Meow

A Novel

Sam Austen

Table of Contents

MEOW

Meow meow meow meow meow, meow. Meow meow meow meow. Meow? Meow.

Meow meow meow meow meow meow meow meow meow meow meow. Meow meow meow meow meow meow meow meow meow meow. Meow meow meow meow meow meow meow meow. Meow meow meow meow meow meow meow. Meow. Meow meow meow meow meow meow meow meow meow meow meow meow.

Meow, meow meow meow meow meow meow meow. Meow meow meow meow meow? Meow meow meow meow meow meow meow? Meow meow meow meow meow. Meow meow meow meow meow. Meow meow meow meow meow meow meow meow meow meow meow meow meow. Meow meow meow meow meow.

Meow meow meow meow meow meow meow meow. Meow meow meow. Meow meow meow meow meow meow meow meow. Meow meow meow meow meow meow meow meow. Meow meow meow meow meow meow. Meow meow meow meow meow meow meow meow meow meow meow meow meow. Meow meow meow meow meow meow meow meow meow meow.

Meow meow meow. Meow meow meow meow meow. Meow meow meow meow meow meow meow meow meow meow meow. Meow meow meow meow meow meow meow meow

1

meow meow meow meow. Meow meow meow meow meow meow meow. Meow meow meow meow. Meow meow meow meow meow.

Meow meow meow meow meow meow meow meow. Meow meow meow meow meow-meow meow meow meow meow meow meow meow meow meow. Meow meow meow meow meow meow meow meow meow meow meow meow meow meow. "Meow meow meow," meow meow meow.

Meow meow meow meow meow meow meow meow meow meow. Meow meow meow meow meow. Meow meow meow meow meow meow meow meow meow meow meow meow meow meow meow meow meow meow meow.

Meow meow meow meow meow meow meow, meow meow-meow meow meow meow meow meow meow meow meow meow, meow meow meow meow. Meow meow meow meow meow meow meow meow meow: meow meow meow, meow meow meow meow, meow meow meow meow-meow meow meow meow meow meow.

Meow meow meow meow meow meow. Meow meow meow meow meow meow meow meow meow meow meow, meow-meow meow meow meow meow meow. Meow meow meow meow. Meow, meow meow, meow meow meow meow meow meow. Meow meow meow meow meow, meow meow meow meow meow meow meow meow.

"Meow meow meow meow meow meow meow meow meow meow meow meow, meow," meow meow meow meow meow meow meow meow-meow meow. "Meow meow meow meow meow meow meow meow. Meow meow meow meow meow meow meow meow?"

Meow meow meow meow meow meow meow meow. Meow, meow meow meow meow meow meow meow meow meow meow meow meow. Meow meow meow meow meow meow

meow. Meow meow meow meow meow meow, meow meow meow meow meow meow meow meow, meow meow, meow meow meow meow meow meow meow, meow meow meow meow meow meow meow, meow meow meow.

Meow meow meow meow meow meow meow meow meow meow meow meow meow. Meow meow meow. Meow meow meow meow meow meow meow meow meow meow meow meow meow meow meow meow meow meow meow meow meow meow meow meow meow meow meow. Meow meow meow meow meow meow meow meow meow meow meow meow meow, meow meow meow meow meow meow meow meow meow meow meow meow meow.

Meow meow meow meow meow, meow meow meow meow meow meow meow meow meow meow meow meow meow, meow meow. Meow meow meow meow meow. Meow meow meow meow meow meow meow.

"Meow meow meow meow meow, meow. Meow meow meow meow meow meow meow," meow meow. Meow meow meow meow meow meow meow meow meow. Meow meow meow meow meow meow, meow meow, meow meow meow meow meow.

Meow meow meow meow meow meow meow meow meow, meow meow meow meow meow meow, meow meow meow meow meow meow meow meow meow meow meow meow meow meow meow meow meow meow meow meow meow meow meow meow. Meow meow, meow meow, meow meow meow meow meow meow meow meow, meow meow Meow, meow meow meow meow meow meow, meow meow meow meow meow meow meow, meow meow meow meow meow meow meow, meow meow meow meow meow meow meow, meow meow meow. Meow, meow meow meow meow meow meow, meow meow meow meow meow, meow meow meow meow meow meow

meow meow meow meow. Meow meow meow meow meow meow meow meow, meow meow meow meow meow meow, meow meow meow meow meow meow meow meow meow. Meow, meow meow meow meow meow meow -- meow meow meow, meow meow meow meow meow, meow meow "meow meow," meow meow meow meow.

Meow meow meow meow meow meow meow meow meow meow meow meow meow meow meow meow meow meow, meow meow meow meow meow meow meow. Meow meow meow meow meow. Meow meow meow meow. Meow meow meow meow meow meow meow meow meow meow meow meow meow meow meow meow meow.

"Meow meow meow, Meow," meow meow meow meow meow meow meow meow meow meow meow meow. Meow meow meow meow meow meow meow meow meow meow meow meow meow meow meow meow meow meow. Meow meow meow, meow meow meow meow meow. Meow meow meow meow meow meow meow meow.

Meow meow meow meow meow meow meow meow meow meow meow, meow meow meow meow meow meow meow meow meow meow meow meow. Meow meow meow meow meow meow meow meow meow meow meow meow, meow meow meow meow Meow meow. Meow meow meow meow meow meow meow meow meow meow meow meow meow meow meow meow. Meow meow meow meow meow meow meow, meow meow meow meow meow meow meow meow meow meow meow meow meow.

Meow meow meow, meow meow meow meow.

Meow meow meow meow meow, meow meow meow meow. Meow meow meow meow. Meow meow meow meow, meow meow meow meow meow meow meow meow. Meow meow meow meow meow meow meow meow, meow meow. Meow

meow meow meow meow meow meow meow meow meow
meow meow meow, meow meow, meow meow meow meow
meow meow meow meow meow meow meow meow meow
meow meow meow. Meow meow meow meow meow meow,
meow meow meow meow Meow meow meow meow meow
meow meow meow meow, meow meow meow meow meow
meow meow. Meow meow meow meow meow meow meow
meow meow meow, meow meow meow meow meow meow
meow.

Meow Meow meow meow meow meow meow meow, meow
meow meow meow. Meow meow. Meow meow meow meow
meow meow meow meow meow meow. Meow meow meow
meow meow-meow meow, meow meow meow meow meow
meow meow meow meow meow.

"Meow, meow meow meow meow meow?' meow meow
meow meow meow meow meow.

Meow meow meow meow meow meow meow meow meow.
Meow meow meow. Meow meow meow meow meow meow:
meow meow meow.

Meow meow meow meow meow meow meow meow meow
meow meow. Meow meow meow meow meow. Meow meow
meow meow meow meow meow meow meow meow. Meow
meow meow meow meow meow meow meow meow. Meow
meow meow, meow meow meow meow meow meow meow.
Meow meow meow meow meow meow meow. Meow meow
meow meow meow meow meow meow. Meow meow meow
meow meow meow meow meow meow meow meow meow
meow, meow meow, meow meow meow meow meow meow
meow meow.

Meow meow, meow meow meow meow. Meow meow meow
meow meow, meow meow meow meow, meow meow meow
meow meow meow meow meow meow meow meow meow

meow meow. Meow. Meow meow meow meow, meow meow
meow meow.

Meow meow meow meow meow meow meow, meow meow
meow meow meow, meow meow meow meow meow meow
meow meow meow. Meow meow meow meow meow meow.
Meow meow meow meow meow meow meow, meow meow
meow meow.

Meow meow meow meow meow meow meow meow meow.
Meow meow meow meow meow meow meow meow, meow meow
meow meow meow meow. Meow meow meow. Meow meow
meow meow meow meow meow, meow meow meow meow
meow meow, meow meow. Meow meow meow meow meow
meow meow meow meow meow, meow meow meow. Meow
meow meow meow meow meow meow meow meow. Meow
meow meow meow meow, meow meow, meow meow meow
meow meow. Meow meow meow meow meow meow meow
meow meow. Meow meow meow meow meow. Meow meow
meow meow meow, meow meow meow meow meow meow meow
meow meow meow meow, meow meow meow meow meow meow
meow. Meow meow meow meow meow meow meow meow.
Meow meow meow meow meow meow meow meow meow.

"Meow meow meow meow meow meow meow. Meow
meow meow."

Meow meow meow meow meow meow meow meow meow
meow, meow meow meow meow meow meow meow meow
meow, meow meow meow meow meow meow meow. Meow
meow meow meow meow meow. Meow meow meow meow
meow meow meow meow meow meow meow.

Meow meow meow meow meow meow meow meow. Meow
meow meow meow meow meow. Meow meow meow. Meow
meow meow meow meow meow. Meow meow meow meow
meow meow, meow meow meow.

Meow. Meow meow. Meow meow meow meow meow meow meow meow meow. Meow meow meow meow meow, meow meow meow meow meow meow meow meow meow meow, meow meow meow meow meow meow. Meow meow meow meow meow meow meow meow. Meow meow meow meow meow meow meow meow. Meow meow meow meow meow meow, meow, meow. Meow meow meow meow meow meow meow meow meow meow. Meow meow meow meow. Meow meow meow meow meow, meow meow meow meow meow meow meow meow. Meow meow meow meow. Meow meow meow meow meow meow meow meow meow meow meow. Meow meow meow meow meow meow meow meow meow meow meow meow meow meow meow meow.

Meow meow meow meow meow meow meow, meow meow. Meow meow meow. Meow meow meow meow meow meow meow meow. Meow meow meow meow meow meow meow. Meow meow meow meow meow meow meow, meow meow meow meow.

"Meow, meow meow meow meow meow meow meow, Meow meow."

Meow meow meow meow meow meow meow. Meow meow meow meow meow. Meow meow meow meow meow meow meow meow meow meow meow meow. Meow meow meow meow meow meow. Meow meow meow meow meow meow meow, meow meow meow. Meow meow meow meow meow meow meow meow meow.

Meow, meow meow meow meow meow meow meow meow meow meow meow meow meow meow. Meow meow. Meow meow meow meow. Meow meow meow meow meow, meow meow meow meow meow meow meow meow. Meow meow meow meow meow, meow meow meow meow meow meow meow meow meow meow meow meow meow meow meow meow.

Meow meow meow meow meow meow meow meow meow meow meow meow meow meow meow. Meow meow meow meow meow meow meow meow meow meow meow meow, meow meow meow meow meow meow meow. Meow meow meow meow meow meow meow meow meow meow, meow meow meow meow meow meow meow meow: meow meow meow meow meow meow meow meow meow meow.

Meow meow meow meow meow meow meow meow meow meow meow meow. Meow meow meow meow meow, meow meow meow meow meow meow meow meow, meow meow, meow meow-meow meow. Meow meow meow meow meow. Meow meow meow. Meow meow meow meow meow meow meow, meow meow meow meow meow meow meow. Meow meow meow, meow meow meow meow meow meow meow meow meow meow, meow meow meow meow. Meow meow meow meow meow meow meow meow meow meow meow meow meow meow meow meow meow.

Meow meow meow meow meow meow meow meow meow meow meow meow meow meow. Meow meow meow meow meow meow. Meow meow meow meow meow meow meow meow meow meow meow meow meow meow meow meow meow. Meow meow meow meow meow meow meow meow meow meow meow meow meow, meow meow meow meow, meow meow meow meow meow meow meow meow meow meow.

Meow meow meow, meow meow meow meow, meow meow meow meow meow meow meow meow. Meow meow meow meow meow meow meow meow meow meow. Meow, meow meow meow meow, meow meow meow meow meow meow meow. Meow meow meow meow meow meow meow meow meow meow meow meow meow. Meow meow meow meow meow

meow, meow meow meow meow meow, meow meow meow meow, meow meow meow.

> *"Meow meow meow meow meow, meow meow*
> *meow meow.*
>
> *Meow."*

Meow meow meow meow meow meow meow meow, meow meow meow meow meow. Meow meow meow meow meow meow meow meow meow meow meow meow meow meow meow meow meow meow meow meow. Meow meow meow meow meow meow meow meow meow meow, meow meow meow meow meow meow meow.

Meow meow meow meow, meow Meow Meow, meow meow meow meow meow meow meow meow meow. Meow meow meow meow meow meow, meow meow. Meow meow meow meow meow meow meow meow meow meow meow meow meow. Meow meow, meow meow meow meow meow meow meow. Meow meow meow meow meow meow, meow meow meow meow meow meow meow, meow meow meow meow meow meow meow, meow meow meow meow meow meow. Meow meow meow meow meow, meow meow meow meow meow meow meow meow.

Meow meow meow meow meow meow meow meow, meow meow meow meow meow meow meow meow meow, meow meow meow meow meow meow. Meow meow meow meow meow meow meow meow meow meow meow meow meow meow. meow meow meow.

Meow meow meow meow meow meow, meow meow meow meow meow. Meow meow meow meow meow meow meow meow meow meow meow meow meow meow, meow meow meow meow meow. Meow meow meow. Meow meow meow meow

meow meow meow meow meow meow meow meow meow.
Meow meow meow meow! Meow meow meow meow meow
meow meow meow meow meow meow, meow meow meow
meow meow meow meow meow meow meow meow.
Meow meow meow meow meow meow meow meow meow
meow. Meow meow meow meow meow meow meow meow.
Meow meow meow meow meow meow. Meow meow meow
meow meow meow. Meow meow meow meow meow meow
meow. Meow meow meow meow meow meow meow meow
meow meow meow. Meow meow meow meow meow meow
meow meow meow meow meow, meow meow meow meow
meow meow meow. Meow meow meow meow meow meow
meow meow meow meow meow meow meow: meow meow,
meow-meow, meow meow meow meow meow meow. Meow
meow meow meow meow meow, meow meow meow meow
meow meow, meow meow meow meow meow meow meow meow.
Meow meow meow meow meow meow meow, meow meow
meow meow meow meow.
Meow meow meow meow meow meow meow. Meow meow
meow meow meow meow meow meow meow meow meow, meow
meow meow meow meow, meow meow meow meow meow
meow, meow meow meow meow, meow meow meow meow
meow meow meow meow meow meow meow meow meow.
(Meow meow meow meow meow meow meow meow meow
meow meow meow meow meow meow meow meow meow
meow meow, meow meow meow meow meow meow meow
mcow. Meow, meow meow, meow meow meow meow meow
meow meow meow. Meow meow meow meow meow, meow
meow meow meow meow meow meow.)
Meow meow meow meow meow meow meow meow meow
meow. Meow meow meow meow meow meow meow meow
meow, meow meow meow meow meow meow meow-meow meow

meow meow meow meow meow meow meow meow meow
meow meow meow meow.
Meow meow meow meow meow meow meow meow meow
meow meow meow. Meow meow meow meow meow meow
meow meow meow. Meow meow meow meow meow meow,
meow meow meow meow meow meow meow meow meow
meow meow meow. Meow meow. Meow.
Meow meow meow meow meow meow meow meow meow
meow meow meow meow meow meow meow meow.
Meow meow meow meow meow meow meow meow meow
meow meow meow meow meow meow meow meow meow.
Meow meow meow. Meow meow meow meow meow meow
meow meow meow meow meow meow meow meow meow
meow meow meow meow. Meow meow meow meow meow,
meow meow meow meow meow meow meow meow meow
meow meow meow meow. Meow meow meow meow, meow
meow meow meow meow. Meow meow meow meow meow
meow meow meow meow meow meow meow meow meow.
Meow meow meow meow meow meow meow meow meow
meow.
Meow meow meow meow meow meow meow meow meow.
Meow meow meow meow meow meow meow meow meow
meow. Meow meow meow meow meow meow meow meow
meow meow meow meow meow meow, meow meow meow
meow meow.
Meow meow meow meow meow meow meow meow meow
meow meow. Meow meow meow meow meow meow meow.
Meow meow meow meow meow meow meow meow meow
meow meow, meow meow meow meow meow meow meow
meow meow meow, meow meow meow. Meow meow meow
meow meow. Meow meow meow meow meow meow meow
meow meow, meow meow meow meow meow meow meow

meow meow meow meow meow, meow meow meow meow meow meow meow.

"Meow meow meow meow meow meow meow meow?," meow meow meow meow.

"Meow meow meow meow meow meow."

"Meow meow?"

"Meow meow meow meow-meow-meow meow meow."

"Meow meow meow meow meow meow meow meow meow meow meow?"

"Meow meow meow meow, meow."

Meow meow meow meow meow meow meow meow meow meow meow meow meow meow meow, meow meow meow meow meow meow, meow meow meow meow. Meow meow meow meow, meow meow. Meow meow meow meow meow meow meow meow meow meow meow.

"Meow meow meow meow?" meow meow.

Meow meow meow meow meow meow meow meow meow meow meow, meow meow meow meow meow meow meow meow meow. Meow meow meow meow meow meow. Meow meow meow meow meow meow meow meow meow meow meow meow meow. Meow meow, meow meow meow meow meow meow. Meow meow meow meow. Meow meow meow meow meow meow meow meow meow. Meow meow meow meow meow meow meow meow meow meow meow meow.

Meow meow meow meow meow meow meow meow meow meow meow meow meow meow. Meow meow meow meow meow meow meow meow. Meow. Meow meow meow meow meow meow meow meow meow meow, meow meow meow meow meow meow meow meow meow meow meow meow, meow meow, meow meow meow meow. Meow meow meow, meow meow meow meow meow meow. Meow meow meow meow

meow, meow meow meow meow meow meow. Meow meow meow meow meow meow. Meow meow meow meow meow meow.

Meow meow meow meow, meow meow. Meow meow meow meow meow meow meow meow meow, meow meow meow meow meow meow meow meow meow, meow meow Meow meow, meow meow, meow meow meow, meow meow meow meow meow, meow meow meow, meow meow meow meow. Meow meow meow meow meow meow meow meow meow meow meow meow meow meow meow meow, meow meow meow meow meow meow meow meow meow meow meow.

Meow meow meow meow meow meow meow meow meow meow meow. Meow meow meow meow. Meow meow meow meow meow meow.

Meow meow meow meow.

Meow meow meow meow meow.

Meow meow.

Meow meow meow meow meow meow. Meow meow meow meow meow meow meow. Meow meow meow meow meow meow meow?

Meow meow meow meow meow meow meow meow meow. Meow meow meow meow meow meow meow meow, meow meow meow meow meow meow meow, meow meow meow meow, meow meow meow. Meow meow meow meow.

"Meow meow meow meow meow, Meow. Meow meow meow meow meow meow meow. Meow meow, meow meow meow meow meow. Meow meow meow meow meow meow meow meow. Meow meow meow."

Meow meow meow meow, meow meow meow meow meow meow, meow meow. Meow meow meow meow meow meow meow. Meow meow meow meow meow meow meow meow meow meow meow meow, meow meow meow meow meow meow.

"Meow meow meow meow," meow meow meow meow. "Meow meow meow meow meow meow meow meow meow meow, meow meow meow meow meow meow meow meow meow meow meow meow."

Meow meow meow meow meow meow meow meow meow meow. Meow meow meow meow meow meow meow meow. Meow meow meow meow meow. Meow meow meow meow meow. Meow meow meow. Meow meow meow meow meow meow, meow meow meow meow, meow meow meow. Meow meow meow meow meow meow meow meow, meow meow meow. Meow meow meow meow meow meow meow, meow meow meow meow meow meow meow. Meow meow meow meow meow.

Meow meow meow meow meow, meow meow meow meow meow meow meow meow meow, meow meow. Meow meow meow meow meow. Meow meow. Meow meow?

Meow meow meow meow meow meow meow meow meow, meow meow meow meow, meow meow meow meow meow meow meow, meow meow meow meow meow meow meow meow meow, meow meow meow meow. Meow meow meow meow meow meow meow meow meow: meow meow meow meow meow meow meow meow meow meow meow meow, meow meow meow, meow meow, meow meow, meow meow meow meow meow meow, meow meow. Meow meow meow meow meow meow meow meow meow meow mcow. Meow meow meow meow meow meow meow meow meow meow meow meow. Mcow meow meow meow meow meow meow. Meow meow meow meow, meow meow meow meow meow meow meow.

"Meow, meow meow meow meow meow meow meow. Meow meow. Meow meow meow meow meow." Meow meow meow meow. Meow meow meow meow meow. Meow meow meow meow. Meow meow meow meow meow meow.

Meow meow meow meow meow meow meow meow, meow meow meow meow meow. Meow meow meow meow meow meow meow meow meow meow. Meow meow. Meow meow. Meow meow meow meow meow meow meow meow meow meow. Meow meow meow meow meow meow. Meow meow meow meow meow meow meow meow meow meow meow. Meow meow meow, meow meow, meow meow meow meow meow. Meow meow meow meow meow meow meow meow meow meow meow meow meow meow, meow meow meow. Meow meow meow meow meow meow meow meow meow meow, meow meow meow meow. Meow meow meow meow meow meow. Meow meow meow meow meow meow meow meow, meow meow meow meow meow meow meow. Meow meow, meow meow meow meow meow meow.

Meow meow meow meow meow meow meow. Meow meow meow meow meow meow meow meow. Meow meow meow, meow. Meow meow meow meow meow meow meow meow. Meow meow meow meow meow. Meow meow meow meow meow meow.

Meow meow meow meow meow, meow meow meow meow meow, meow meow meow meow meow meow meow meow meow. Meow meow meow meow. Meow meow meow meow meow meow meow meow meow meow meow meow meow meow. Meow meow meow meow meow meow. Meow meow meow meow, meow meow meow. Meow meow meow meow. Meow meow meow.

Meow meow meow meow meow meow, meow meow meow meow.

Meow meow meow meow meow meow meow meow meow. Meow meow. Meow meow. Meow meow meow meow meow meow meow meow. Meow meow meow, meow meow meow Meow Meow. Meow meow meow Meow meow meow meow

meow. Meow meow meow. Meow meow meow meow meow. Meow meow meow, meow meow meow meow meow meow meow. Meow meow meow meow meow meow meow meow meow meow meow meow meow meow. Meow meow meow meow meow meow meow meow meow meow meow meow meow meow meow meow meow meow meow meow meow, meow meow meow meow meow meow, meow meow meow meow. Meow meow meow meow meow meow meow meow meow meow meow meow. Meow meow meow meow meow meow meow meow meow meow meow meow meow meow meow meow meow meow meow. Meow meow meow meow meow meow meow meow meow meow meow meow. Meow meow meow meow meow meow meow meow meow meow meow meow meow meow meow meow meow meow meow Meow.

Meow meow meow meow meow meow, meow meow meow meow meow meow meow meow meow meow meow meow meow. Meow meow meow meow meow meow meow meow, meow meow meow. Meow meow meow meow meow meow. Meow meow meow meow meow meow meow meow meow, meow meow meow meow, meow meow meow meow meow, meow meow meow meow meow meow.

"Meow! Meow meow meow," meow meow meow meow meow meow.

"Meow?"

"Meow."

"Meow meow meow meow meow meow meow meow meow?"

"Meow meow meow meow."

Meow meow meow meow meow meow meow meow. Meow meow meow meow, meow, meow meow. Meow meow meow meow meow meow meow meow, meow meow meow, meow meow meow meow meow meow. Meow meow meow meow, meow meow meow meow meow, meow meow meow meow

meow meow meow meow. Meow meow meow meow. Meow meow meow meow meow meow meow meow meow meow.

Meow meow meow meow meow meow, meow. Meow meow meow, meow, meow. Meow meow meow meow meow meow, meow meow meow meow meow meow. Meow meow meow meow meow meow meow, meow meow meow meow meow meow meow meow. Meow meow meow meow. Meow meow meow meow meow meow meow meow. Meow meow meow meow meow meow meow meow meow meow. Meow meow meow meow meow.

Meow meow meow meow meow meow meow meow meow meow meow meow meow meow meow meow meow meow meow. Meow meow meow meow meow meow meow meow meow meow, meow meow meow meow meow meow meow meow, meow meow meow meow, meow meow meow. Meow meow meow meow meow meow meow.

Meow meow meow, meow meow meow meow.

Meow meow meow, meow meow meow meow. Meow meow meow meow meow, meow meow meow meow meow meow meow, meow meow meow meow meow meow meow meow meow, meow meow meow meow meow meow. Meow meow meow meow. Meow meow meow meow. Meow meow meow meow meow meow meow meow meow. Meow meow meow meow meow meow meow meow meow meow meow meow meow meow.

Meow meow meow meow meow. Meow meow. Meow meow meow meow meow meow meow meow meow meow, meow meow meow meow. Meow meow meow, meow meow meow meow meow meow. Meow meow meow, meow meow meow meow meow, meow meow meow. Meow meow meow meow meow meow. Meow meow meow, meow meow meow meow, meow meow meow. Meow.

"Meow meow meow meow meow?" meow meow meow.

"Meow, meow. Meow meow meow meow meow. Meow meow meow meow. Meow meow meow meow."

"Meow. Meow meow meow meow?"

"Meow, meow meow meow. Meow meow meow meow. Meow meow meow meow, meow meow."

"Meow meow."

Meow meow meow meow meow meow, meow meow meow meow meow meow meow meow meow meow. Meow meow meow meow meow meow meow meow meow meow meow, meow meow meow meow meow meow meow meow, meow meow meow meow. Meow meow meow meow meow meow. Meow meow meow meow meow meow, meow meow meow meow meow meow meow. Meow meow meow meow meow meow meow meow. Meow meow meow meow meow meow meow.

Meow meow meow meow meow meow meow meow meow meow meow. Meow meow meow. Meow meow meow meow meow meow meow meow. Meow meow meow, meow meow meow. Meow meow. Meow meow meow meow meow, meow meow meow meow meow meow meow.

"Meow meow meow meow meow meow meow meow meow meow. Meow meow meow meow meow meow meow meow meow meow meow meow, meow?"

"Meow meow, Meow. Meow meow meow meow meow meow meow meow meow. Meow meow meow, meow meow meow meow. Meow meow meow meow meow. Meow meow meow meow meow meow meow, meow meow meow meow."

"Meow meow," meow meow. Meow meow meow meow meow meow, meow meow, meow meow meow meow meow meow meow meow. Meow meow meow meow meow, meow meow meow meow. Meow meow, meow. Meow meow meow meow

meow. Meow meow meow meow meow meow meow. Meow meow meow, meow meow, meow meow. Meow meow meow meow meow meow. Meow meow meow meow. Meow meow meow, meow meow meow, meow meow meow meow. Meow meow. Meow meow meow, meow meow. Meow meow meow meow meow meow meow meow meow meow meow meow meow meow.

MEOW, MEOW MEOW

Meow meow meow meow meow meow meow meow meow meow meow meow meow meow. Meow meow meow meow meow, meow meow meow. Meow meow meow meow meow meow meow meow meow meow, meow meow meow meow meow meow. Meow meow meow meow meow meow meow meow meow meow meow meow meow meow meow meow meow meow meow, meow meow meow meow meow meow, meow meow meow meow meow meow meow meow meow meow meow. Meow meow meow meow meow meow meow. Meow meow meow meow meow meow meow meow meow, meow-meow meow, meow meow meow meow meow meow meow. Meow meow meow meow meow meow. Meow meow meow meow meow meow. Meow meow meow meow meow meow meow meow meow, meow meow meow meow meow meow, meow meow meow meow meow meow meow meow meow meow meow meow meow meow meow meow meow.

Meow meow meow meow meow meow, meow meow meow meow meow meow meow meow meow meow meow meow meow meow meow meow meow meow meow meow, meow meow meow meow meow meow meow, meow meow meow meow meow, meow meow meow meow meow, meow meow meow meow meow meow meow meow. Meow meow meow meow meow meow, meow meow meow meow meow meow meow. Meow meow meow meow meow meow

meow meow meow meow, meow meow meow meow meow meow meow meow meow.

Meow meow. Meow meow meow meow. Meow meow meow meow meow meow, meow meow meow meow meow meow.

Meow meow meow meow meow meow. Meow meow meow meow meow meow meow meow meow meow meow meow meow, meow meow meow meow, meow meow meow. Meow meow meow meow meow, meow meow meow. Meow meow meow meow meow meow meow-meow meow. Meow meow meow meow meow meow meow meow. Meow meow, meow meow meow meow meow.

Meow meow meow meow meow meow meow/meow meow meow meow meow meow meow meow meow meow meow meow. Meow meow meow meow meow meow meow meow. Meow meow meow meow. Meow meow. Meow meow meow meow meow meow meow. Meow meow meow meow meow, meow meow meow meow meow. Meow meow meow meow meow meow meow meow, meow meow meow, meow meow meow meow meow meow meow meow meow meow, meow meow meow meow meow meow, meow meow meow meow meow meow meow meow meow. Meow meow meow meow meow meow meow meow, meow meow meow meow meow, meow meow meow meow meow meow meow meow meow meow meow meow. Meow meow meow meow meow meow meow, meow meow meow meow meow meow meow meow meow meow meow meow meow meow meow meow meow meow meow meow meow meow meow.

Meow meow meow meow meow meow meow meow meow, meow meow meow meow meow meow meow meow meow meow. Meow meow meow meow meow meow meow meow meow meow meow meow. Meow meow meow meow meow meow meow meow meow meow meow meow meow

meow meow meow meow meow meow meow meow meow.
Meow meow meow meow.

Meow meow meow meow meow meow meow meow meow
meow meow meow. Meow meow meow meow meow meow
meow meow meow meow. Meow meow meow meow meow
meow meow meow meow meow, meow, meow meow. Meow
meow meow meow meow meow meow meow meow meow
meow meow meow meow. Meow meow meow meow meow
meow meow meow meow meow meow meow, meow meow
meow meow meow meow meow meow meow meow, meow
meow meow meow meow meow. Meow meow meow meow
meow meow.

Meow meow meow meow meow meow meow meow meow,
meow meow meow meow meow meow meow meow meow
meow, meow meow meow, meow meow meow meow meow
meow. Meow meow meow meow meow meow meow meow
meow meow meow. Meow meow meow meow meow meow
meow.

Meow meow meow. Meow meow meow.

Meow meow meow meow meow meow meow meow meow
meow meow meow meow, meow meow meow meow meow
meow meow meow meow meow meow meow meow meow
meow meow meow meow meow meow meow meow, meow
meow meow meow meow meow meow, meow meow meow
meow meow. Meow meow meow meow meow meow meow
meow meow meow, meow-meow meow, meow mcow Meow
meow Meow Meow. Meow meow meow meow meow meow,
meow meow meow meow meow meow meow meow meow,
meow meow meow meow meow meow meow meow meow
meow. Meow meow meow meow meow meow meow meow
meow meow, meow meow meow meow meow meow meow
meow meow meow meow meow meow meow meow meow meow.

Meow meow meow meow meow, meow meow meow meow meow meow meow meow meow meow meow meow meow meow meow meow meow meow. Meow meow meow meow meow. Meow meow meow meow meow meow meow meow. Meow meow.

Meow meow meow meow meow meow meow meow. Meow meow meow meow meow meow meow meow meow meow meow.

Meow meow meow meow meow meow meow meow meow meow meow. Meow meow meow meow meow meow meow meow meow meow meow meow meow meow meow meow. Meow meow meow meow meow meow meow meow meow meow, meow meow meow. Meow meow meow meow, meow meow meow meow meow meow meow meow meow.

Meow meow meow meow meow meow meow meow meow meow, meow meow meow meow meow meow meow meow meow meow meow meow meow meow meow, meow meow meow meow meow meow meow meow meow meow meow meow meow meow meow meow meow meow meow, meow meow meow meow meow meow meow, meow meow meow meow meow. Meow meow meow meow meow meow meow meow meow meow meow meow meow meow meow meow Meow meow meow meow meow meow. Meow meow meow meow meow meow meow meow. Meow meow meow meow meow meow.

Meow meow meow meow meow meow meow meow meow meow, meow meow meow meow meow meow meow meow. Meow meow meow meow meow meow meow meow meow meow meow meow meow meow meow meow meow meow. Meow meow meow meow meow meow, meow meow meow meow meow meow meow meow. Meow meow meow meow meow meow meow meow meow meow meow meow meow meow meow meow meow meow. Meow meow meow meow meow meow meow meow

meow. Meow meow meow meow meow meow, meow meow meow meow meow meow meow.

Meow meow meow meow meow meow meow meow. Meow meow meow meow meow meow meow meow meow meow meow. Meow meow meow meow meow meow meow meow meow meow meow meow meow meow meow meow meow meow meow meow meow meow meow meow meow meow meow meow meow meow.

Meow meow meow meow meow meow meow. Meow meow meow meow meow meow meow meow, meow meow meow. Meow meow meow meow meow meow meow meow meow meow meow meow meow: meow, meow meow, Meow.

Meow meow. Meow meow meow meow meow. Meow meow meow meow meow meow meow meow meow meow meow meow meow meow meow meow meow meow meow meow meow, meow meow meow meow meow meow meow meow meow meow meow meow meow meow meow meow meow. Meow meow meow meow meow meow meow meow meow meow. Meow meow meow meow meow meow meow. Meow meow, meow meow meow meow meow meow meow meow meow meow meow meow meow meow. Meow meow meow meow meow meow meow meow meow meow meow.

Meow meow meow meow meow meow meow meow meow meow meow, meow meow meow meow meow meow meow meow. Meow meow meow meow. Meow meow meow meow meow meow meow meow meow, meow meow meow meow meow meow meow meow meow meow meow. Meow meow meow meow meow meow meow meow. Meow meow meow meow meow, meow meow meow meow meow, meow meow meow meow.

Meow meow meow meow meow meow. Meow meow meow meow.

Meow meow meow meow meow meow, meow meow meow meow meow meow meow meow meow meow meow, meow meow meow. Meow meow meow meow meow meow meow meow meow meow meow. Meow meow meow meow meow meow meow, meow meow meow meow meow meow meow.

"Meow meow meow meow, meow," meow meow Meow meow meow meow meow meow, meow meow meow meow Meow, meow meow meow meow meow meow.

"Meow meow, meow meow meow meow."

Meow meow meow meow meow meow meow meow meow meow meow. Meow meow meow meow meow meow meow meow meow meow meow meow. Meow meow meow meow meow meow meow meow. Meow meow meow meow. Meow meow meow meow meow. Meow meow meow meow. Meow meow meow meow meow.

Meow meow meow meow meow. Meow meow meow meow meow. Meow meow meow meow meow meow meow meow meow. Meow meow meow meow meow meow meow, meow meow. Meow meow meow meow meow meow meow. Meow meow meow meow meow.

"Meow meow meow meow meow meow meow meow meow, meow. Meow meow meow meow meow meow meow. Meow meow meow meow meow. Meow meow meow meow meow meow meow meow meow."

"Meow meow meow, meow. Meow meow meow meow meow meow meow."

"Meow meow meow meow. Meow meow meow."

Meow meow meow meow meow meow meow meow meow, meow meow, meow meow meow meow meow meow meow meow meow meow. Meow meow meow meow meow meow meow meow meow meow meow. Meow meow meow meow. Meow meow meow

meow meow Meow meow meow. Meow meow. Meow meow meow meow meow meow meow meow meow meow meow?

Meow meow meow meow meow meow meow meow meow meow meow meow. Meow meow meow meow, meow meow meow meow meow meow meow meow. Meow meow meow meow meow meow meow, meow meow meow meow meow meow meow meow: meow meow meow meow meow meow meow Meow meow.

Meow meow meow meow meow meow meow meow. Meow meow meow meow meow meow meow. Meow meow meow meow meow, meow meow meow meow meow meow meow, meow meow meow meow meow meow meow, meow meow meow meow, meow meow meow meow meow meow meow meow meow meow meow meow. Meow meow meow meow meow meow meow meow meow meow meow meow. Meow meow meow meow meow meow meow meow meow meow, meow meow meow, meow meow meow, meow meow meow meow meow meow.

"Meow meow meow. Meow meow meow meow."

Meow meow meow meow meow meow meow meow meow meow meow meow meow meow meow meow.

"Me'meow meow meow meow meow?" Meow meow meow meow meow meow meow. "Meow meow meow meow meow?"

"Meow, meow meow meow meow meow meow meow."

"Meow. Meow... meow meow meow meow meow?"

"Meow. Meow meow meow meow meow meow."

Meow meow meow meow meow meow meow meow, meow meow meow, meow meow meow meow, meow meow meow meow. Meow meow meow meow. Meow meow.

"Meow meow," meow meow.

"Meow meow meow?"

"Meow."

"Meow. Meow meow meow meow meow."
Meow meow meow meow meow meow meow, Meow meow meow meow meow meow. Meow meow. Meow meow meow meow meow meow meow meow meow meow. Meow meow meow meow meow meow. Meow meow meow meow, meow meow meow meow meow meow.

Meow meow meow meow meow meow meow. Meow meow meow, meow meow meow meow meow meow meow meow meow. Meow meow meow meow meow meow, meow meow. Meow meow meow meow meow meow meow, meow meow meow meow, meow meow meow meow meow. Meow meow meow meow meow meow.

"Meow meow meow meow meow meow meow meow meow, Meow Meow?"

"Meow, meow meow meow meow meow meow meow, meow meow meow meow."

"Meow meow," meow meow meow meow meow meow meow meow, meow meow meow meow meow meow meow meow. Meow. Meow meow meow. Meow meow meow meow. Meow meow meow meow meow meow meow meow meow meow meow meow. Meow meow meow meow meow meow meow meow meow meow meow meow meow meow, meow meow meow.

Meow meow meow meow meow meow meow meow meow meow meow, meow meow meow meow meow meow, meow meow meow meow meow, meow meow, meow meow meow meow, meow meow meow meow. Meow meow meow meow Meow meow meow, meow meow meow meow meow meow meow meow. Meow meow meow meow meow meow meow meow meow meow meow, meow meow meow meow meow meow meow meow meow meow meow meow meow meow meow meow meow meow meow meow meow meow meow meow meow

meow meow, meow meow, meow meow meow meow meow meow.

"Meow meow meow meow meow meow meow... meow meow meow meow, meow meow meow meow meow," meow meow meow meow meow meow meow meow meow meow meow.

Meow meow meow meow meow.

Meow meow meow meow meow meow meow.

Meow meow meow Meow Meow, meow meow meow meow meow meow meow. Meow meow meow meow meow meow meow meow meow meow meow meow. Meow meow meow meow meow meow meow meow meow meow meow, meow meow meow meow meow. Meow meow meow meow meow meow meow meow meow meow meow. Meow meow meow meow meow meow meow.

Meow meow meow meow meow meow meow meow, meow meow meow meow meow meow meow meow meow meow meow meow meow. Meow meow meow meow meow meow meow meow meow meow, meow meow meow.

Meow meow meow meow meow meow meow meow meow meow meow meow. Meow meow meow meow meow meow meow meow meow. Meow meow meow meow meow meow meow meow, meow meow meow meow meow. Meow meow meow meow meow meow meow meow meow meow, meow meow meow meow. Meow meow meow meow meow meow. Meow meow meow meow meow meow meow meow meow meow meow meow meow. Meow meow meow meow meow meow meow meow, meow meow meow. Meow, meow meow meow meow meow.

Meow meow meow meow meow meow meow. Meow meow meow meow meow meow meow meow meow meow. Meow

meow meow meow meow meow meow meow, meow meow meow meow meow meow.

"Meow meow meow?"

"Meow meow, meow meow meow." Meow meow meow meow meow meow meow meow meow meow meow meow. Meow meow meow meow meow, meow meow meow meow meow. Meow meow meow meow meow. Meow meow meow meow meow meow.

"Meow meow meow meow. Meow meow meow meow. Meow meow meow," meow meow.

Meow meow meow meow meow. Meow meow meow meow meow meow meow meow, meow meow meow meow meow meow. Meow meow meow. Meow meow meow meow meow meow meow meow meow meow meow meow. Meow meow meow meow meow meow meow. Meow meow meow meow meow, meow meow.

"Meow meow meow meow meow meow?" meow meow meow.

"Meow meow meow meow meow meow meow meow meow meow meow."

MEOW MEOW MEW MEOW MEOW

Meow meow meow meow meow meow meow meow meow meow meow meow meow meow. Meow meow meow meow meow meow. Meow, meow meow meow meow meow meow meow meow meow, meow meow meow meow meow meow, meow meow meow meow meow meow meow meow meow meow. Meow meow meow meow meow meow meow meow meow meow meow meow meow meow meow meow meow.

Meow meow meow meow meow meow, meow meow meow meow meow. Meow meow meow meow meow meow meow meow meow meow meow meow meow meow meow, meow meow meow meow meow meow meow. Meow meow meow meow meow meow, meow meow. Meow meow meow meow meow meow meow meow, meow meow meow meow meow meow meow. Meow meow meow meow meow meow meow meow, meow meow meow. Meow meow meow meow meow meow meow meow meow meow, meow meow meow meow meow.

Meow meow meow meow meow meow meow meow meow meow meow. Meow meow meow meow meow meow meow meow meow meow "meow meow," meow meow meow meow meow meow meow meow meow. Meow meow meow meow

meow meow. Meow meow meow meow meow meow meow meow meow, meow meow meow meow meow, meow meow meow meow meow meow meow meow meow meow meow. Meow meow meow meow meow. Meow meow meow meow meow meow meow meow meow meow meow meow meow meow meow meow meow meow. Meow meow meow meow meow meow meow meow meow meow meow meow meow meow meow.

Meow meow meow meow meow meow meow meow meow meow meow meow meow meow, meow meow meow meow meow meow meow meow meow meow meow meow meow meow.

Meow meow meow meow meow meow meow meow, meow meow meow meow meow meow. Meow meow meow meow meow meow meow meow "Meow, meow meow meow." Meow meow meow meow, meow meow meow meow meow meow meow meow meow meow meow meow-meow meow. Meow meow meow.

"Meow, meow meow meow meow," meow meow meow meow.

Meow meow meow meow meow meow meow meow meow meow meow meow meow meow meow meow meow meow meow. Meow meow meow meow meow, meow meow meow. Meow meow meow meow meow meow meow.

"Meow, meow meow meow meow meow meow meow meow meow meow meow, meow?" meow meow meow meow meow meow.

"Meow meow meow meow meow meow meow."

Meow meow meow meow, meow meow meow meow meow meow meow meow meow meow meow meow meow meow meow meow. Meow meow meow meow meow meow meow meow meow meow meow. Meow meow meow, meow meow. Meow meow meow. Meow. Meow. Meow meow meow meow meow

meow meow meow meow meow. Meow meow meow meow meow meow meow meow meow meow.

Meow meow meow meow meow meow meow meow meow meow meow meow meow meow meow meow meow meow meow meow meow meow meow meow. Meow meow meow meow meow meow meow meow, meow meow meow meow meow meow meow meow meow meow meow. Meow meow meow meow meow, meow meow. Meow meow meow meow meow meow meow meow, meow meow meow.

Meow meow meow meow meow meow meow meow meow meow meow meow meow meow meow meow meow. Meow meow meow meow meow meow meow meow meow meow, meow meow meow meow meow meow.

Meow meow meow meow meow meow meow meow meow meow, meow meow meow meow meow meow. Meow meow meow meow meow meow meow meow meow. Meow meow meow meow meow meow meow meow meow meow meow meow meow meow meow meow meow. Meow meow, meow meow meow meow meow meow meow meow meow meow meow meow meow, meow meow meow meow meow meow meow meow meow meow.

Meow meow meow meow meow meow-meow meow meow meow meow meow meow meow meow meow meow meow meow meow meow meow. Meow meow meow meow meow meow meow meow mcow. Meow meow meow meow meow meow, meow meow, meow meow meow meow.

* * * * * * *

Meow Meow, meow meow meow meow meow meow, meow meow meow meow meow meow meow, meow meow meow. Meow meow meow meow meow, meow meow meow meow

meow meow meow, meow meow meow meow meow meow meow meow meow meow meow, meow meow meow meow meow meow meow meow meow meow.

Meow meow meow meow meow meow meow meow meow, meow meow meow meow meow meow meow: meow meow meow meow meow meow Meow Meow. Meow meow meow meow meow meow meow. Meow meow meow meow. Meow meow meow, meow meow meow meow meow meow meow meow meow meow meow meow.

Meow meow meow meow meow meow meow. Meow meow meow meow meow meow meow meow meow. Meow meow meow meow meow, meow meow meow meow meow meow meow. Meow meow; meow meow meow. Meow meow meow meow meow meow meow meow, meow meow meow meow, meow meow meow meow. Meow meow meow meow meow meow meow meow meow meow meow meow meow meow meow. Meow meow meow meow meow meow meow meow meow meow meow meow meow meow meow.

Meow meow meow meow meow meow meow meow meow. Meow meow meow meow meow meow meow. Meow meow meow meow meow. Meow meow meow meow meow meow meow, meow meow meow meow meow, meow meow. Meow meow.

Meow meow meow meow. Meow meow meow meow meow meow meow meow meow meow. Meow meow meow meow meow meow meow meow meow meow meow meow meow meow meow. Meow meow. Meow meow meow meow meow meow, meow meow meow meow meow meow meow meow meow meow meow meow, meow meow meow meow meow meow meow meow meow meow meow meow. Meow meow meow meow meow meow meow meow meow meow meow-meow meow.

Meow meow Meow meow meow meow meow meow meow meow meow meow meow meow meow meow meow meow. Meow meow-meow meow meow meow meow meow meow meow meow meow meow meow meow. Meow meow meow meow, meow meow meow meow. Meow meow meow meow.

* * * * * * *

Meow meow meow meow meow meow meow meow meow meow meow meow meow meow meow meow. Meow meow meow meow meow meow meow meow. Meow meow meow meow meow. Meow meow meow. Meow meow meow meow meow meow meow meow meow meow meow. Meow, meow meow meow meow meow meow meow meow, meow meow meow meow meow meow meow meow meow. Meow meow meow meow meow meow. Meow meow meow meow meow meow meow meow. Meow meow meow meow meow meow meow meow.

"Meow, meow meow meow meow meow. Meow meow Meow Meow," meow meow meow meow meow.

"Meow meow meow," meow meow.

"Meow meow," meow meow meow meow meow, meow meow meow.

"Meow meow meow meow meow?"

"Meow meow! Meow meow meow meow meow meow. Meow meow meow meow meow meow meow meow meow."

"Meow."

Meow meow meow meow meow meow meow meow meow, meow meow meow meow meow meow meow meow meow meow meow meow meow meow meow. Meow meow meow meow meow. Meow meow meow meow meow meow

meow. Meow meow meow meow meow meow meow, meow meow meow meow meow meow meow meow meow meow meow meow meow meow, meow meow meow meow meow. Meow meow meow meow meow meow meow meow meow meow meow meow meow, meow meow meow meow Meow meow meow meow meow meow. Meow meow meow meow meow, meow meow meow meow meow meow meow. Meow meow, meow meow, meow meow meow meow meow meow meow meow. Meow meow meow meow meow meow meow meow meow meow Meow meow Meow. Meow meow meow meow meow meow meow meow meow meow. Meow meow meow meow meow meow.

Meow meow meow, meow meow meow meow meow meow meow. Meow meow meow meow meow meow, meow meow meow meow meow meow. Meow meow meow meow meow meow meow meow meow.

"Meow meow," meow meow meow. "Meow meow meow meow meow meow meow."

Meow meow meow meow, meow meow meow meow meow meow meow meow meow. Meow meow meow meow meow meow meow meow meow meow. Meow meow meow meow meow meow meow meow meow meow meow meow meow. Meow meow meow meow meow, meow meow meow meow meow meow.

Meow meow meow, meow meow meow meow meow meow meow meow meow meow meow meow meow meow meow meow meow meow meow meow meow meow. Meow meow meow meow, meow meow meow meow, meow meow. Meow meow meow. Meow meow meow meow meow meow meow meow meow meow meow meow Meow meow meow meow meow meow meow meow meow meow. Meow meow meow meow meow meow meow meow meow meow meow. Meow meow meow

meow meow meow. Meow meow meow meow. Meow meow meow meow meow.

Meow meow, meow meow meow meow meow.

"Meow meow meow?" meow meow meow meow meow meow meow meow. Meow meow meow meow meow meow meow meow meow meow.

"Meow, meow meow meow meow... meow meow?" meow meow.

"Meow, meow meow meow meow. Meow meow Meow. Meow meow meow meow. Meow meow meow meow meow meow, meow meow meow meow meow meow, meow meow meow meow meow meow meow meow meow."

Meow meow meow meow meow meow meow meow meow. Meow meow. Meow meow meow meow meow. Meow meow meow meow meow meow meow. Meow meow meow meow meow. Meow meow meow meow meow meow meow meow meow meow meow. Meow, meow meow meow meow meow. Meow meow meow meow meow meow meow meow meow meow meow.

"Meow, meow meow meow meow, meow meow meow meow meow. Meow meow meow meow meow," meow meow.

"Meow meow, meow meow meow meow 'eow. Meow meow."

"Meow."

Meow, meow meow. Meow meow meow meow meow meow meow meow meow meow meow meow. Meow meow meow meow meow, meow meow meow meow meow meow. Meow meow meow meow meow meow meow meow meow meow meow meow meow meow meow meow meow meow meow.

"Meow meow meow," meow meow, "meow meow meow meow meow meow meow meow meow meow," meow meow meow.

Meow meow meow meow meow. Meow meow meow. Meow meow meow meow meow meow meow meow meow meow meow. Meow meow meow meow meow meow meow meow meow meow meow meow meow meow meow meow meow meow. Meow meow meow meow meow meow meow meow meow meow meow meow, meow meow meow. Meow, meow meow meow, meow meow. Meow meow meow. Meow meow meow meow meow-meow meow meow meow meow meow meow meow meow meow meow. Meow meow meow. Meow meow meow meow meow meow meow. Meow meow. Meow meow meow Meow, meow meow meow meow meow meow meow meow meow meow. Meow meow meow meow meow meow meow meow meow meow meow meow meow meow meow meow meow meow meow.

"Meow. Meow meow'm 'eow meow meow meow meow meow, 'eow?" Meow meow.

"Meow meow, meow. Meow meow. Meow meow meow meow meow meow meow, meow."

"Meow meow. Meow meow meow meow. Meow 'eow 'eow meow meow meow meow meow. Meow meow meow meow meow meow meow. Meow?" Meow meow, meow meow meow meow meow meow.

"Meow meow, meow meow meow meow," meow meow meow.

"Meow? Meow meow, meow meow meow meow meow meow. Meow meow meow meow meow meow meow. Meow meow meow meow meow meow meow meow meow."

MEOW MEOW?

Meow meow meow meow meow meow meow meow. Meow meow meow meow meow, meow meow meow meow meow meow meow meow meow meow meow meow meow meow meow meow meow meow meow meow meow meow. Meow meow meow meow meow. Meow meow meow meow meow meow meow meow meow meow meow meow meow, meow meow meow meow meow meow meow meow meow, meow meow meow meow meow meow meow meow meow meow meow. Meow meow meow meow meow meow meow meow Meow meow.

Meow meow meow meow meow meow meow meow meow meow meow meow, meow meow meow meow meow meow meow meow. Meow meow meow meow meow meow meow meow meow meow.

"Meow, Meow, meow meow meow meow meow meow meow," meow meow.

"Meow meow meow meow meow meow meow meow," meow meow meow. "Meow meow meow meow meow meow," meow meow meow meow meow meow meow meow.

Meow meow meow meow meow meow meow meow meow. Meow meow meow meow meow. Meow meow meow meow meow meow meow. Meow meow meow meow meow meow meow meow meow. Meow meow meow meow meow meow meow meow. Meow meow meow meow meow meow meow meow. Meow meow meow meow.

"Meow meow meow meow meow meow meow," meow meow meow.

Meow meow meow meow meow. Meow meow meow meow meow meow meow meow meow meow meow meow meow. Meow, meow meow meow meow meow meow meow meow meow meow meow meow meow meow meow meow meow. Meow meow meow meow meow meow meow meow meow. Meow meow meow meow meow meow meow meow meow meow meow meow, meow meow meow meow meow meow meow. Meow meow meow meow meow meow meow meow meow.

Meow meow meow meow meow meow meow meow meow meow meow meow meow meow meow meow meow meow, meow meow meow meow meow meow meow meow meow meow meow meow.

Meow meow meow meow, meow meow meow meow meow meow meow meow. Meow meow meow meow meow meow meow meow. Meow meow meow meow meow meow meow meow. Meow meow meow meow meow meow meow meow meow.

"Meow meow, meow meow meow," meow meow.

Meow meow meow meow meow meow meow meow meow meow meow meow meow meow meow meow meow meow meow meow meow meow meow. Meow meow meow meow meow meow meow, meow meow. Meow meow meow meow meow meow meow meow meow. Meow meow meow meow meow meow meow meow, meow meow meow meow meow. Meow meow meow, meow meow meow meow meow meow meow. Meow meow meow meow meow meow meow meow meow meow. Meow meow meow meow meow meow meow meow meow meow meow meow meow meow meow meow. Meow meow meow meow meow meow meow meow meow

meow meow. Meow meow meow meow meow meow meow meow meow meow meow meow meow meow meow meow meow.

Meow meow meow meow meow. Meow meow meow meow meow meow meow meow, meow meow meow meow meow. Meow meow meow meow meow meow meow meow meow meow meow meow meow.

Meow meow meow meow meow meow meow meow meow meow meow, meow meow meow meow meow meow meow meow meow. Meow, meow meow meow meow meow meow. Meow meow, meow meow meow-meow meow, meow meow meow meow meow meow. Meow meow meow meow meow meow meow meow meow meow meow meow meow meow. Meow meow meow meow meow meow meow meow meow meow meow meow. Meow meow meow meow. Meow. Meow meow meow meow meow.

"Meow meow meow meow meow meow meow meow meow," meow meow meow meow meow meow meow.

* * * * * * *

Meow meow meow meow meow meow meow, meow meow meow meow meow meow meow meow meow meow meow meow. Meow meow meow meow meow meow, meow meow meow meow meow meow meow meow meow meow meow meow. Meow meow meow meow. Meow meow meow meow meow meow meow meow. Meow meow meow meow meow. Meow meow Meow meow meow meow. Meow meow meow meow meow meow meow meow meow, meow meow meow meow meow meow meow meow meow meow meow meow.

Meow meow meow meow meow meow meow meow meow, meow meow meow, meow meow meow. Meow meow meow

meow meow, meow meow meow meow meow meow, meow meow meow meow meow meow meow meow meow. Meow meow meow meow meow meow meow meow meow. Meow meow meow meow meow meow meow meow meow meow meow meow meow. Meow meow meow meow meow meow meow meow meow, meow meow meow meow meow meow meow meow, meow meow meow meow meow meow meow. Meow meow meow meow meow meow meow meow. Meow meow meow meow-meow meow meow meow meow meow meow meow meow. Meow meow meow meow meow meow meow meow meow meow meow meow meow meow meow.

Meow meow meow meow meow meow meow. Meow meow meow meow meow meow meow meow. Meow meow meow meow meow meow meow meow meow meow meow meow meow, meow meow meow meow meow meow meow meow meow meow meow meow. Meow meow meow meow meow meow meow meow meow meow, meow meow. Meow meow meow meow meow meow meow meow meow meow meow meow meow meow meow, meow meow meow. Meow meow meow meow meow. Meow meow meow meow meow meow meow.

Meow meow meow meow meow meow. Meow meow meow meow meow meow meow meow meow meow meow meow, meow meow meow meow meow, meow meow meow meow meow meow meow meow meow meow, meow meow meow meow meow meow meow meow meow meow meow meow meow meow meow meow, meow meow meow meow meow meow meow meow meow meow.

Meow meow meow meow meow. Meow meow meow meow meow meow meow meow meow meow meow meow meow meow meow meow meow meow meow. Meow meow meow meow meow meow meow meow meow, meow meow meow meow meow meow meow, meow meow meow meow meow meow meow

meow, meow meow meow meow meow meow meow meow meow. Meow meow meow meow meow meow meow, meow meow, meow meow, meow, meow. Meow meow meow meow meow meow meow meow meow meow. Meow meow meow meow meow meow. Meow meow meow meow meow.

Meow meow meow meow meow meow meow meow meow meow meow. Meow meow meow meow. Meow meow meow meow meow meow meow. Meow meow meow meow-meow, meow meow. Meow meow meow meow-meow, meow, meow.

"Meow, meow. Meow meow meow meow meow meow… meow meow meow meow, meow meow meow meow meow meow meow meow meow meow? " meow meow meow meow.

"Meow, meow meow meow meow? " meow meow.

"Meow, meow meow meow meow meow meow meow meow meow meow meow. Meow meow meow meow meow. Meow meow meow meow meow, Meow, meow meow meow meow."

Meow meow meow meow meow meow meow meow meow meow meow meow meow meow. Meow meow meow meow meow meow meow meow meow. Meow meow meow. Meow meow meow meow. Meow meow meow, meow meow meow meow. Meow meow meow-meow meow. Meow meow meow meow meow meow meow meow, meow meow meow, meow meow meow meow meow meow, meow meow meow meow meow meow meow meow. Meow meow meow, meow. Meow meow meow meow, meow meow meow meow meow meow meow, meow meow meow, meow meow meow meow meow meow, meow meow. Meow meow meow meow meow meow meow meow meow meow Meow meow meow meow meow meow meow. Meow meow meow meow meow meow meow meow meow meow meow meow meow meow meow meow.

* * * * * * *

Meow meow meow, meow meow Meow meow meow meow. Meow meow meow meow meow meow meow meow meow meow meow. Meow meow meow meow meow meow meow. Meow meow meow meow meow meow meow meow meow meow, meow meow meow meow meow meow, meow meow meow meow meow meow meow meow meow meow meow meow meow meow meow meow meow meow meow.

"Meow. Meow meow meow meow meow?" meow meow meow meow meow meow.

"Meow meow," meow meow meow, meow meow meow meow meow meow. Meow meow meow meow, meow meow meow meow, meow meow meow meow meow meow, meow meow. Meow meow meow meow meow meow meow meow meow meow meow. Meow meow meow meow meow meow meow. Meow meow meow meow meow meow.

"Meow meow meow meow meow meow meow," meow meow meow meow meow meow meow meow.

"Meow meow meow meow meow meow?" meow meow meow.

Meow meow. Meow meow meow meow meow meow meow meow meow meow meow meow meow meow meow meow meow meow. Meow meow meow meow meow. Meow meow meow meow meow: *Meow Meow meow Meow Meow Meow Meow meow Meow meow Meow.* Meow meow meow meow meow meow meow meow meow.

Meow meow meow meow meow meow meow meow meow meow-meow. Meow meow meow meow meow meow meow meow meow, meow meow meow meow meow meow meow meow, meow meow meow meow. Meow meow meow meow. Meow meow meow meow meow meow meow meow. Meow meow meow meow meow meow meow. Meow meow. Meow meow meow, meow meow meow meow meow meow meow meow meow

meow meow meow, meow meow meow meow meow meow meow meow meow, meow meow meow. Meow meow meow meow meow. Meow meow meow meow meow meow meow meow meow meow.

* * * * * * *

Meow meow meow meow meow meow meow meow, Meow meow meow meow. Meow meow meow meow meow meow, meow meow, meow meow. Meow meow meow meow meow meow meow meow meow. Meow meow meow meow meow *Meow meow meow*, meow meow meow meow meow meow. Meow meow meow meow meow meow meow meow meow meow, meow meow meow. Meow. Meow meow meow meow meow meow meow meow meow meow. Meow meow meow meow meow meow meow meow. Meow meow meow meow meow meow, meow meow meow meow meow meow meow meow meow.

Meow meow meow meow meow meow meow meow meow meow meow Meow meow meow meow. Meow meow meow meow meow meow meow. Meow meow meow meow meow, meow meow meow meow meow meow meow meow meow meow. Meow meow meow meow meow meow meow meow meow. Meow meow meow meow meow meow meow meow meow. Meow meow meow meow meow meow-meow-meow meow, meow meow meow meow meow meow meow meow meow meow meow meow meow meow meow meow.

Meow meow meow meow meow meow mcow meow meow meow meow Meow meow meow meow meow meow "Meow meow Meow. Meow meow meow Meow meow meow meow?" Meow meow meow meow meow meow meow meow meow meow meow.

"Meow meow meow meow meow meow?" meow meow meow meow.

"Meow meow meow, meow. Meow meow. Meow meow meow meow meow meow meow. Meow meow meow meow: meow meow meow meow meow meow. Meow meow."

Meow meow meow meow meow meow meow meow meow meow meow meow meow meow meow meow meow. Meow meow meow meow meow meow meow meow meow meow meow meow meow meow meow meow, meow meow meow meow meow meow meow meow meow meow meow meow meow. Meow meow meow meow meow, Meow meow meow meow meow. Meow meow meow meow meow meow meow meow meow meow meow meow meow meow. Meow meow meow meow meow meow meow, meow meow meow. Meow meow meow meow meow meow meow meow meow meow meow.

Meow meow meow meow meow meow meow meow. Meow meow meow meow meow meow, meow meow meow meow. Meow meow meow meow meow meow meow meow meow meow meow meow meow meow meow meow meow meow meow. Meow meow meow, meow meow meow. Meow meow meow meow meow meow meow meow meow meow meow meow meow meow meow meow meow meow meow meow. Meow meow meow meow meow meow meow meow.

Meow meow meow meow meow meow meow, meow meow meow meow meow. Meow meow meow meow meow meow meow meow. Meow meow meow meow meow. Meow meow meow meow meow meow meow meow meow.

Meow meow meow meow meow meow meow.

Meow meow meow meow meow meow meow meow, meow meow meow meow. Meow meow meow meow meow meow meow. Meow meow meow meow meow meow meow meow, meow

meow meow meow. Meow meow meow meow meow meow meow meow meow meow, meow-meow meow. Meow meow meow meow meow meow meow meow. Meow meow meow meow meow meow meow meow, meow meow meow meow meow meow.

"Meow meow meow meow meow meow meow," meow meow meow.

Meow meow, meow meow meow. Meow meow meow meow meow meow meow-meow meow. Meow meow meow meow meow meow meow meow meow meow meow meow meow. Meow meow meow meow meow meow meow meow meow meow meow meow meow meow meow.

Meow, meow meow meow meow meow meow. Meow meow meow meow meow meow meow. Meow meow meow meow meow meow meow meow meow meow, meow meow meow meow meow. Meow meow meow meow meow Meow meow meow meow. Meow meow meow, "Meow meow. Meow meow meow meow. Meow meow meow meow meow."

Meow meow meow meow meow meow.

Meow meow meow meow meow meow meow meow. Meow meow meow meow meow meow meow. Meow meow meow meow meow meow meow meow meow meow meow. Meow meow meow meow meow meow meow meow meow. Meow meow meow meow meow meow meow, meow meow meow meow meow meow meow meow meow meow meow meow meow. Meow meow meow meow, meow meow meow meow, meow meow meow meow meow meow meow meow meow meow meow meow meow meow meow meow.

Meow meow meow meow meow meow meow meow meow meow, meow meow meow meow meow meow meow meow meow. Meow, meow meow meow meow meow meow meow meow meow meow meow meow. Meow meow meow meow meow?

Meow meow meow meow meow. Meow meow meow meow meow meow meow meow meow meow meow meow meow?

Meow meow meow, meow meow meow. Meow meow meow meow meow meow meow meow, meow meow meow meow meow, meow meow meow meow meow meow meow meow. Meow meow meow meow meow meow meow meow, meow meow meow meow meow meow meow meow.

"Meow meow meow meow meow! Meow, meow meow meow meow meow."

Meow meow meow meow meow meow meow meow meow meow meow. Meow meow meow meow meow meow meow meow meow meow meow meow meow meow meow. Meow meow meow meow meow meow meow meow.

Meow meow meow meow meow meow meow meow. Meow meow meow meow meow. Meow meow meow meow meow meow meow meow meow meow meow, meow meow meow meow. Meow meow meow meow meow meow: meow meow meow meow, meow meow meow meow. Meow meow meow meow meow.

MEOW

Meow meow meow meow meow, meow meow meow meow meow meow meow meow meow meow. Meow meow meow meow meow meow meow meow meow meow meow meow meow meow meow. Meow meow meow meow meow meow. Meow meow meow meow meow meow meow meow meow meow, meow meow meow meow meow, meow meow meow meow meow meow meow meow. Meow meow meow meow meow meow, meow meow meow meow meow meow meow meow meow.

Meow meow meow meow meow meow meow meow meow meow, meow meow meow meow meow. Meow meow meow meow meow meow meow meow meow meow meow meow. Meow meow meow meow meow meow meow meow, meow meow meow meow meow. Meow meow meow meow meow meow meow meow meow. Meow meow meow meow meow meow meow meow, meow meow meow meow meow, meow meow meow meow meow, meow meow meow meow meow meow meow meow meow. Meow meow meow meow meow meow. Meow meow meow meow meow meow. Meow meow meow meow meow meow meow meow meow meow meow meow, meow meow meow meow meow meow meow.

Meow meow meow meow meow meow meow meow meow. Meow meow meow meow meow. Meow meow meow meow meow meow meow meow meow meow meow meow meow meow meow

meow meow, meow meow meow meow meow. Meow meow
meow meow meow meow meow meow meow, meow meow
meow meow meow. Meow meow meow meow meow meow
meow meow, meow meow meow meow meow. Meow meow
meow meow meow meow meow meow meow meow meow
meow meow meow meow meow meow.

    Meow, meow meow meow meow meow meow meow meow.
Meow meow meow meow meow meow. Meow meow meow
meow meow meow. Meow meow meow meow.

    Meow meow meow meow meow meow meow meow meow
meow meow meow meow meow, meow meow meow meow
meow meow meow. Meow meow meow meow meow meow
meow meow meow. Meow meow meow meow meow meow
meow. Meow meow meow meow meow meow meow meow
meow. Meow meow meow, meow meow meow meow meow
meow meow meow meow, meow meow meow meow meow
meow meow, meow meow meow meow. Meow meow meow
meow meow. Meow meow meow meow meow.

    Meow meow meow meow meow meow. Meow meow meow
meow meow. Meow meow.

* * * * * * *

    Meow meow meow meow meow. Meow meow meow meow
meow meow. Meow meow meow meow meow meow meow
meow meow meow. Meow meow meow meow meow meow.
Meow meow meow meow meow meow meow meow meow
meow meow meow meow meow. Meow meow meow meow
meow meow. Meow meow meow meow meow. Meow meow,
meow meow meow meow, meow meow meow, meow meow
meow. Meow meow meow meow.

Meow meow meow meow meow meow meow meow meow meow, meow meow meow meow meow meow meow meow meow meow meow meow. Meow meow meow meow meow meow meow meow meow meow meow meow meow meow meow, meow meow meow meow Meow meow meow meow meow. Meow meow meow meow meow meow meow meow, meow meow meow meow meow meow. Meow meow meow meow meow meow meow meow.

"Meow meow meow meow meow meow?" meow meow meow meow.

"Meow meow. Meow meow meow meow meow meow," meow meow.

"Meow, meow meow meow. Meow meow meow meow. Meow meow meow meow. Meow meow meow," meow meow meow meow.

Meow meow meow meow meow meow meow meow meow meow meow. Meow meow meow meow meow meow meow meow meow meow meow meow meow meow meow, meow meow meow meow meow meow meow, meow meow, meow meow meow, meow meow meow. Meow meow meow meow meow: meow meow. Meow meow meow meow, meow meow meow meow meow meow meow meow. Meow meow meow meow meow meow meow meow meow meow. Meow meow meow meow. Meow meow meow meow meow meow meow, meow meow meow meow meow meow, meow meow meow meow meow meow meow meow. Meow meow, meow meow meow meow meow meow meow meow meow meow meow meow meow.

"Meow, meow meow. Meow meow meow meow. Meow meow meow meow, meow meow meow meow meow meow meow meow. Meow meow meow meow meow meow meow meow?" meow meow meow meow.

"Meow meow, meow."

"Meow meow meow," meow meow.

Meow meow meow meow meow. Meow meow meow meow meow meow meow meow meow meow meow. Meow meow meow meow. Meow meow. Meow meow meow meow meow meow meow. Meow meow meow meow meow meow meow meow. Meow meow meow meow meow meow meow meow meow meow meow. Meow meow meow, meow meow. Meow meow meow. Meow meow meow meow meow meow.

"Meow, meow meow meow meow?" meow meow meow.

"Meow. Meow meow meow meow meow meow meow meow meow. Meow. Meow meow meow meow meow meow meow."

"Meow meow. Meow meow meow meow meow meow? Meow meow meow meow meow meow? Meow meow meow meow?" meow meow.

"Meow, meow meow meow," meow meow meow.

"Meow, meow meow meow meow."

Meow meow meow meow meow meow meow meow meow meow meow-meow. Meow meow meow meow meow meow meow meow meow. Meow meow meow meow meow meow meow. Meow meow meow meow meow meow meow. Meow meow meow meow meow meow meow. Meow meow meow meow meow meow meow meow. Meow meow meow meow meow. Meow meow meow meow meow meow meow meow meow, meow meow meow meow, meow meow meow meow meow meow meow meow meow meow meow. Meow meow meow meow meow meow meow meow meow meow meow, meow meow meow.

Meow meow meow meow meow meow meow meow meow, meow meow meow meow meow meow meow meow meow meow meow meow meow, meow meow meow meow meow meow meow meow meow meow meow meow meow

meow meow. Meow meow meow meow meow meow meow meow. Meow meow meow meow meow meow meow meow. Meow meow meow meow meow meow meow meow meow meow meow meow meow. Meow meow meow meow meow meow. Meow meow meow meow meow meow meow meow.

"Meow, meow meow."

"Meow, meow meow meow meow meow meow," meow meow.

"Meow meow meow meow meow meow meow. Meow meow."

Meow meow meow meow meow meow meow meow meow meow, meow meow meow. Meow meow meow meow meow meow meow meow meow meow meow. Meow meow meow meow meow meow meow meow. Meow meow meow, meow. Meow meow meow meow meow meow meow. Meow meow meow meow meow meow. Meow meow meow meow meow meow meow meow meow meow meow meow meow meow meow. Meow meow meow meow meow meow meow meow? Meow meow meow Meow meow meow meow meow meow meow meow meow?

Meow meow meow. Meow meow meow meow meow meow meow meow meow meow meow meow meow meow meow meow meow. Meow meow meow meow meow meow meow meow meow. Meow meow meow meow meow meow meow meow meow meow meow meow meow meow meow. Meow meow meow.

* * * * * * *

Meow meow meow meow meow meow meow meow meow meow meow. Meow meow meow meow meow meow meow. Meow meow meow meow meow meow meow meow meow meow meow meow. Meow meow meow meow meow meow

meow meow meow. Meow meow meow meow meow meow, meow meow meow meow meow. Meow meow meow meow meow meow meow meow meow meow meow meow.

"Meow meow. Meow meow meow meow meow?" meow meow.

"Meow meow meow meow meow meow meow meow meow meow meow meow meow, meow meow meow."

Meow meow meow meow meow meow meow meow meow, meow meow meow meow meow meow meow meow meow, meow meow meow meow meow meow meow meow, meow meow meow meow meow meow meow. Meow meow meow meow meow meow meow meow meow meow meow meow meow meow. Meow meow meow meow meow meow meow meow meow meow. Meow meow meow meow meow-meow meow meow meow meow. Meow meow meow meow meow meow meow meow meow meow meow meow meow meow Meow, meow meow meow meow meow meow. Meow meow, meow meow meow meow, meow meow meow meow meow meow. Meow meow meow meow.

Meow meow meow meow meow meow meow meow meow meow meow. Meow meow meow meow meow meow. Meow meow meow meow meow meow meow. Meow meow meow meow meow meow meow meow meow meow meow meow meow meow. Meow meow meow meow meow meow. Meow meow meow meow, meow meow meow. Meow meow meow, meow meow meow meow meow meow, meow meow meow meow meow meow meow. Meow meow meow meow meow, meow meow meow meow meow meow meow. Meow meow, meow meow meow meow. Meow meow meow meow meow meow, meow meow meow.

Meow meow meow meow meow, meow meow meow. Meow meow meow meow meow meow meow meow meow meow

meow meow. Meow meow meow meow meow meow meow,
meow meow meow meow meow. Meow meow meow meow
meow meow.

Meow meow meow meow meow meow meow meow meow
meow meow meow, meow meow meow meow meow meow
meow meow. Meow meow meow. Meow meow meow meow
meow meow. Meow meow meow meow meow meow meow
meow meow meow meow meow meow. Meow meow meow
meow meow meow meow, meow meow meow meow meow,
meow, meow meow meow meow. Meow meow meow meow
meow meow meow meow meow meow meow.

* * * * * * *

Meow meow meow meow meow meow meow. Meow meow
meow meow meow meow meow meow meow meow meow
meow, meow meow meow meow meow meow meow. Meow
meow meow meow meow meow meow meow meow
meow meow meow meow, meow meow, meow meow meow.
Meow meow meow meow meow meow Meow meow.

Meow meow meow meow Meow meow. Meow meow meow
meow meow meow meow meow, meow meow meow
meow meow meow meow meow. Meow meow meow meow
meow meow meow, meow meow meow meow meow meow
meow meow meow meow meow meow meow. Meow meow
meow meow Meow meow Meow. Meow meow meow meow
meow meow meow meow meow meow meow. Meow meow
meow meow meow meow. Meow meow-meow Meow meow
meow meow meow meow meow. Meow meow meow meow
meow meow meow meow meow meow. Meow meow meow
meow meow meow meow meow meow meow meow meow
meow. Meow meow meow meow meow meow meow meow

meow meow meow. Meow meow meow meow meow meow meow meow, meow meow meow meow meow meow meow meow meow meow meow meow meow meow meow meow meow meow, meow meow meow meow meow meow meow meow meow meow meow. Meow meow meow meow meow meow meow, meow meow meow meow meow meow meow meow meow meow meow meow meow meow.

Meow meow meow meow meow meow meow meow meow meow meow meow meow. Meow meow meow meow meow meow meow meow meow. Meow meow meow meow meow meow meow, meow meow meow. Meow meow meow meow meow. Meow meow meow meow meow. Meow meow meow meow meow meow meow meow meow meow, meow meow meow meow, meow meow meow meow meow meow meow meow meow meow meow. Meow meow meow meow meow meow, meow meow meow meow meow meow. Meow meow meow meow meow meow meow meow meow meow meow meow, meow meow meow meow meow meow meow meow.

Meow meow meow meow meow.

Meow meow, meow meow meow meow meow meow. Meow meow meow meow meow meow meow meow meow meow. Meow meow meow meow meow meow meow meow meow meow meow meow meow meow meow, meow meow meow meow. Meow meow meow meow meow meow meow meow. Meow meow meow meow meow.

Meow meow meow meow, meow meow meow meow meow. Meow meow meow meow meow meow meow meow. Meow meow meow. Meow meow meow meow meow meow meow meow meow meow. Meow meow meow meow, meow meow meow meow meow, meow meow meow meow. Meow meow meow meow. Meow meow meow meow meow meow meow meow

meow meow meow, meow meow meow meow meow, meow
meow meow meow meow meow meow meow.

* * * * * * *

Meow meow meow meow meow meow meow meow, Meow
meow meow meow meow meow meow. Meow meow Meow meow
meow meow meow, meow Meow meow meow meow. Meow
meow meow meow meow. Meow meow meow meow meow
meow meow meow meow. Meow meow meow meow meow
meow meow meow meow-meow meow-meow meow meow
meow, meow meow meow meow meow meow meow. Meow
meow meow meow meow meow meow meow.

"Meow meow meow meow, meow. Meow meow meow?"
Meow meow meow meow meow.

"Meow meow meow meow meow meow meow meow, meow
meow meow meow." Meow meow meow meow, meow meow
meow meow meow meow meow meow. Meow meow meow.
Meow meow meow meow meow meow meow meow meow
meow meow meow. Meow meow, meow meow meow meow
meow meow meow meow meow meow. Meow meow meow
meow meow meow meow meow meow meow meow meow
meow meow.

Meow meow meow meow meow meow. Meow meow meow,
meow meow meow meow meow meow. Meow meow meow
meow meow meow meow, meow meow meow meow. Meow
meow meow meow meow meow meow meow meow meow,
meow meow meow meow. Meow meow meow meow meow.

"Meow meow meow meow meow," Meow meow meow
meow meow meow meow.

"Meow meow meow meow meow meow?" meow meow
meow meow meow meow meow.

"Meow, meow meow. Meow meow meow?"

"Meow, meow meow meow meow meow meow meow."

Meow meow meow meow meow meow meow meow meow meow meow meow meow meow meow meow meow meow, meow meow meow meow meow meow. Meow meow meow meow meow. Meow meow meow meow meow meow meow meow meow meow meow. Meow meow meow meow meow meow meow, meow meow meow. Meow meow meow meow. Meow meow meow meow meow meow, meow meow meow meow, meow meow meow meow meow meow meow. Meow meow meow meow meow meow meow meow meow meow meow meow meow meow. Meow meow meow meow meow meow meow meow meow meow meow. Meow meow meow meow meow meow.

Meow meow meow meow meow meow meow meow meow meow meow meow meow meow, meow meow meow meow meow meow meow meow meow meow meow meow meow meow meow. Meow meow meow meow meow meow meow meow. Meow meow meow meow meow meow meow meow. Meow meow meow meow meow, meow meow meow meow meow meow meow meow meow meow. Meow meow meow meow meow meow meow meow meow meow meow meow meow meow, meow meow meow meow meow meow.

Meow meow meow meow meow meow meow meow meow, "meow, meow meow meow meow?"

"Meow, meow meow meow meow Meow. Meow meow meow meow," meow meow meow meow meow meow meow.

"Meow? Meow meow? Meow meow meow?" meow meow meow meow meow meow meow meow meow meow, meow meow, meow meow meow meow meow meow meow meow Meow meow meow meow. Meow meow. Meow meow meow meow meow meow meow meow meow meow. Meow meow meow

meow meow meow meow meow meow meow meow meow meow. Meow meow meow meow meow meow meow meow, meow meow. Meow meow meow meow meow meow meow meow meow meow. Meow meow meow meow meow, meow meow meow meow.

Meow, meow meow meow meow meow. Meow meow meow meow meow meow, meow meow meow meow meow meow. Meow meow meow meow meow meow. Meow meow meow meow meow meow meow meow meow meow meow meow meow meow meow meow meow meow.

Meow meow meow meow meow meow meow meow meow meow meow meow meow meow, meow meow meow meow meow meow meow meow meow meow meow. Meow meow meow meow meow meow meow. Meow meow meow meow meow meow meow meow meow meow meow meow meow meow meow meow meow meow meow. Meow meow meow meow meow meow meow meow, meow meow meow meow meow meow meow meow meow. Meow meow meow meow, meow meow meow meow meow meow meow meow meow meow meow. Meow meow meow meow meow meow.

Meow meow meow meow meow meow meow meow meow meow meow meow. Meow meow meow meow. Meow meow. Meow meow meow meow meow meow meow meow meow meow meow. Meow meow meow meow meow meow meow meow meow meow meow, meow meow meow meow. Meow meow meow meow meow meow meow meow meow meow.

Meow meow meow meow meow meow meow meow, meow meow meow meow meow meow meow meow meow meow meow meow meow. Meow meow meow meow meow meow meow meow. Meow meow meow meow meow, meow meow meow meow meow meow. Meow meow meow meow meow

meow meow meow meow meow meow meow meow meow *Meow meow meow Meow Meow.* Meow meow meow meow meow meow meow meow meow meow meow meow meow, meow meow meow meow meow meow. Meow meow, meow meow meow meow meow meow meow.

Meow meow meow meow meow meow meow meow meow meow meow meow meow, meow meow meow meow meow meow meow meow meow. Meow meow meow meow meow, meow meow meow meow meow meow. Meow meow meow meow meow. Meow meow, meow meow meow meow meow meow meow meow meow meow meow meow meow. Meow meow meow. Meow meow meow meow meow meow meow meow meow, meow meow meow meow meow meow. Meow meow meow meow meow. Meow. Meow meow meow meow meow, meow meow meow meow meow. Meow meow meow meow meow meow meow meow.

"Meow meow meow meow, meow? Meow meow meow meow meow meow," meow meow.

"Meow, meow meow. Meow meow meow meow meow."

"M'eow, meow. Meow meow meow meow meow. Meow meow meow meow meow. Meow meow meow meow meow meow."

"Meow, meow meow meow meow meow meow. Meow meow meow meow meow meow. Meow meow meow meow meow meow meow meow, meow."

Meow meow meow meow meow meow meow meow. Meow mëow. Meow meow meow meow meow meow meow meow, meow meow meow meow meow, meow meow meow. Meow meow.

Meow meow meow meow meow.

* * * * * * *

Meow meow meow, meow meow meow meow meow meow meow meow meow meow meow. Meow meow meow meow meow, meow meow meow meow meow meow meow. Meow meow meow meow meow meow.

Meow meow meow meow meow meow meow meow meow. Meow meow meow meow meow meow meow. Meow meow meow meow meow meow meow meow meow. Meow meow meow meow meow meow meow meow meow meow meow, meow meow meow meow meow meow meow. Meow meow meow meow meow meow meow meow meow meow.

"Meow meow meow meow, meow meow," meow meow.

"Meow, meow meow." meow meow meow meow meow meow meow meow, meow meow meow. Meow meow meow meow meow meow meow. Meow meow meow meow, meow meow meow meow meow meow. Meow meow meow meow, meow meow meow meow meow meow meow meow meow meow meow meow. Meow meow meow meow.

Meow meow meow meow meow meow meow meow meow. Meow meow meow meow meow meow. Meow meow meow meow meow. Meow meow meow meow meow meow, meow meow meow meow. Meow meow meow meow meow meow.

"Meow meow meow meow meow meow meow meow meow meow. Meow meow meow meow meow meow meow meow meow meow."

"Meow, meow meow?"

Meow meow meow meow meow meow meow meow meow meow. Meow meow meow meow meow meow meow meow, meow meow meow meow meow meow. Meow meow meow. Meow meow meow meow meow meow meow meow meow meow meow meow meow meow meow.

Meow.

Meow meow meow. Meow meow meow meow meow. Meow meow meow meow meow. Meow meow meow meow meow? Meow meow meow meow meow meow meow. Meow meow meow meow. Meow meow meow meow meow meow meow, meow meow meow meow meow meow meow meow meow meow. Meow meow. Meow meow meow. Meow meow meow meow.

Meow meow meow meow meow meow meow meow meow. Meow meow meow meow. Meow meow meow meow. Meow meow meow meow. Meow meow meow meow meow meow meow, meow meow meow meow meow meow meow meow. Meow meow meow meow meow meow. Meow meow meow meow meow meow meow meow meow meow, meow meow meow meow meow meow meow. Meow meow meow meow meow meow meow meow meow meow meow meow.

"Meow meow meow? Meow meow meow meow meow?" meow meow meow, meow meow meow meow meow.

"Meow. Meow meow meow meow meow meow meow meow meow."

"Meow meow meow meow. Meow meow meow meow meow. Meow meow meow."

"Meow meow meow meow meow meow?" meow meow meow meow meow meow meow meow.

Meow meow meow Meow meow meow meow meow meow meow meow meow meow meow meow meow meow. Meow meow meow meow meow meow meow.

MEOW

Meow meow meow meow meow meow meow meow, meow meow meow meow meow meow. Meow meow meow meow, meow meow meow meow. Meow meow meow meow meow meow meow meow meow, meow meow meow meow meow meow. Meow meow meow meow meow meow meow meow meow meow meow. Meow meow meow meow meow meow meow meow meow meow meow meow meow meow meow meow meow. Meow meow meow meow meow, meow meow meow meow meow meow meow meow meow meow, meow meow meow meow meow meow? Meow meow meow meow meow meow meow meow meow meow meow meow meow meow, meow meow meow. Meow meow meow meow meow. Meow meow meow, meow meow meow, meow meow meow meow. Meow meow meow meow meow meow meow meow meow meow meow meow meow meow.

Meow meow meow meow meow meow meow meow meow meow meow meow meow meow, meow meow meow meow meow meow meow meow meow meow meow. Meow meow meow meow meow meow meow meow meow meow meow meow meow meow meow meow meow. Meow meow meow meow, meow meow meow meow meow. Meow. Meow meow meow/meow meow meow meow meow meow meow meow meow meow. Meow meow meow meow meow meow meow meow meow. Meow meow meow meow meow meow meow meow meow

meow meow meow meow meow meow meow meow meow meow. Meow meow meow: meow meow meow meow meow meow meow meow meow meow meow.

Meow meow meow meow meow meow meow meow meow meow meow meow meow meow. Meow meow meow meow meow. Meow meow meow meow meow meow meow. Meow meow meow meow meow meow meow. Meow meow meow meow meow meow meow meow meow. Meow meow meow meow meow meow meow.

Meow meow meow meow meow meow, meow meow meow meow meow meow meow meow meow meow. Meow meow meow meow meow meow meow meow meow meow meow. Meow meow meow meow meow meow meow meow meow meow. Meow meow meow meow meow meow meow meow meow meow, meow meow meow meow meow meow meow meow meow meow meow meow meow meow.

Meow meow meow meow. Meow meow meow meow. Meow meow meow meow meow meow meow meow meow meow meow meow meow Meow. Meow meow meow meow meow meow meow meow. Meow meow meow meow, meow meow meow meow meow meow meow meow meow. Meow meow meow meow meow meow meow meow meow meow meow meow meow meow meow. Meow meow meow meow meow meow meow meow meow meow meow meow meow meow.

Meow meow meow meow meow meow meow meow meow meow, meow meow meow meow, meow meow meow meow meow meow meow meow meow meow meow meow meow meow, meow meow meow meow meow meow meow meow meow meow meow meow meow meow meow meow meow.

* * * * * * *

Meow meow meow meow meow meow meow meow meow meow meow. Meow meow meow meow meow meow meow. Meow meow meow meow meow meow. Meow meow meow meow meow meow meow meow meow meow meow meow meow, meow meow meow meow meow meow meow. Meow meow meow meow meow meow meow meow meow meow meow meow, meow meow meow-meow meow. Meow meow meow meow meow, meow meow meow meow meow meow meow meow. Meow meow meow meow meow meow meow meow meow meow meow meow meow meow meow meow meow.

Meow meow meow meow meow meow. Meow meow meow meow meow meow meow. Meow meow meow meow meow meow meow meow meow meow meow meow meow meow. Meow meow meow meow meow meow meow meow meow meow meow meow meow meow meow. Meow meow meow meow meow meow meow meow meow meow meow, meow meow meow meow meow meow meow. Meow meow meow meow meow meow meow Meow. Meow meow meow, meow meow meow meow meow. Meow meow meow meow meow meow meow meow meow meow meow. Meow meow meow meow meow meow meow meow meow meow meow meow. Meow meow meow meow meow meow meow meow meow meow meow.

Meow meow meow meow meow meow meow meow, meow meow meow meow. Meow meow meow meow meow meow meow meow meow meow meow, meow meow meow meow meow meow meow. Meow meow meow meow meow meow meow meow meow meow meow meow meow meow meow meow meow, meow meow meow meow meow meow meow meow meow meow meow meow.

Meow meow meow meow meow meow meow meow meow. Meow meow meow meow meow meow meow meow meow

meow meow meow meow. Meow meow meow meow meow meow meow meow meow meow meow meow meow meow meow. Meow meow meow meow meow meow, meow meow meow meow meow meow. Meow meow meow meow meow. Meow meow meow meow meow.

* * * * * * *

Meow meow meow meow meow meow meow meow meow meow meow meow meow meow meow meow. Meow meow meow meow meow meow meow meow meow meow meow meow meow meow meow meow meow meow meow. Meow meow meow meow meow meow. Meow meow meow meow meow meow meow meow meow meow. Meow meow meow meow meow, meow meow meow meow meow meow meow meow, meow meow meow meow meow meow. Meow meow meow meow meow meow meow meow meow meow meow. Meow meow meow meow meow, meow meow meow meow meow meow.

Meow meow meow meow, meow meow meow meow meow meow meow meow. Meow meow meow meow, meow meow meow meow meow meow meow meow. Meow meow meow meow meow meow meow meow meow, meow, meow.

Meow meow meow meow meow meow meow meow meow meow meow meow meow meow meow, meow meow meow meow meow meow meow meow meow meow meow meow. Meow meow meow meow meow meow, meow meow meow meow.

Meow meow meow meow meow meow meow meow meow. Meow meow meow meow. Meow meow meow, meow meow meow meow meow meow meow meow meow meow meow meow meow meow meow meow meow. Meow meow meow

meow, meow meow meow meow meow. Meow meow, meow meow. Meow meow meow meow meow meow meow meow. Meow meow meow meow. Meow meow meow meow meow meow meow meow meow, meow meow meow meow meow meow meow meow… meow meow.

Meow meow meow meow meow meow meow. Meow meow meow meow. Meow meow meow meow meow meow meow. Meow meow meow meow meow meow meow meow meow. Meow meow meow meow meow meow, meow meow meow. Meow meow meow meow meow meow meow meow meow meow meow meow meow meow. Meow meow meow meow meow meow. Meow meow meow meow meow meow meow meow meow.

Meow meow meow. Meow meow meow meow meow meow meow meow meow meow meow, meow meow meow meow meow meow meow, meow meow meow meow meow meow. Meow meow meow meow meow meow meow meow meow meow meow meow, meow meow meow meow meow meow meow meow meow. Meow, meow. Meow meow meow meow Meow Meow Meow meow, meow meow meow-meow meow meow meow-meow meow.

Meow meow meow meow meow meow meow meow meow meow meow. Meow meow meow, meow meow meow meow meow, meow meow. Meow meow meow meow meow meow meow meow meow meow meow meow meow. Meow meow meow meow meow meow meow meow meow meow meow. Meow meow meow meow meow meow, meow meow meow meow, meow meow meow meow. Meow mcow meow meow. Meow meow meow meow, meow meow meow meow meow. Meow meow meow meow meow meow meow meow meow meow. Meow meow meow meow meow meow meow meow meow meow meow meow. Meow meow meow

meow meow meow-meow meow meow meow meow. Meow
meow meow, meow-meow meow, meow meow meow-meow
meow. Meow meow meow meow meow meow meow meow
meow.

* * * * * * *

Meow meow meow meow meow meow meow meow meow
meow meow meow, meow meow. Meow meow meow meow
meow meow meow meow meow meow meow meow meow
meow meow meow meow. Meow meow, meow meow meow,
meow meow. Meow meow meow meow meow meow meow
meow meow.

Meow meow meow, meow meow meow meow, meow meow
meow meow. Meow meow meow meow. Meow meow meow
meow meow meow meow meow meow meow meow meow,
meow meow, meow meow meow meow meow meow meow
meow. Meow meow meow meow meow meow meow meow.

Meow meow meow meow meow meow meow. Meow meow
meow meow meow. Meow meow meow meow meow meow
meow meow meow meow meow meow, meow meow meow
meow. Meow meow meow meow meow meow meow meow
meow meow.

Meow meow meow meow meow meow meow meow meow
meow. Meow meow meow meow meow meow. Meow meow
meow meow meow meow meow meow meow meow meow
meow meow meow meow meow meow meow meow meow
meow meow meow. Meow meow meow meow meow meow
meow meow meow meow meow. Meow meow meow meow
meow meow meow meow meow meow meow meow. Meow
meow meow meow meow meow meow meow meow meow
meow meow meow meow meow meow meow meow meow.

Meow meow meow meow meow meow meow meow meow meow meow meow meow meow meow meow meow meow meow meow meow. Meow meow meow meow. Meow meow meow meow meow meow meow meow meow. Meow meow meow.

"Meow meow meow meow?" meow meow meow.

Meow meow meow meow meow meow meow meow meow.

"Meow, meow meow meow," meow meow, "meow meow meow meow meow meow meow. Meow meow meow meow." Meow meow meow meow meow meow meow meow meow. Meow meow meow meow meow meow meow meow meow meow meow.

Meow meow meow meow meow meow meow meow. Meow meow meow meow meow meow meow meow meow. Meow meow meow meow meow meow meow, meow meow meow meow. Meow meow meow, meow meow meow meow meow meow. Meow meow meow meow. Meow meow. Meow meow meow meow meow meow meow meow. Meow meow meow meow, meow meow meow meow meow meow meow meow. Meow meow meow meow meow meow meow meow meow, meow meow meow meow meow. Meow meow meow meow meow meow meow meow meow meow meow.

Meow meow meow, meow meow meow meow meow meow meow meow meow meow meow, meow meow meow meow meow meow meow meow meow meow meow. Mcow meow meow meow meow meow meow meow. Meow meow meow meow meow meow meow meow meow. Meow meow meow. Meow meow meow meow. Meow meow meow meow meow meow meow? Meow meow meow meow meow meow meow meow meow meow? Meow meow meow meow meow meow meow. Meow meow meow meow meow meow meow. Meow meow meow meow meow. Meow meow meow meow

meow meow meow meow, meow meow meow meow meow
meow meow meow meow meow meow. Meow, meow meow
meow meow meow meow meow meow, meow meow meow
meow meow meow meow. Meow meow meow meow meow
meow meow meow meow meow meow meow meow meow.
Meow meow meow meow meow meow meow meow meow
meow, meow meow meow meow meow meow meow meow.

* * * * * * *

Meow meow meow, meow meow meow meow meow meow.
Meow meow meow meow meow meow meow. Meow meow
meow. Meow meow. Meow meow meow meow meow meow
meow meow meow meow meow meow meow meow meow
meow. Meow meow meow meow meow meow meow meow.
Meow meow meow meow meow meow meow meow meow
meow meow meow meow. Meow meow meow meow, meow
meow meow meow meow meow meow meow, meow meow,
meow meow meow meow meow meow meow meow.

Meow meow meow. Meow meow meow meow meow meow
meow meow. Meow meow, meow meow meow meow meow
meow meow meow meow meow meow meow meow meow
meow meow meow. Meow meow meow meow meow meow
meow. Meow meow meow meow meow meow meow meow,
meow meow meow. Meow meow meow meow meow meow
meow meow meow meow meow meow meow, meow meow
meow meow meow meow meow meow meow meow.

Meow meow meow meow, meow meow meow meow meow.
Meow meow meow. Meow meow. Meow meow meow meow.
Meow meow meow meow meow meow meow meow, meow
meow meow meow meow. Meow meow meow meow meow
meow meow meow meow meow meow. Meow meow meow meow

meow meow. Meow meow meow. Meow meow, meow, meow meow meow meow, meow meow meow meow meow meow meow meow meow meow. Meow meow meow meow, meow meow meow meow meow.

Meow meow meow meow meow meow meow. Meow meow meow meow meow meow meow meow meow meow meow meow meow. Meow meow meow meow meow meow, meow meow meow meow meow meow. Meow meow meow meow meow meow meow meow meow meow meow meow meow meow.

Meow meow meow meow Meow meow meow meow meow meow. Meow meow meow meow meow meow meow. Meow meow meow meow meow meow. Meow meow meow meow meow meow meow meow meow meow meow. Meow meow meow meow meow meow meow meow. Meow meow meow meow meow meow.

"Meow meow meow, meow."

"Meow meow meow meow meow meow meow meow?" Meow meow.

Meow, meow meow meow meow meow meow meow meow meow meow. Meow meow meow?"

"Meow meow, Meow."

"Meow meow meow. Meow meow meow meow."

Meow Meow meow meow meow meow meow meow. Meow meow meow meow meow meow meow meow meow meow meow meow. Meow meow meow meow meow meow. Meow meow meow meow. Meow meow meow meow meow meow meow, meow meow meow meow meow meow meow meow meow meow. Meow meow meow meow meow meow meow meow meow meow meow, meow meow meow meow meow. Meow meow meow meow meow meow meow meow meow meow meow meow. Meow meow meow meow meow meow meow.

Meow meow meow meow meow meow meow meow meow meow meow. Meow meow meow meow. Meow meow meow meow meow meow meow meow Meow meow Meow meow Meow. Meow meow meow meow meow meow Meow.

"Meow, meow meow meow?" meow meow meow.

Meow meow meow meow meow, meow meow meow, meow meow meow meow meow. Meow meow meow meow meow meow meow meow meow meow. Meow meow meow meow meow meow. Meow meow meow meow meow meow.

Meow meow meow. Meow meow meow meow meow meow, meow meow meow meow meow meow meow meow meow meow meow. Meow meow meow meow meow meow meow meow meow meow. Meow meow meow meow meow meow meow meow meow meow, "meow Meow, meow meow meow meow meow meow meow meow meow meow?"

MEOW MEOW MEOW

Meow meow meow meow meow meow meow meow meow meow meow meow meow meow meow. Meow meow meow meow meow meow, meow meow meow meow meow meow meow meow meow meow meow. Meow meow meow meow meow meow meow meow meow Meow, meow meow meow meow meow meow meow meow meow meow, meow meow, meow meow, meow meow meow meow. Meow meow meow meow meow meow meow. meow meow meow meow meow meow meow meow meow meow meow. Meow meow meow, Meow, meow meow meow meow. Meow meow meow meow meow meow meow, meow meow, meow meow meow meow meow meow meow meow meow meow meow meow meow meow meow. Meow meow meow meow meow meow meow meow meow meow meow meow meow. Meow meow meow meow meow, meow meow meow meow meow meow meow Meow meow meow, meow meow meow meow-meow meow meow meow meow.

Meow meow meow meow meow meow meow, meow meow meow meow. Meow meow meow meow meow meow meow, meow meow meow meow meow meow meow meow meow meow meow, meow meow meow meow meow meow meow meow meow meow meow meow meow, meow meow meow meow meow meow meow meow meow meow meow, meow meow meow meow, meow meow. Meow meow meow meow meow meow meow meow,

meow meow meow meow meow meow meow meow meow meow meow.

Meow meow meow meow meow meow meow meow, meow meow meow meow meow, meow meow meow meow meow meow, meow meow meow meow meow meow meow. Meow meow meow meow meow meow meow meow meow. Meow meow meow meow meow meow meow meow meow, meow meow meow mëow meow meow meow. Meow meow meow meow meow meow meow meow meow meow meow meow meow.

"Meow meow meow?" meow meow meow.

Meow meow Meow meow meow meow meow, meow meow meow meow meow meow meow meow meow meow meow. Meow meow meow meow meow meow meow meow meow meow meow. Meow meow meow meow meow meow, meow meow meow meow meow meow meow meow meow.

"Meow meow meow meow meow meow, meow? Meow meow meow meow meow meow meow meow meow meow meow meow meow meow meow meow meow meow meow meow meow meow meow meow meow meow meow. Meow meow meow meow meow meow meow meow meow."

"Meow, meow meow meow?" meow meow meow.

"Meow meow meow meow meow meow meow meow."

"Meow? Meow?" meow meow meow meow meow meow meow. Meow meow meow. Meow meow meow meow meow meow. Meow meow meow meow meow meow meow, meow meow meow meow, meow meow meow meow meow meow meow meow. Meow meow meow, meow meow meow meow meow meow. Meow meow meow meow meow meow meow meow, meow meow meow meow meow meow meow meow meow. Meow meow meow.

"Meow meow meow meow, meow meow meow meow meow." Meow meow meow meow, meow meow meow meow.

Meow meow meow meow meow meow meow meow meow meow meow meow meow, meow meow meow meow meow meow meow meow. Meow meow meow. Meow meow meow meow meow meow meow, meow meow meow meow meow. Meow meow meow meow meow meow meow. Meow meow meow meow meow meow meow meow meow meow meow meow meow meow meow meow meow meow meow meow meow.

Meow meow meow meow meow meow meow, meow meow meow meow meow. Meow meow meow meow meow meow meow, meow meow meow meow meow meow. Meow meow meow meow meow meow meow meow, meow, meow meow meow meow meow meow meow meow meow. Meow meow meow, meow meow meow meow. Meow meow meow meow meow meow meow meow meow meow meow, meow meow meow meow meow meow, meow meow meow meow meow. Meow meow meow meow meow meow meow meow meow meow. Meow meow meow meow meow meow meow. Meow, meow meow meow meow meow meow meow meow, meow meow meow meow meow meow meow meow meow meow meow meow meow. Meow meow meow meow meow meow meow meow meow. Meow meow meow meow meow meow meow / meow meow. Meow meow meow meow meow meow meow.

Meow meow meow meow meow meow meow meow meow meow meow, meow meow meow meow meow. Meow meow, meow meow. Meow meow meow meow meow meow, meow meow meow meow meow meow meow meow meow meow meow, meow meow, meow meow meow meow meow meow meow meow meow meow. Meow meow meow meow meow meow, meow meow meow meow meow meow meow meow. Meow meow meow meow meow meow meow Meow meow meow meow meow meow Meow Meow. Meow meow meow Meow meow. Meow meow meow meow meow meow

meow meow meow meow. Meow meow meow meow meow meow Meow meow meow meow.

Meow meow meow meow, meow meow meow meow, meow meow meow meow meow meow meow meow meow meow meow, meow meow meow meow meow meow meow meow. Meow meow meow meow meow meow meow meow meow meow meow meow meow, meow meow meow meow meow meow meow. Meow meow meow meow meow meow meow meow meow meow, meow meow meow meow meow meow, meow meow meow meow meow meow, meow meow meow meow meow meow meow meow meow, meow meow meow meow meow.

Meow meow meow meow meow meow meow meow meow meow meow meow meow meow meow meow. Meow meow meow meow meow meow meow meow-meow meow meow, meow meow meow, meow meow meow meow meow meow meow meow. Meow meow meow meow meow meow meow meow meow, meow meow meow meow. Meow meow meow meow, meow meow meow meow, meow meow, meow meow meow meow. Meow meow meow meow meow, meow meow meow meow. Meow meow meow, meow meow meow meow meow Meow meow meow meow meow meow meow. Meow meow meow meow meow meow meow meow meow meow, meow meow meow meow meow meow meow meow meow meow meow, meow meow meow meow meow, meow meow meow meow meow meow meow meow meow meow meow meow meow.

Meow meow, meow meow meow meow meow meow meow. Meow meow meow meow meow meow meow meow meow meow, meow meow meow meow meow. Meow meow meow meow meow meow meow meow meow meow meow meow meow meow. Meow meow meow meow meow meow meow meow meow meow, meow meow, meow meow meow meow meow, meow meow

meow meow, meow meow, meow meow meow meow meow meow meow meow. Meow meow meow meow meow meow meow meow meow meow meow meow meow meow. Meow Meow meow meow meow meow meow meow meow meow meow meow meow meow, meow meow meow meow meow meow meow, meow meow meow meow meow, meow meow meow meow meow meow meow meow meow.

Meow meow meow meow meow, meow meow meow. Meow meow meow meow meow meow meow meow meow. Meow meow meow meow meow meow meow meow meow meow meow meow meow meow meow, meow meow meow meow meow meow meow meow, meow meow meow meow meow.

Meow meow. Meow meow meow meow meow meow meow meow, meow meow meow meow meow meow meow meow meow meow meow meow meow meow. Meow meow meow meow meow meow meow meow meow meow meow meow meow, meow meow meow meow meow meow meow meow meow. Meow meow meow meow.

* * * * * * *

Meow meow, meow meow meow meow meow. Meow meow meow meow meow meow meow. Meow meow meow meow meow, meow meow meow meow meow meow meow meow meow meow. Meow meow meow meow meow meow. Meow meow meow meow meow meow meow meow meow meow meow meow meow meow meow meow.

Meow meow meow meow meow meow meow meow meow meow meow meow meow meow. Meow meow Meow Meow meow Meow Meow Meow. Meow meow meow, meow meow meow meow, meow meow meow meow meow meow meow meow meow. Meow meow meow meow meow, meow meow

meow meow meow meow meow meow meow meow. Meow meow meow meow meow meow meow meow, meow meow meow meow meow meow meow meow, meow meow meow meow-meow meow meow meow meow meow meow meow meow meow meow meow meow meow.

"Meow, meow meow," meow meow. Meow meow meow meow meow meow meow meow. Meow meow meow meow meow meow meow, meow meow meow meow meow meow meow meow meow meow meow. Meow meow, meow meow meow meow meow meow, meow meow meow meow meow meow meow meow meow, meow meow meow meow meow meow, meow meow meow meow meow meow meow meow meow meow meow meow. Meow meow meow meow meow meow meow, meow meow.

"Meow, meow meow meow meow meow meow meow, meow meow meow meow meow meow meow, meow meow meow meow meow meow Meow Meow meow meow meow."

Meow meow meow meow meow meow meow meow Meow. Meow meow meow meow meow meow meow meow meow meow, meow meow meow meow meow meow meow meow meow meow meow meow meow. Meow meow meow meow meow meow meow meow meow meow meow meow meow meow meow meow meow meow meow meow meow meow meow meow meow meow meow, meow meow meow meow meow Meow meow meow meow meow meow. Meow meow meow meow meow meow meow.

"Meow meow meow," meow meow meow, "meow meow meow meow meow meow meow."

Meow meow meow meow meow meow meow meow, meow Meow meow meow meow meow meow meow meow. Meow meow meow meow meow meow meow meow meow meow meow. Meow meow meow meow meow meow meow. Meow

meow. Meow. Meow meow meow meow meow meow meow, meow meow meow meow meow meow meow. Meow meow meow meow meow meow meow meow meow, meow meow meow meow meow meow. Meow meow meow meow meow, meow meow meow meow Meow meow meow, meow meow meow meow meow meow meow meow,

Meow meow meow meow meow meow meow meow meow meow. Meow meow meow meow, meow meow meow Meow meow meow meow, meow meow meow meow meow meow meow. Meow meow meow meow. Meow meow meow meow meow meow meow meow meow meow. Meow meow meow meow meow, meow meow meow meow meow meow meow, meow meow meow meow meow meow meow meow meow meow meow meow meow meow meow, meow meow meow meow meow meow meow meow. Meow meow meow meow meow meow meow meow. Meow meow meow meow meow meow meow meow meow.

Meow meow meow meow. Meow meow meow Meow. Meow. "Meow meow meow meow meow?" meow meow, meow meow.

"Meow meow meow meow meow meow meow," Meow meow meow meow. Meow meow meow meow meow, meow meow.

"Meow meow meow meow Meow?" meow meow.

Meow meow meow meow meow meow. Meow meow meow meow meow, meow meow meow meow meow meow meow meow meow meow meow meow meow meow meow meow. Meow meow. Meow meow meow meow meow meow meow meow meow meow meow.

Meow meow meow meow meow meow meow meow Meow meow meow meow meow meow. Meow meow meow meow meow meow, meow meow meow meow meow meow meow meow meow meow meow meow meow meow. Meow meow meow,

Meow meow meow meow meow. Meow meow meow meow meow meow meow meow, meow meow meow meow, meow meow meow meow meow meow meow meow. Meow meow meow meow meow, meow meow meow meow meow meow meow meow meow meow, meow meow meow meow meow meow meow meow meow meow meow meow. Meow, meow meow meow meow meow meow meow meow meow meow meow meow, meow meow meow meow meow meow meow meow meow, meow meow meow.

Meow meow Meow meow meow meow meow, meow meow meow meow meow meow meow meow meow. Meow meow meow meow meow meow meow meow Meow, meow meow meow meow meow meow. Meow meow. Meow Meow meow meow, meow meow meow, meow meow meow meow.

Meow meow meow meow meow meow Meow Meow. Meow meow meow meow meow meow meow meow meow meow meow Meow. Meow meow, meow meow meow meow meow. Meow meow meow meow meow Meow meow, meow meow meow Meow meow meow meow meow meow.

Meow meow meow, meow meow meow meow meow meow meow. Meow meow meow meow meow meow. Meow meow meow meow meow meow meow meow, meow meow meow meow meow meow meow, meow meow meow meow meow. Meow meow Meow meow meow meow meow meow, Meow meow meow meow meow meow, meow meow meow meow. Meow meow meow meow meow meow meow meow meow meow, meow meow meow meow meow.

Meow meow meow meow meow Meow meow. Meow meow meow meow meow meow meow meow meow meow meow meow. Meow meow meow meow meow meow, meow meow meow meow meow meow meow meow. Meow meow meow meow

meow meow meow meow meow meow. Meow meow meow meow meow. Meow meow meow meow meow, meow meow meow meow meow meow meow meow meow meow meow meow. Meow meow meow meow meow meow meow. Meow meow meow meow meow meow, meow meow meow meow. Meow meow meow meow meow meow meow meow meow meow.

Meow meow meow meow meow meow Meow. Meow meow meow meow meow meow, meow meow meow meow meow meow meow meow meow. Meow meow. Meow meow meow meow. Meow meow meow meow meow meow meow meow meow meow meow, meow meow meow meow meow. Meow meow meow meow meow meow meow meow. Meow meow. Meow meow meow meow meow meow meow meow meow. Meow meow meow meow meow meow. Meow meow meow meow meow meow meow. Meow meow meow, meow. Meow meow meow meow, meow meow meow meow meow meow meow meow meow, meow meow meow meow meow meow, meow meow meow meow meow meow meow meow. Meow meow meow meow meow meow meow. Meow meow meow meow meow meow meow, meow meow meow meow meow meow meow meow meow, meow meow meow meow meow meow.

Meow meow meow meow meow meow meow, meow meow meow meow. Meow meow meow meow. Meow meow meow, meow meow meow meow meow meow meow. meow meow meow meow meow meow meow meow meow meow meow meow meow.

Meow meow meow meow meow meow meow meow meow meow. Meow meow meow meow, meow meow meow meow meow meow meow meow meow meow meow meow meow meow meow meow meow meow meow meow meow. Meow meow meow meow meow meow meow. Meow Meow, meow meow meow

meow meow meow meow meow meow meow. Meow meow meow meow meow meow meow meow, meow meow meow meow meow meow meow meow meow. Meow meow meow meow, Meow meow meow meow meow meow meow, meow meow meow, meow meow meow meow.

Meow meow meow meow meow meow meow, meow meow meow meow meow.

* * * * * * *

Meow meow meow meow meow meow meow, meow. Meow meow meow meow meow meow meow meow meow meow, meow meow meow meow meow meow meow meow meow meow meow meow, meow meow meow meow meow, meow meow meow meow meow meow meow meow meow meow. Meow meow meow meow: meow meow meow meow meow.

Meow meow meow meow meow meow meow meow meow meow meow meow meow. Meow meow meow meow meow meow, meow. Meow meow meow meow meow. Meow meow meow meow meow meow. Meow meow meow meow meow. Meow meow meow meow meow, meow meow meow meow meow meow meow meow. Meow meow meow meow meow meow meow meow meow meow. Meow meow meow, meow meow meow meow meow meow meow meow meow. Meow meow meow meow meow meow meow meow meow. Meow meow meow meow, meow meow meow meow.

Meow meow meow meow. Meow meow meow meow, meow, meow meow meow meow Meow meow meow meow meow. Meow meow, meow meow. Meow meow meow meow meow, meow meow meow meow meow. Meow meow meow meow.

Meow meow meow meow meow meow meow meow, meow meow meow meow meow meow meow meow meow meow

meow meow meow. Meow meow meow. Meow meow meow. Meow meow meow meow meow meow meow meow meow. Meow meow meow meow meow.

Meow meow meow meow meow meow meow meow meow meow meow meow Meow meow meow meow meow meow meow. Meow meow meow meow meow meow meow meow meow meow meow. Meow meow meow meow meow meow meow meow. Meow meow meow meow meow meow meow meow Meow meow meow, meow meow meow meow meow. Meow meow meow meow meow, meow meow meow meow meow. Meow meow meow meow meow meow meow, meow meow meow meow.

"Meow meow meow meow," meow meow.

Meow meow meow meow meow, meow meow meow meow meow meow meow meow meow meow meow meow meow meow Meow. Meow meow meow meow meow meow meow meow, meow meow meow meow, meow meow meow meow meow meow meow meow meow meow meow… meow meow.

Meow meow meow meow meow, meow meow meow meow meow meow meow meow meow meow meow, meow meow meow meow meow meow meow meow, meow meow meow meow meow meow meow meow. Meow meow meow meow meow meow meow meow. Meow meow meow meow meow meow meow meow meow, meow meow meow meow meow meow meow meow meow meow meow meow meow meow meow. meow.

MEOW MEOW MEOW MEOW

Meow, meow meow, meow meow meow meow meow. Meow meow meow meow meow meow, meow meow meow, meow meow meow meow, meow meow meow meow meow. Meow meow meow meow meow meow meow meow: meow meow, meow meow, meow meow-meow meow. Meow meow meow meow meow meow meow meow, meow meow meow meow meow meow meow meow meow meow, meow meow meow meow meow. Meow meow meow meow meow meow, meow meow meow meow meow meow meow meow meow meow, meow. Meow meow meow meow meow meow, meow meow meow meow meow meow.

Meow meow meow meow meow meow meow meow meow meow meow meow meow, meow meow meow meow meow meow meow meow meow meow, meow meow meow meow meow. Meow meow meow meow meow meow. Meow meow meow meow meow, meow meow meow meow meow meow. Meow meow meow, meow meow meow meow. Meow meow meow meow meow meow meow meow.

Meow meow meow meow meow. Meow meow meow meow meow meow meow, meow meow meow meow meow meow meow meow meow meow meow meow meow meow, meow meow meow meow meow meow meow meow meow meow meow. Meow meow meow meow meow meow meow

meow meow. Meow meow meow meow meow, meow meow meow meow meow meow meow meow, meow meow meow meow meow meow. Meow meow meow meow meow meow meow meow meow meow, meow meow meow meow meow meow meow meow meow meow meow meow meow meow meow, meow meow meow meow meow meow.

Meow meow meow meow meow meow meow meow meow meow meow meow, meow meow meow meow meow, meow meow meow meow meow meow meow, meow meow meow meow meow meow. Meow meow meow meow meow meow meow meow meow meow meow meow meow, meow meow meow meow meow meow. Meow meow meow meow. Meow meow meow. Meow meow meow meow meow meow, meow meow meow Meow. Meow meow meow meow meow meow meow meow meow meow meow, meow meow meow meow meow meow meow meow meow. Meow meow meow meow meow meow meow meow meow, meow meow meow meow meow meow meow meow meow meow. Meow meow meow meow meow.

Meow meow meow meow meow meow, meow meow meow meow meow meow meow meow. Meow meow meow meow meow meow meow, meow meow meow meow meow meow meow, meow meow meow. Meow meow, meow meow meow meow meow meow meow meow meow. Meow meow meow meow meow, meow meow meow meow meow meow, meow meow meow meow meow meow Meow. Meow meow meow, meow meow meow meow meow meow Meow meow meow meow meow, meow meow meow meow meow meow meow meow meow meow meow meow, meow meow meow meow meow meow meow meow meow meow meow.

Meow meow meow meow meow, meow meow meow meow meow meow meow meow meow. Meow meow meow meow meow

meow meow meow meow meow meow meow meow meow meow meow meow. Meow meow meow meow meow meow meow, meow meow meow meow meow. Meow meow meow meow meow meow meow meow meow, meow meow meow meow, meow meow meow meow meow, meow meow meow meow meow meow meow meow meow. Meow meow meow meow, meow meow meow meow meow meow. Meow meow meow meow meow.

"Meow meow meow meow meow," meow meow meow, meow meow meow meow meow. "Meow meow meow meow, meow meow meow meow meow meow."

Meow meow meow meow meow. Meow meow meow. Meow meow meow meow meow meow meow meow meow meow meow meow meow. Meow meow meow meow meow meow, meow meow meow, meow meow meow.

"Meow meow, meow meow meow?"

"Meow meow meow meow meow. Meow meow meow meow meow meow meow meow. Meow meow meow meow meow. Meow meow meow meow meow meow meow meow."

Meow meow meow meow, meow meow meow meow meow meow, meow meow meow meow meow, meow meow meow meow meow meow meow. Meow meow meow meow meow meow meow meow meow meow meow, meow meow. Meow meow meow, meow meow meow meow meow meow meow meow. Meow meow meow meow meow meow meow, meow meow meow meow meow meow meow. Meow meow meow meow meow meow meow meow meow meow meow meow meow meow.

Meow meow meow meow meow meow, meow meow meow meow meow meow. Meow meow meow meow meow meow meow meow meow meow meow. Meow meow meow meow meow meow meow meow meow, meow meow meow meow meow meow meow meow meow meow meow meow.

"Meow meow?" meow meow meow, meow meow meow meow meow meow meow meow. Meow meow meow meow meow meow meow meow meow meow meow meow meow. Meow meow meow meow meow meow meow. Meow meow meow meow meow meow meow meow. Meow meow meow meow meow meow, meow. Meow meow meow meow meow meow meow meow. Meow meow meow meow meow meow, meow meow meow meow meow meow meow meow meow meow meow, meow meow meow meow meow meow meow.

"Meow meow meow meow meow," meow meow meow. Meow meow meow meow meow meow meow meow. Meow meow meow meow meow meow meow, meow meow. Meow meow meow meow meow meow meow. "Meow meow meow meow, meow meow meow meow. Meow meow meow."

"Meow, meow meow meow meow, meow meow meow meow meow meow meow." Meow meow meow meow meow, meow meow meow meow meow meow, meow meow, meow meow.

Meow meow meow meow. Meow meow meow meow meow meow meow meow meow meow meow meow meow, meow meow meow meow meow meow meow. Meow, meow meow meow meow meow, meow meow meow meow, meow meow meow meow. Meow meow meow. Meow meow meow meow. Meow meow meow, meow meow meow meow meow meow meow meow meow, meow meow meow meow meow.

Meow meow meow meow meow meow meow meow meow meow meow. Meow meow meow meow meow meow meow meow mcow. Meow meow, meow meow meow meow meow meow meow. Meow meow meow meow, meow meow meow meow meow meow. Meow meow meow meow meow meow meow meow meow.

"Meow meow meow meow meow meow, meow?" meow meow meow meow meow meow meow meow.

Meow meow meow meow meow meow meow meow meow, meow meow meow meow meow, meow meow meow meow meow meow meow meow. Meow meow meow meow meow meow. Meow meow meow meow meow meow meow meow meow. Meow meow meow meow meow meow meow meow meow meow meow meow meow meow.

"Meow, meow meow? Meow meow meow meow meow meow. Meow meow meow meow meow meow meow meow. Meow meow meow meow meow," meow meow meow meow meow, meow meow meow meow meow. Meow meow meow meow meow meow meow, meow meow meow. Meow meow meow meow, meow meow meow meow meow meow meow. Meow meow meow meow meow meow meow, meow meow meow meow meow meow meow meow meow meow meow meow meow meow meow meow meow meow meow meow meow meow meow meow meow meow meow meow. Meow meow meow meow meow meow meow meow, meow meow meow.

Meow meow meow, Meow. Meow meow meow meow, meow meow meow meow. Meow meow meow meow meow meow meow meow meow. Meow meow meow meow meow meow meow. Meow meow meow meow meow meow meow meow meow, meow meow meow meow meow meow, meow meow meow meow meow meow.

"Meow Meow, meow meow meow?" meow meow meow.

Meow meow meow meow meow meow, meow meow meow meow meow meow meow meow. Meow meow meow meow meow meow meow meow meow. Meow meow meow meow meow meow meow meow meow, meow meow meow meow meow meow meow meow.

"Meow Meow, meow meow meow meow. Meow meow meow meow meow meow meow meow meow. Meow meow meow meow meow meow meow. Meow meow meow meow

meow meow," meow meow meow meow meow meow meow meow meow meow meow meow meow meow meow. Meow meow meow meow meow meow meow meow meow meow meow meow meow meow, meow meow meow meow meow. Meow meow meow meow meow meow meow meow meow. Meow meow meow meow meow meow, meow meow meow meow meow meow.

"Meow meow meow meow, meow meow meow meow meow meow meow meow," Meow meow.

"Meow Meow, meow meow meow meow," meow meow meow meow meow meow meow meow. Meow meow meow meow meow meow meow meow. Meow meow meow meow meow, meow meow meow. Meow meow meow meow meow meow meow meow meow meow meow meow, meow meow meow meow meow meow. Meow meow meow meow meow meow meow meow meow meow meow meow meow meow. Meow meow meow meow meow meow meow meow meow meow.

Meow meow meow meow, meow meow meow meow meow meow, meow meow meow meow meow. Meow meow meow meow meow meow meow meow meow. Meow meow meow meow meow meow meow meow meow meow meow meow meow. Meow meow meow meow meow meow.

Meow meow meow, meow meow meow. Meow meow meow meow meow meow meow meow meow. Meow Meow meow Meow. Meow meow meow meow. Meow meow meow meow meow meow meow. Meow meow meow meow meow. Meow meow meow meow meow. Meow meow meow meow meow meow, meow meow meow meow meow meow meow.

Meow meow meow meow meow meow, meow meow meow meow meow meow meow meow meow meow meow. Meow meow meow meow meow meow meow meow. Meow meow meow meow meow, meow meow meow meow meow.

* * * * * * *

Meow meow meow, meow meow meow meow meow meow meow. Meow meow meow meow meow meow meow meow, meow meow meow meow meow meow. Meow meow meow meow meow meow, meow meow meow meow meow meow meow meow meow.

Meow meow meow meow, meow meow meow meow meow meow meow meow meow meow. Meow meow meow meow meow meow meow meow meow meow meow. Meow meow meow meow. Meow.

Meow meow meow meow meow meow meow.

MEOW, MEOW, MEOW MEOW MEOW MEOW

Meow meow meow meow meow meow meow meow meow meow meow. Meow meow meow meow meow meow meow meow meow meow meow. Meow meow meow meow meow meow meow meow meow meow, meow meow meow meow meow. Meow meow meow meow meow meow meow meow meow. meow meow meow meow meow meow meow meow meow meow.

Meow meow meow meow meow meow meow, meow meow meow meow meow. Meow meow meow meow meow meow. Meow meow meow meow meow meow meow meow meow meow meow meow meow meow meow meow. Meow meow meow meow meow meow meow meow, meow meow meow. Meow meow meow meow meow. Meow meow meow meow meow meow. Meow meow meow meow meow. Meow meow meow meow meow meow meow meow meow meow. Meow meow meow meow meow meow meow, meow meow meow meow meow. Meow meow meow meow meow meow meow meow meow meow meow meow meow, meow meow meow meow meow meow meow. Meow meow mcow. Meow meow.

Meow meow meow meow meow meow meow meow meow meow meow meow, meow meow meow meow meow meow.

Meow. Meow meow meow. Meow meow. Meow meow meow meow meow meow meow meow. Meow meow meow meow meow meow, meow meow meow meow. Meow meow meow meow meow meow meow meow meow meow meow meow. Meow meow meow meow meow meow meow meow meow, meow meow meow meow meow meow meow meow meow meow meow meow meow meow. Meow meow meow meow meow meow meow meow meow meow meow meow, meow meow meow meow meow meow meow. Meow meow meow meow meow meow meow meow. Meow meow meow meow meow meow meow meow meow meow meow meow meow. Meow meow meow meow. Meow meow, meow meow meow meow meow meow meow meow meow meow meow meow meow meow meow meow meow meow meow.

Meow meow meow meow meow meow, meow meow meow meow meow meow meow. Meow meow meow meow meow meow meow, meow meow meow meow meow meow meow meow-meow. Meow meow meow meow meow meow meow meow. Meow meow meow meow meow meow meow meow meow meow meow meow meow. Meow meow meow, meow meow, meow meow meow MEOW MEOW MEOW. Meow meow, meow meow meow meow. Meow meow, meow meow meow meow meow meow meow. Meow meow meow meow meow meow meow meow meow meow meow meow meow. Meow meow meow meow, meow meow meow meow meow meow meow meow meow meow meow, meow meow meow meow meow meow, meow meow meow meow meow meow. Meow meow meow meow meow meow meow meow meow meow meow meow meow meow meow meow meow. Meow meow meow meow meow meow meow meow meow, meow meow meow meow meow meow meow meow meow.

Meow meow meow meow meow meow meow meow meow meow meow meow. Meow meow meow meow meow meow meow meow meow meow meow meow meow. Meow meow meow meow meow meow meow meow, meow meow meow meow meow meow meow meow meow meow, meow meow meow meow meow meow meow. Meow meow meow meow meow, meow meow meow meow meow meow meow meow meow meow meow. Meow meow meow meow meow meow meow, meow meow meow meow meow meow meow. Meow meow meow meow meow, meow meow meow meow meow meow meow meow meow.

Meow meow meow meow meow meow meow. Meow meow meow meow meow meow meow meow meow meow. Meow meow meow meow meow. Meow meow meow meow meow meow meow meow meow meow meow meow meow?

Meow meow meow meow meow meow meow meow meow meow meow meow meow meow meow meow meow, meow meow meow meow meow meow meow meow meow meow. Meow meow meow meow. Meow meow meow meow meow meow-meow meow meow meow. Meow meow meow meow meow meow meow meow meow meow meow, meow meow meow meow meow meow meow Meow, meow meow meow meow meow meow meow meow meow meow meow meow meow meow-meow meow meow meow. Meow meow meow meow meow meow meow meow meow meow meow meow meow meow meow.

Meow meow meow meow meow meow meow, meow meow meow meow, Meow meow meow meow meow meow meow, meow meow meow meow meow meow meow meow meow meow meow meow meow meow. Meow meow meow meow meow meow meow meow meow. Meow meow meow meow

meow meow, meow meow meow meow meow meow meow meow meow meow meow meow meow meow, meow meow meow meow meow, meow meow meow meow meow meow meow meow meow meow meow meow meow meow, meow meow meow meow meow meow meow meow meow meow meow meow meow meow meow meow.

* * * * * * *

Meow meow meow meow meow meow meow. Meow meow meow meow meow meow meow meow meow. Meow meow meow meow, meow meow meow meow meow meow meow meow. Meow meow meow meow meow meow, meow meow meow meow meow meow. Meow meow meow meow meow meow meow meow meow, meow meow meow meow meow meow meow meow meow meow meow meow meow. Meow meow meow.

Meow meow meow meow meow meow, meow meow meow meow, meow meow meow meow meow meow meow. Meow meow meow meow meow meow meow meow meow meow meow meow meow meow, meow meow meow meow meow meow meow meow meow meow meow. Meow meow meow meow meow, meow meow meow meow meow meow meow meow meow meow.

Meow meow meow meow meow meow meow, meow meow meow meow meow meow meow. Meow meow meow meow meow meow meow, meow meow meow meow meow. Meow meow meow meow meow meow, meow meow meow meow meow meow meow meow. Meow meow meow meow meow.

"M'eow meow meow, meow meow," meow meow meow meow meow meow meow meow meow meow. Meow meow meow meow meow meow meow meow. Meow meow meow meow. Meow meow meow, meow meow meow meow,

meow meow meow meow meow. Meow meow meow meow. Meow meow meow meow. Meow meow meow meow meow meow meow meow. Meow meow meow meow meow meow meow meow meow meow meow meow meow meow meow meow meow. Meow meow meow meow meow meow meow, meow meow meow meow meow meow, meow meow meow meow. Meow meow meow meow meow meow meow meow, meow meow meow meow meow meow meow meow, meow meow meow meow meow meow meow. Meow meow meow. Meow meow meow meow meow meow meow meow, meow meow meow meow meow meow meow meow. Meow meow. Meow meow meow meow meow meow meow. Meow meow meow meow meow meow meow meow meow meow, meow meow meow meow meow meow meow meow meow meow meow meow meow, meow meow meow meow meow meow meow meow meow meow, meow meow meow meow meow meow meow, meow meow meow meow meow meow.

"Meow meow meow? Meow meow?" meow meow meow meow.

"Meow meow, meow. Meow meow meow," meow meow, "meow meow meow meow meow?"

Meow meow meow meow meow meow, meow meow meow meow meow meow meow. Meow meow meow meow meow meow meow meow meow, meow meow meow meow meow. Meow meow meow meow meow. Meow meow meow meow meow. Meow meow meow meow meow meow meow.

"Meow meow meow meow meow meow. Meow meow meow meow," meow meow meow. "Meow meow meow meow meow meow?"

Meow meow. Meow meow meow meow. Meow meow meow meow meow meow meow. Meow meow meow meow meow, meow meow meow meow meow meow meow, meow

meow meow meow meow meow. Meow meow meow meow meow meow meow.

"Meow meow meow meow meow. Meow meow meow meow meow. Meow meow."

Meow meow meow meow meow meow. Meow meow meow meow meow meow meow meow meow meow meow. Meow meow meow meow meow meow. Meow meow meow meow. Meow meow meow meow meow meow meow meow. Meow meow meow meow meow meow meow meow meow. Meow meow meow meow meow meow meow, meow meow meow meow meow meow meow meow meow meow meow meow. Meow meow meow meow meow meow meow meow meow meow meow, meow meow meow meow meow meow. Meow meow meow meow meow meow meow meow meow meow meow. Meow meow meow. Meow meow meow meow meow meow. Meow meow meow meow. Meow meow meow meow.

"Meow meow meow, meow meow meow. Meow meow meow meow meow? Meow meow meow meow meow?" meow meow meow meow meow meow meow meow meow. Meow meow meow meow meow, meow meow meow meow, meow meow meow meow meow. Meow meow meow meow meow meow meow meow. Meow meow meow. Meow meow meow meow meow meow meow meow, meow meow meow, meow meow meow-meow meow meow.

"Meow Meow," meow meow meow meow meow meow meow, meow meow meow meow meow, meow meow meow meow. "Meow meow. Meow meow meow meow meow meow meow. Meow meow meow meow. Meow meow."

"Meow, meow, meow meow," meow meow meow meow meow meow, meow meow meow meow meow meow meow meow meow meow meow. Meow meow meow meow meow meow

meow. Meow meow meow meow, meow meow meow Meow-meow-Meow, meow meow meow meow meow. Meow meow meow meow, meow meow meow meow meow, meow meow meow meow meow meow. Meow meow meow meow meow meow meow meow meow, meow meow meow meow meow meow meow meow. Meow meow meow meow meow meow meow meow meow meow meow meow meow meow meow, meow meow meow meow meow meow, meow meow meow meow meow meow.

Meow meow meow meow meow meow meow meow meow, meow meow meow meow meow meow meow meow. Meow meow meow meow meow meow meow meow. Meow meow meow meow meow, meow meow meow meow meow meow meow meow meow meow meow meow.

"Meow meow meow meow, Meow," meow meow meow meow meow meow meow. Meow meow meow meow meow meow meow meow, meow meow meow meow meow meow. Meow meow meow meow meow meow meow meow. Meow meow meow meow meow meow meow, meow meow Meow Meow meow meow meow meow meow. Meow meow meow meow, meow meow meow meow, meow meow meow meow meow meow meow. Meow meow meow meow meow meow meow meow meow meow meow meow meow meow meow meow meow meow meow meow. Meow meow meow meow meow meow, meow meow meow meow meow, meow meow meow meow meow meow meow meow.

Meow meow meow meow meow, meow meow. Meow meow meow meow meow meow, meow meow meow meow meow meow. Meow meow meow meow meow meow meow meow meow meow meow meow meow meow. Meow meow meow meow meow meow meow meow meow. Meow meow meow meow meow meow, meow meow meow meow meow. Meow meow

meow meow meow meow meow meow meow meow, meow meow meow meow meow, meow meow meow meow. Meow meow meow meow meow meow meow meow meow, meow meow meow. Meow meow meow meow meow meow. Meow meow meow meow.

Meow meow meow, meow meow meow meow meow meow meow meow meow meow. Meow meow meow meow, meow meow. Meow meow meow meow meow meow meow. Meow meow. Meow meow meow meow meow meow meow meow meow meow meow meow meow meow meow meow. Meow meow meow meow meow meow meow meow meow.

"Meow meow meow?" meow meow meow meow meow meow meow meow meow meow.

"Meow, meow meow. Meow meow meow. Meow meow meow meow."

"Meow, meow. Meow meow meow."

"Meow meow meow meow meow meow, meow?"

MEOW: MEOW MEOW

Meow meow meow, meow meow meow meow meow meow meow meow, meow meow meow meow meow meow meow. Meow meow meow meow meow meow meow meow meow meow meow, meow meow meow meow, meow meow meow meow. Meow meow meow meow meow meow meow meow, meow meow meow meow meow meow meow meow meow meow meow. Meow meow meow, meow meow meow meow meow meow. Meow meow meow meow meow meow meow meow meow meow meow meow meow meow, meow meow meow meow meow. Meow meow meow meow meow meow meow meow meow meow meow meow meow meow meow meow meow meow meow meow meow meow. Meow meow meow meow meow meow meow meow meow meow, meow meow meow meow meow meow meow meow.

Meow meow meow meow meow meow meow meow meow meow meow meow meow meow meow meow meow. Meow meow-meow meow meow meow meow meow meow meow meow, meow meow meow meow meow meow meow meow meow meow meow, meow meow meow meow meow meow meow, meow meow meow meow, meow meow meow meow meow. Meow meow meow meow meow. Meow meow meow meow meow meow meow meow, meow meow meow meow meow meow meow. Meow meow meow meow meow meow meow. Meow meow meow meow meow meow meow meow. Meow

meow meow meow meow, meow meow meow meow meow. Meow meow meow meow meow meow meow meow meow meow meow meow.

Meow meow meow meow meow meow meow? Meow meow meow meow meow meow meow meow meow meow. Meow meow meow meow meow meow-meow meow meow meow meow. Meow meow meow meow meow meow meow. Meow meow meow meow meow meow, meow meow meow meow meow meow meow meow meow. Meow meow meow meow meow meow meow meow meow meow meow meow meow meow meow, meow-meow. Meow meow meow meow meow meow meow meow meow meow, meow meow meow meow meow meow meow meow. Meow meow meow meow meow meow meow.

Meow meow meow meow meow meow. meow meow meow meow meow meow meow, meow meow meow meow meow meow meow, meow meow meow meow meow meow meow meow meow meow, meow meow meow meow meow meow meow meow meow meow meow. Meow meow meow meow meow meow meow meow meow meow meow meow.

Meow meow meow meow meow meow, meow meow meow meow meow, meow meow meow meow meow, meow meow meow meow meow meow meow meow meow meow. Meow meow meow meow meow meow meow meow meow meow meow meow meow meow meow meow meow meow meow meow, meow meow meow. Meow meow meow meow meow.

Meow meow meow meow, meow meow meow. Meow meow meow. Meow meow meow meow meow meow. Meow meow meow meow meow meow meow meow meow meow meow. Meow meow meow meow meow meow meow meow meow meow meow. Meow meow meow meow.

Meow meow meow meow meow meow meow, meow meow meow meow. Meow meow. Meow meow meow meow meow meow meow meow meow meow meow meow. Meow meow meow meow meow, meow meow meow meow meow. Meow meow meow meow meow meow, meow meow meow meow meow meow meow meow meow meow meow meow meow meow meow meow meow. Meow meow meow meow meow meow meow meow meow meow meow meow. Meow meow meow meow meow, meow meow meow. Meow meow meow. Meow meow meow meow meow meow meow meow meow meow, meow meow meow meow meow meow meow meow meow meow meow meow. Meow meow meow meow meow meow meow meow meow meow meow meow meow, meow meow.

Meow meow meow meow meow meow meow meow, meow meow meow meow meow meow meow meow meow meow meow. Meow meow meow meow meow meow meow meow meow, meow meow meow meow meow meow meow meow meow meow meow. Meow.

Meow meow meow meow meow meow meow meow meow meow, meow meow meow meow meow meow meow meow meow meow meow meow. Meow meow meow, meow meow meow meow meow meow meow meow meow meow meow, meow meow meow meow meow meow. Meow meow meow meow meow meow meow meow meow. Meow meow meow meow meow meow meow meow.

Meow meow, meow meow meow.

Meow meow meow, meow meow meow meow meow meow. Meow meow meow meow meow meow meow meow meow meow meow meow, meow meow meow meow. Meow meow meow meow meow meow meow meow meow meow meow meow. Meow meow meow meow meow, meow meow meow meow meow meow meow meow meow meow.

Meow meow meow meow meow meow. Meow meow meow meow. Meow, meow meow meow meow meow meow meow meow meow, meow meow meow meow. Meow meow meow meow meow meow meow, meow meow meow. Meow meow meow meow meow, meow meow meow meow meow, meow meow meow meow meow meow meow meow meow meow. Meow meow meow.

Meow meow meow meow meow meow meow meow meow meow meow meow meow. Meow meow meow meow meow meow meow Meow, meow meow meow meow meow meow meow meow meow meow meow meow meow, meow meow meow meow meow meow meow meow. Meow meow meow meow meow meow meow meow meow meow meow meow. Meow meow meow meow meow meow meow, meow meow meow meow meow meow meow meow. Meow meow meow meow meow meow meow meow meow meow meow meow meow meow, meow meow meow meow meow meow meow.

Meow meow meow meow meow meow, meow meow meow meow meow, meow meow meow meow meow meow. Meow meow meow meow meow. Meow meow meow meow meow meow meow meow meow, meow meow meow meow meow meow meow meow meow meow. Meow, meow meow, meow meow meow meow meow, meow meow meow meow meow meow meow.

"Meow, meow, meow meow meow meow meow?" Meow meow.

Meow meow meow meow, meow. Meow meow meow meow meow meow meow, meow meow meow meow meow. Meow meow meow meow meow meow meow meow meow. Meow meow meow meow meow meow. Meow meow meow meow meow meow meow meow meow, meow meow meow,

meow meow meow meow, meow meow. Meow meow meow meow meow meow meow meow. Meow meow meow meow meow meow meow meow meow meow. Meow meow meow meow meow meow meow meow meow meow meow. Meow meow meow meow meow meow, meow meow meow meow meow meow meow meow meow meow meow meow meow meow meow meow meow meow meow. Meow meow Meow meow meow meow meow meow meow meow, meow meow meow, meow meow meow meow meow meow meow meow meow meow. Meow meow meow meow meow, meow meow meow meow. Meow meow meow, meow meow meow meow. Meow meow meow meow meow meow meow.

Meow meow meow meow meow meow meow meow meow meow meow, meow meow meow meow meow meow meow. Meow meow meow meow meow meow meow meow meow, meow meow meow meow meow meow meow meow meow meow meow. Meow meow meow meow meow meow meow meow, meow meow meow meow meow meow meow meow meow. Meow meow meow meow meow meow meow meow meow meow, meow meow meow meow meow meow meow meow meow meow meow meow meow meow meow meow meow. Meow, meow meow meow meow meow, meow meow meow meow meow meow meow meow meow meow. Meow meow meow meow meow meow. Meow meow meow meow meow meow meow meow meow, meow meow meow meow. Meow meow meow meow meow, meow meow meow meow meow meow meow meow meow meow meow.

Meow meow meow meow meow meow meow meow meow meow, meow meow meow meow meow meow meow meow meow. Meow meow meow. Meow meow meow meow meow. Meow meow meow meow meow meow meow meow meow meow meow meow, meow meow meow meow. Meow meow meow

meow meow meow meow meow meow. Meow meow meow meow meow, meow meow meow meow meow meow. meow meow meow meow meow meow, meow meow meow meow meow meow meow. Meow meow meow meow meow meow meow meow meow. Meow meow meow meow meow meow meow meow.

Meow meow meow meow Meow, meow "Meow, meow meow meow," meow meow meow meow meow meow meow meow meow meow. Meow meow meow meow. Meow meow meow meow meow meow meow meow meow. Meow meow meow meow meow meow meow meow meow meow, meow meow meow meow meow meow meow meow.

Meow meow meow meow meow meow meow meow meow meow meow meow. Meow meow meow meow meow meow meow meow meow meow. Meow meow meow meow meow meow meow meow meow meow meow meow meow. Meow meow meow meow, meow meow meow meow meow meow meow meow meow meow.

Meow meow meow meow meow meow meow meow, meow meow meow meow meow meow meow. Meow meow meow meow meow meow meow, meow meow meow meow meow. Meow meow meow meow meow. Meow meow meow meow meow meow meow meow, meow meow meow meow.

Meow meow meow meow meow meow meow meow meow meow meow. Meow meow meow. Meow meow meow meow meow meow meow meow meow, meow meow meow meow meow meow meow meow meow meow. Meow, meow meow meow meow. Meow meow meow meow meow meow.

Meow meow meow meow meow meow. Meow meow meow meow meow meow meow meow meow. Meow meow meow meow meow meow, meow meow meow meow meow meow. Meow meow meow meow meow meow meow meow meow

meow. Meow meow meow meow meow meow meow meow meow meow.

"Meow meow," meow meow Meow, "Meow meow meow meow meow meow, meow meow meow, meow meow meow meow meow."

Meow Meow meow meow meow, meow meow meow meow meow meow meow meow meow meow meow meow. Meow meow meow meow meow meow meow meow, meow, meow meow meow meow meow meow, meow meow meow meow meow meow. Meow meow meow meow meow meow meow meow. Meow meow meow meow meow meow. Meow meow meow meow meow meow meow. Meow meow meow meow meow meow meow meow meow meow meow meow.

Meow meow meow meow meow meow meow meow meow meow meow meow meow meow, meow meow meow, meow meow meow. Meow meow meow, meow meow. Meow meow meow meow meow, meow meow meow meow meow meow meow. Meow meow meow meow meow. Meow, meow meow meow meow meow meow, meow meow meow meow meow Meow meow Meow meow Meow meow meow meow meow, meow meow, meow meow meow meow meow meow. Meow meow meow. Meow meow meow meow meow meow meow, meow meow meow meow meow meow meow. Meow meow meow meow meow meow meow meow meow meow meow meow meow meow meow meow meow meow, meow meow meow meow. Meow meow meow meow meow meow meow meow meow meow meow. Meow meow meow meow meow meow. Meow meow meow meow meow Meow meow meow meow meow. Meow meow, meow meow meow meow, meow meow meow meow.

Meow meow meow meow meow meow meow meow, meow meow meow meow meow meow meow meow meow, meow meow

meow meow meow meow meow meow meow, meow meow, meow meow meow meow meow meow meow meow meow. Meow Meow meow meow meow meow meow meow, meow meow meow meow meow meow meow, meow meow meow meow, meow meow, meow meow meow meow meow meow meow.

Meow meow meow meow, Meow meow meow meow meow meow meow. Meow meow meow meow meow meow meow meow meow meow meow, meow meow meow meow meow meow meow meow. Meow meow meow, meow meow meow meow meow meow. Meow meow meow meow meow meow meow meow meow meow meow meow, meow meow meow meow meow meow, meow meow meow meow meow meow meow meow meow meow meow meow.

MEOW

Meow meow meow, meow meow meow meow meow meow meow meow. Meow meow meow meow, meow meow meow meow meow meow meow meow. Meow meow meow meow meow meow meow meow, meow meow meow meow. Meow meow meow meow, meow meow meow meow meow meow, meow meow meow meow. Meow meow meow meow, meow. Meow meow meow meow meow meow, meow meow meow meow meow, meow meow meow meow meow meow meow meow meow. Meow meow meow meow meow meow meow meow meow meow meow meow meow.

Meow meow meow meow meow meow meow, meow meow meow meow meow meow meow meow meow meow meow, meow meow meow meow meow. Meow meow meow meow meow meow meow meow meow meow meow meow meow. Meow meow meow meow. Meow meow meow meow meow meow. Meow Meow, meow meow meow meow meow meow meow meow meow meow meow meow, meow meow meow meow meow meow meow meow meow meow meow meow meow meow meow meow meow. Meow, meow meow meow meow meow meow meow, meow meow meow meow meow. Meow meow meow meow meow meow meow meow, meow meow meow meow meow meow, meow meow mcow meow meow meow meow meow meow.

Meow meow meow meow meow meow meow meow meow meow, meow meow meow meow meow meow meow meow meow meow, meow meow meow meow meow meow. Meow meow meow meow meow meow meow meow meow meow meow meow, meow meow meow. Meow meow meow meow meow meow meow meow meow meow meow, meow meow meow meow meow meow meow meow meow meow meow. Meow meow meow meow-meow meow. Meow meow meow meow meow. Meow meow meow meow meow. Meow meow meow meow meow. Meow meow meow meow meow meow meow meow meow.

Meow meow meow meow meow meow meow meow meow meow. Meow meow meow meow meow meow meow. Meow meow meow meow meow meow meow. Meow meow meow meow meow meow meow meow, meow meow meow meow, meow meow meow meow meow meow meow.

Meow meow meow meow meow.

Meow meow meow meow meow meow.

Meow meow meow meow.

Meow meow meow, meow meow meow meow meow meow meow meow, meow meow meow meow meow, meow meow meow meow meow meow meow, meow meow meow meow meow meow meow. Meow meow meow meow meow meow meow meow meow meow, meow meow meow meow meow, meow meow meow meow meow meow meow meow, meow meow meow meow meow meow meow meow meow meow meow meow meow meow meow. Meow meow meow meow meow meow meow meow meow meow meow meow meow meow, meow meow meow meow meow meow meow meow meow meow, meow meow meow. Meow meow meow meow meow meow meow meow, meow meow meow meow meow meow

meow meow, meow meow meow meow meow meow meow meow meow.

Meow meow meow, meow meow meow meow meow. Meow meow meow meow meow meow meow meow, meow meow meow meow meow meow meow meow, meow meow meow meow meow meow meow meow meow meow.

Meow meow meow meow meow, meow meow meow. Meow meow meow meow meow meow meow, meow meow meow meow meow meow meow meow meow, meow meow meow meow meow. Meow meow meow meow meow meow meow meow meow meow meow, meow meow meow meow meow meow meow. Meow meow meow meow meow meow meow meow.

Meow meow, meow meow meow meow meow meow meow meow meow. Meow meow meow meow meow. Meow meow meow meow meow, meow meow meow meow meow meow meow meow meow meow meow. Meow meow meow meow meow meow meow meow meow meow. Meow meow meow meow meow meow meow meow meow meow meow meow meow meow meow meow. Meow meow meow meow meow meow meow, meow meow meow meow meow meow meow meow meow. Meow meow meow meow meow meow meow, meow meow meow meow meow meow.

"Meow, meow meow meow meow meow meow?" meow meow.

Meow meow meow meow meow meow meow. Meow meow meow meow meow meow meow meow. Meow meow meow meow meow meow meow meow, meow meow meow meow meow meow meow. Meow meow meow. Meow meow, meow meow meow meow meow meow. Meow meow meow meow meow meow.

Meow meow meow meow meow meow. Meow meow meow meow meow, meow meow meow meow meow meow meow meow

meow meow meow. Meow, meow, meow meow meow meow, meow meow meow meow, meow meow meow-meow. Meow meow meow meow meow meow meow meow meow meow meow meow, meow meow meow. Meow meow meow meow meow meow meow meow meow, meow meow meow meow meow. Meow. Meow meow meow meow, meow meow. Meow meow meow meow meow meow meow meow. Meow meow meow. Meow meow meow meow meow. Meow meow meow meow meow, meow meow meow meow meow meow meow meow meow meow. Meow meow meow meow meow meow meow meow meow.

Meow meow meow meow meow meow meow meow meow meow meow, meow meow meow meow. Meow meow meow meow meow meow meow meow.

Meow meow meow meow meow meow meow. Meow meow meow, Meow meow meow meow. Meow meow meow meow meow meow meow. Meow meow meow meow-meow meow, meow meow meow meow meow meow meow. Meow meow meow meow meow meow meow meow meow, meow meow meow meow meow meow meow meow. Meow meow meow, meow-meow meow meow meow meow meow meow meow meow. Meow meow meow meow, meow meow meow meow. Meow meow meow meow. Meow meow meow meow meow. Meow meow meow meow meow meow meow meow. Meow meow, meow meow meow meow meow meow meow meow meow meow meow. Meow meow meow meow meow meow meow meow meow meow, meow meow meow meow meow meow meow, meow meow meow meow meow meow meow meow. Meow meow meow meow meow, meow meow meow meow meow meow meow meow meow meow meow. Meow meow meow meow, meow meow meow meow meow meow meow. Meow meow meow meow meow meow meow meow meow meow.

"Meow meow meow meow meow meow meow meow meow meow meow meow meow," meow meow meow meow meow. Meow meow meow meow meow, meow meow meow meow meow. "Meow?"

"Meow, meow meow meow," meow meow.

"Meow meow meow meow."

"Meow meow meow meow meow meow? Meow? Meow meow meow meow."

"Meow meow meow meow meow meow meow meow meow meow? Meow meow? Meow meow?"

"Meow meow. Meow meow meow."

"Meow meow meow? Meow meow?"

"Meow."

"Meow, meow meow meow meow meow meow meow meow meow meow?"

"Meow meow."

Meow meow. Meow meow meow meow meow meow meow meow meow meow. Meow meow meow meow meow meow meow meow meow meow meow meow meow, meow meow. Meow meow meow meow meow. Meow meow meow meow meow meow meow, meow meow meow meow meow meow.

"Meow, meow meow meow meow meow meow meow meow meow."

Meow meow meow meow meow meow meow meow meow meow meow meow meow meow meow. Meow meow meow meow meow meow meow meow meow meow meow. Meow meow meow meow. Meow meow meow meow.

Meow meow meow meow meow meow meow meow, meow meow meow meow meow, meow meow meow meow meow meow meow meow meow meow meow meow. Meow meow, meow meow meow meow meow meow. Meow meow meow meow meow meow meow meow meow meow meow. Meow meow

meow meow meow meow, meow meow meow meow. Meow meow meow meow meow meow meow, meow meow meow meow meow meow meow. Meow meow meow meow meow meow meow meow.

Meow meow meow meow, meow meow meow meow meow meow. Meow meow meow. Meow meow meow meow. Meow meow. Meow meow, meow meow meow meow meow, meow meow meow meow.

"Meow."

"Meow, Meow Meow. Meow meow Meow Meow Meow, meow meow meow meow Meow."

Meow meow meow meow, meow meow meow meow meow meow meow meow meow meow meow meow. Meow Meow Meow meow meow meow meow meow meow meow, meow meow meow meow meow meow meow meow meow meow meow. Meow meow meow meow meow meow meow.

"Meow, meow meow meow meow," meow meow meow meow. "Meow meow meow meow meow meow. Meow meow meow meow meow meow meow."

Meow meow meow meow meow. Meow meow meow meow meow meow meow meow meow meow. Meow meow meow meow, meow. Meow meow meow. "Meow, meow meow meow meow meow meow?" meow meow meow meow.

Meow meow meow meow meow meow meow meow meow meow meow. Meow meow meow meow meow meow Meow Meow Meow meow meow meow meow. Meow meow meow meow meow meow meow meow meow meow meow meow meow, meow meow meow meow meow, meow meow meow meow. Meow meow meow meow meow meow meow.

"Meow meow, meow meow meow meow, meow."

"Meow, meow meow meow meow. Meow meow meow meow meow."

Meow meow meow meow, meow meow meow meow meow, meow Meow Meow Meow meow meow meow meow meow meow. Meow meow meow meow meow meow meow meow.

Meow Meow Meow meow meow meow meow meow meow. Meow meow meow. Meow meow meow meow meow meow, meow meow meow meow meow meow meow, meow meow meow meow meow meow meow. Meow meow meow meow meow meow. Meow meow meow meow meow meow meow, meow meow meow. Meow meow meow meow meow meow meow.

"Meow meow meow, meow meow meow meow meow meow meow. Meow meow meow." meow meow meow. Meow meow meow meow meow meow meow meow meow. Meow meow meow meow meow meow meow, meow meow meow meow meow meow, meow meow meow meow meow meow.

"Meow meow, meow meow meow meow. Meow meow meow meow meow meow meow meow meow meow. Meow meow meow meow meow meow meow meow meow meow meow. Meow, meow meow. Meow meow meow meow meow meow meow meow. Meow meow meow meow meow meow?"

"Meow meow meow."

Meow meow meow meow meow. Meow meow meow.

"Meow meow meow meow meow meow. Meow meow meow meow meow?"

"Meow meow meow meow meow meow meow meow meow."

Meow meow meow meow meow meow meow meow meow meow meow meow meow. Meow meow meow meow meow meow meow, meow meow meow meow meow meow meow meow meow. Meow meow meow meow meow meow meow meow meow meow. Meow meow meow meow, meow meow

meow meow, meow meow meow meow meow meow. Meow meow meow, meow meow meow meow meow meow.

Meow meow meow meow. Meow meow meow meow. Meow meow meow meow meow meow meow meow meow, meow meow meow meow meow? Meow meow meow meow meow meow meow meow meow meow meow meow meow meow, meow meow meow meow. Meow meow meow meow meow meow meow meow meow meow meow. Meow meow meow meow meow meow meow meow meow meow meow meow meow meow meow. Meow meow meow meow meow meow. Meow meow meow meow meow meow meow. Meow meow meow meow meow meow meow meow meow meow meow. Meow meow meow meow meow meow meow meow meow meow meow meow meow, meow meow meow meow meow meow meow meow.

"Meow meow meow?" meow meow meow meow meow meow, meow meow meow meow meow meow meow meow meow meow. Meow meow meow meow meow meow, meow meow meow meow meow meow meow meow meow meow.

"Meow meow meow meow meow meow meow meow meow meow, meow. Meow meow?"

Meow meow meow meow meow. Meow meow meow meow meow meow, meow meow meow meow meow meow meow meow, meow meow meow meow meow meow meow, meow meow meow meow meow meow meow meow meow, meow meow meow meow-meow-meow meow.

"Meow, meow meow meow," meow meow.

"Meow meow meow meow meow meow meow meow meow."

"Meow meow."

Meow meow meow meow meow meow meow. meow meow meow meow. Meow meow meow meow meow meow meow,

meow meow meow meow meow. Meow meow. Meow meow meow meow meow meow. Meow meow meow meow meow meow, meow meow meow meow meow meow meow meow meow meow meow meow meow meow.

Meow meow meow meow meow meow, meow meow meow meow, meow meow meow meow, meow meow meow meow meow meow, meow meow meow. Meow meow meow meow. meow meow meow meow meow. Meow meow meow. Meow meow meow meow meow meow meow meow meow meow meow meow meow meow. Meow meow meow.

Meow meow meow, meow meow meow meow meow meow, meow meow meow meow meow meow meow. Meow meow meow meow meow meow meow meow meow meow meow, meow meow meow meow meow meow meow meow. Meow meow meow meow meow meow meow meow, meow meow meow meow meow meow meow meow meow.

Meow meow meow, meow meow meow meow meow meow meow meow meow. Meow meow meow meow meow. Meow meow meow meow meow meow meow meow meow meow meow meow meow meow meow meow meow. Meow meow meow meow meow meow meow meow, meow meow meow meow meow meow meow meow meow meow. Meow meow meow meow meow meow meow meow meow meow. Meow meow meow meow, meow meow meow meow meow meow meow? Meow meow meow meow, meow meow. Mcow meow meow meow meow, meow meow meow meow meow meow meow meow meow meow meow meow.

Meow meow meow meow meow, meow meow meow mcow meow meow meow meow meow meow meow meow. Meow meow meow meow meow meow meow meow meow meow meow meow meow meow meow. Meow meow meow meow meow meow meow meow meow, meow meow meow meow meow meow

meow meow meow meow. Meow meow meow meow meow meow meow meow meow meow meow. Meow meow meow meow meow meow meow meow meow, meow meow meow meow meow meow meow meow meow meow meow. Meow meow meow meow meow meow meow meow meow meow meow meow meow meow meow.

Meow meow, meow meow, meow meow meow meow meow meow. Meow meow meow meow meow. Meow meow meow meow meow meow meow meow meow. Meow meow. Meow meow meow meow. Meow meow meow meow meow meow meow, meow meow. Meow meow meow meow meow meow meow, meow meow. Meow meow meow meow meow meow, meow meow meow meow meow. Meow meow meow meow meow meow meow meow meow.

Meow meow meow meow meow meow meow meow meow meow meow, meow meow meow meow meow meow meow. Meow meow meow. Meow meow meow meow, meow meow meow meow, meow meow meow meow meow, meow meow meow meow. Meow meow meow meow meow.

Meow meow meow meow meow meow meow.

Meow meow meow meow meow meow meow meow, meow meow meow meow meow. Meow meow meow. Meow meow meow meow meow meow meow meow. Meow meow meow meow meow meow meow. Meow meow meow meow meow meow. Meow meow meow meow meow, meow meow.

MEOW?

Meow meow meow meow meow meow meow meow meow meow. Meow meow meow. Meow meow meow meow meow meow meow meow meow, meow meow meow meow meow meow meow meow meow, meow meow meow meow meow meow meow. Meow meow meow meow. Meow meow meow meow meow meow meow. Meow meow meow meow meow meow meow meow. Meow meow meow meow meow meow meow, meow meow meow meow, meow meow meow meow meow meow meow meow meow meow meow. Meow meow meow meow meow meow meow meow meow meow meow meow meow meow meow meow meow. Meow meow meow meow. Meow meow meow meow meow meow. Meow meow meow meow meow meow meow meow meow. Meow meow meow.

Meow meow meow meow meow meow meow meow. Meow meow meow meow meow meow meow meow, meow meow meow meow meow meow meow meow meow meow meow meow meow meow meow meow meow meow meow meow meow, meow meow meow meow meow meow meow meow meow meow meow meow meow. Meow meow meow meow meow meow meow meow meow meow meow. Meow meow meow meow meow meow meow. Meow meow meow meow meow. Meow meow meow meow meow meow meow meow. Meow meow meow meow meow meow. Meow meow meow

meow meow meow meow. Meow meow. Meow meow meow meow meow meow meow meow meow. Meow meow meow meow meow meow meow meow meow meow, meow meow meow meow meow meow meow meow meow meow. Meow meow meow meow. Meow meow meow meow meow meow meow meow meow meow meow meow meow meow, meow meow meow meow meow meow.

Meow meow meow meow meow. Meow meow meow meow meow meow meow meow, meow meow meow meow meow. Meow meow meow meow meow. Meow. Meow meow meow meow meow meow meow meow meow. Meow meow meow meow. Meow meow meow meow meow meow meow meow meow meow meow meow meow meow, meow meow.

Meow meow meow meow meow meow meow meow meow. Meow meow meow meow meow meow meow meow meow meow. Meow meow meow meow meow meow meow meow meow, meow meow meow meow meow meow meow meow meow meow meow. Meow meow meow meow meow, meow meow meow meow meow meow meow. Meow meow meow meow.

"Meow meow, Meow, meow meow meow meow meow meow, meow meow meow meow meow meow meow meow," meow meow meow meow meow meow meow meow meow meow.

Meow meow, meow meow meow meow. Meow meow meow meow meow, meow meow meow meow meow meow meow. Meow meow meow meow meow meow meow meow meow. Meow meow meow meow meow meow, meow meow meow, meow meow meow meow, meow meow meow. Meow meow meow meow meow, meow meow meow meow meow meow meow meow meow meow meow.

* * * * * * *

Meow meow meow meow meow meow meow meow meow. Meow meow meow meow meow meow meow. Meow meow meow meow meow meow meow meow meow. Meow meow meow meow meow meow meow, meow meow meow meow meow meow meow. Meow meow meow Meow meow meow meow. Meow meow meow meow meow meow meow, meow meow meow meow. Meow meow meow meow meow meow meow, meow meow meow meow meow. Meow meow meow meow meow meow meow meow meow, meow meow meow meow meow.

Meow meow meow meow meow meow meow meow meow meow meow meow, meow meow meow meow Meow meow meow meow meow meow. Meow meow meow meow meow meow meow meow meow meow meow meow meow: meow meow meow, meow meow meow. Meow meow meow meow meow meow. Meow meow.

Meow meow meow meow meow meow meow meow, meow meow meow meow meow meow meow meow meow meow, meow meow meow meow meow meow, meow meow meow meow meow meow. Meow meow meow meow. Meow meow meow meow meow meow meow, meow meow meow meow. Meow meow meow meow. Meow meow meow meow meow meow meow meow meow meow meow meow meow. Meow meow meow meow, meow meow meow meow meow meow meow meow.

Meow meow meow meow meow, meow meow meow meow, meow meow meow meow meow meow meow meow meow. Meow meow meow meow meow, meow meow meow meow meow meow meow meow meow meow meow. Meow meow meow meow meow. Meow meow meow meow meow meow meow meow meow meow meow meow meow meow. Meow meow meow meow meow meow meow, meow meow

meow meow meow meow, meow meow meow meow meow meow meow meow meow meow meow meow.

Meow meow meow meow meow meow. Meow meow meow meow meow meow meow meow meow meow meow. Meow meow meow meow meow meow meow meow meow meow, meow meow meow meow meow, meow meow meow meow meow, meow meow meow, meow meow meow meow meow meow meow meow meow meow meow meow meow.

Meow meow meow meow meow. Meow meow meow meow meow meow meow meow meow, meow meow meow meow. Meow meow meow meow meow meow meow. Meow meow meow, meow meow meow meow meow meow meow meow meow, meow meow meow meow meow. Meow meow.

Meow meow meow meow meow meow, meow meow meow meow meow, meow meow meow meow meow meow meow meow meow. Meow meow meow meow meow meow. Meow meow meow meow meow meow. Meow meow meow. Meow. Meow meow meow meow. Meow meow meow meow.

Meow meow meow, meow meow Meow, meow Meow. Meow meow meow meow, meow meow meow meow meow, meow meow meow meow meow meow meow meow meow meow. Meow meow meow meow meow meow meow meow meow meow meow meow meow. Meow meow meow meow meow meow. Meow meow meow meow meow meow meow meow meow meow meow meow meow, meow meow meow meow meow. Meow meow meow meow meow meow meow meow meow meow meow meow meow, meow meow meow meow meow meow meow. Meow meow meow meow meow meow meow meow meow meow. Meow meow meow meow meow meow meow meow meow meow, meow meow meow, meow meow meow meow meow meow meow meow meow meow meow meow meow meow meow. Meow

meow meow meow meow meow. Meow meow meow meow meow.

Meow meow meow meow, meow meow meow meow meow. Meow meow meow meow meow meow meow meow, meow meow. Meow meow meow meow meow meow meow meow, meow meow meow meow meow meow meow meow meow meow meow meow meow. Meow meow meow meow meow meow meow meow, meow meow meow meow meow meow meow meow, meow meow meow meow meow, meow meow meow meow meow meow. Meow meow meow meow meow meow meow meow, meow meow meow.

Meow meow meow meow meow meow meow meow meow meow meow meow meow meow meow meow. Meow meow meow, meow meow meow meow meow meow meow, meow meow. Meow meow meow. Meow meow meow meow meow meow Meow meow Meow meow meow meow meow.

Meow meow meow meow meow, meow meow meow meow meow meow meow. meow meow meow meow meow meow meow meow meow meow. Meow meow meow meow meow meow meow meow. Meow meow meow meow meow. Meow meow meow meow meow meow meow?

Meow meow meow meow meow. Meow meow meow, meow meow meow meow meow, meow meow Meow meow meow. Meow meow meow meow. Meow meow meow, meow meow, meow meow meow meow meow meow meow meow. Meow Meow meow meow meow meow. Meow meow meow meow meow meow meow meow meow meow meow meow meow. Meow meow meow meow meow, meow. Meow meow meow, meow meow meow, meow meow meow meow meow meow meow meow meow meow. Meow. Meow meow meow meow?

Meow meow meow meow meow meow meow meow meow meow meow meow meow. Meow meow meow meow meow

meow meow meow meow meow meow meow meow meow meow meow.

Meow meow meow meow, meow meow meow. Meow meow meow meow meow meow meow meow meow meow. Meow meow, meow meow meow meow meow meow meow meow. Meow meow meow meow, meow meow meow meow meow meow, meow meow meow meow meow meow.

"Meow, meow meow meow, m-meow, m-meow meow meow meow meow meow meow meow," meow meow meow meow. "Meow meow meow meow meow meow meow meow meow meow meow meow."

Meow meow meow meow meow meow. meow meow meow meow meow meow meow meow meow meow meow meow. Meow meow meow meow meow Meow meow meow meow meow meow meow meow meow meow, meow meow meow meow meow meow meow meow meow. Meow meow Meow meow meow meow meow. Meow meow meow meow meow meow meow meow meow meow, meow meow meow meow meow meow meow meow meow meow. Meow meow meow meow meow meow, meow meow meow meow meow meow meow Meow, meow meow meow meow.

"Meow meow meow meow meow meow, Meow?" Meow meow meow. Meow, meow meow meow meow, meow meow meow. Meow meow meow meow meow meow meow meow meow meow. Meow meow meow meow meow meow. Meow meow meow meow, meow.

"Meow meow, Meow. Meow meow meow, meow meow meow meow? Meow meow meow meow meow meow."

"Meow meow meow," Meow meow meow meow meow meow.

Meow meow meow Meow, Meow meow meow meow meow. Meow meow meow meow, meow meow meow meow meow.

Meow meow meow meow. Meow meow meow meow meow meow meow meow meow meow meow meow meow meow.

Meow meow meow meow. Meow meow meow meow meow meow, meow meow meow meow meow meow meow. Meow meow meow meow meow meow meow. Meow meow meow meow meow meow meow meow meow meow meow meow meow meow meow meow meow meow meow meow meow meow meow. Meow meow meow meow meow meow meow meow meow meow meow.

Meow meow meow meow meow. Meow meow meow meow, meow meow meow meow. Meow meow meow meow meow meow meow meow meow, meow meow meow meow meow meow meow. Meow meow meow meow meow meow meow meow, meow meow, meow meow meow meow. Meow meow meow meow meow meow meow meow meow meow meow, meow meow meow meow, meow meow meow meow meow meow meow. Meow meow meow meow meow meow meow meow meow, meow meow meow meow meow meow meow meow meow meow meow meow meow meow meow.

* * * * * * *

Meow meow meow meow meow meow meow meow. Meow meow meow meow meow meow meow meow, meow meow meow meow meow meow meow meow. Meow meow meow meow meow meow meow meow meow meow meow, meow meow meow meow meow meow meow meow meow meow meow meow meow Meow. Meow meow meow, meow meow meow Meow meow meow meow, Meow meow meow, meow meow meow meow meow meow. Meow meow meow meow meow meow. Meow meow meow

meow meow meow meow, meow meow meow meow meow meow.

Meow meow meow meow meow meow meow meow meow. Meow meow meow, meow meow, meow meow Meow meow, meow meow meow meow meow meow meow meow. Meow meow meow meow meow, meow meow meow meow meow. Meow meow meow meow meow meow meow meow meow meow meow meow.

Meow meow meow. Meow meow meow meow meow. Meow meow meow meow meow. Meow meow meow meow, meow meow meow meow meow meow meow meow meow meow meow. Meow meow meow meow meow meow meow meow meow meow meow.

Meow meow meow, meow meow meow meow meow meow meow meow meow. Meow meow meow meow meow. Meow meow meow meow meow. Meow meow meow meow meow meow meow meow, meow. Meow meow meow meow. Meow meow meow meow meow meow meow. Meow meow meow meow meow, meow meow meow. Meow meow meow meow meow, meow meow meow meow meow meow, meow meow meow meow meow meow meow meow. Meow meow meow meow. Meow meow meow, meow meow meow meow.

Meow meow meow meow meow.

Meow meow meow meow meow. Meow meow meow Meow meow meow meow meow meow, meow meow meow. Meow meow meow, meow Meow meow meow meow. Meow meow. Meow meow meow meow meow meow meow meow meow meow. Meow meow meow meow meow meow meow meow Meow. Meow meow meow meow meow meow. Meow meow meow meow, meow meow meow meow. Meow meow meow meow, meow meow meow, meow meow meow Meow meow meow. Meow meow meow meow, meow meow meow meow.

"Meow meow meow meow meow," meow meow.

Meow meow meow meow meow meow meow meow meow meow meow. Meow meow meow meow meow meow meow meow, meow meow meow. Meow meow meow meow meow. Meow meow meow meow meow meow.

"Meow Meow meow?" meow meow meow meow meow meow meow meow meow.

Meow meow meow meow, meow meow meow meow meow meow meow meow meow meow. Meow meow meow meow meow meow meow meow meow, meow meow meow meow meow meow meow.

"Meow meow meow, meow meow?" Meow meow meow.

"Meow."

"Meow meow meow, meow," meow meow meow meow meow meow, meow meow meow meow. Meow meow meow meow meow. Meow meow meow meow, meow meow meow meow meow meow, meow meow. Meow meow meow meow meow meow meow meow meow meow meow meow meow.

"Meow meow meow meow. Meow meow meow meow meow meow, meow meow."

"Meow, meow meow meow meow. Meow meow meow meow, meow meow meow meow," meow meow meow meow.

Meow meow meow meow meow. Meow meow meow meow meow meow. Meow meow meow meow meow meow meow meow meow meow meow meow meow meow. Meow meow meow meow meow meow meow meow meow, meow meow meow meow meow meow meow meow meow meow.

"Meow meow meow meow meow meow," meow meow meow meow meow meow meow meow meow. Meow meow meow meow meow meow, meow meow meow meow meow meow. Meow meow meow meow meow meow, meow meow meow meow meow meow meow meow meow. Meow meow

meow meow meow meow meow meow meow meow meow meow. Meow meow, meow meow meow, meow meow meow meow meow meow, meow meow meow meow meow meow meow meow meow meow meow. Meow meow meow meow meow meow, meow meow meow meow meow meow.

Meow meow meow meow meow meow meow. Meow meow meow meow. Meow meow meow meow meow meow meow meow meow meow meow meow meow meow, meow meow meow meow meow meow meow meow. Meow meow meow meow meow meow, meow meow meow meow meow meow. Meow meow meow meow meow meow meow meow meow.

Meow meow meow meow, meow meow meow meow meow meow meow. Meow meow meow meow meow meow meow meow, meow meow meow meow meow meow. Meow meow meow meow meow meow meow. Meow meow meow meow meow meow meow. Meow meow meow meow meow meow meow meow meow meow. Meow meow. meow meow meow meow meow meow, meow meow, meow meow meow meow meow meow meow meow meow meow. Meow meow meow meow meow meow meow meow meow meow meow, meow meow meow meow meow meow meow meow, meow meow meow meow meow meow meow meow.

Meow meow meow meow meow meow, meow meow meow meow, meow meow meow meow meow meow meow. Meow meow meow meow meow, meow meow meow meow. Meow meow meow meow meow meow meow meow, meow meow meow meow. Meow meow meow meow, meow meow meow meow meow meow meow, meow meow Meow meow meow. Meow meow meow meow meow meow meow. Meow meow meow meow meow meow?

"Meow meow meow meow meow?" meow meow meow, meow meow meow meow meow meow meow meow meow,

meow meow meow meow meow meow, meow meow meow meow meow meow meow meow meow.

"Meow meow meow meow meow, meow. Meow meow. Meow meow. Meow meow meow meow meow. Meow meow meow meow meow meow meow meow. Meow meow meow," meow meow meow.

"Meow meow meow, meow, meow meow meow meow meow," meow meow meow meow meow meow meow meow meow meow. Meow meow meow meow, meow meow meow meow meow meow meow. Meow meow meow meow meow meow meow, meow meow meow. Meow meow meow meow meow meow meow. Meow meow meow meow meow meow meow meow, meow meow meow meow meow meow meow meow meow meow meow meow. Meow meow meow meow meow meow meow meow meow meow meow, meow meow meow meow meow meow meow. Meow meow meow meow meow meow, meow meow meow meow meow, meow meow meow meow meow meow meow meow meow meow meow.

Meow meow meow meow meow meow meow meow, meow meow meow meow meow, meow meow meow meow meow meow meow. Meow meow meow meow meow meow meow meow meow. Meow meow meow meow, meow meow meow meow meow meow. Meow meow meow meow meow meow meow.

Meow meow meow meow meow meow meow, meow meow meow meow. Meow meow meow meow meow meow meow, meow meow meow meow meow meow meow, meow meow meow meow meow meow meow. Meow meow meow meow meow meow meow meow meow.

Meow meow meow meow meow meow meow meow meow. Meow meow meow meow meow meow meow meow

meow. Meow meow meow meow meow meow meow meow. Meow meow. Meow meow meow meow, meow meow meow meow meow meow meow meow meow meow meow. Meow meow meow meow meow meow meow meow. Meow meow meow meow meow meow meow meow meow meow. Meow meow meow meow meow meow meow meow, meow meow meow meow meow meow. Meow meow meow meow meow meow meow meow meow Meow meow meow meow, meow, meow meow meow meow meow meow meow meow, meow meow meow meow meow. Meow meow meow meow meow, meow meow meow meow, meow meow meow meow meow meow meow meow meow.

Meow meow meow meow meow meow, meow meow meow, meow meow meow meow meow meow meow meow meow meow meow meow meow. Meow meow meow meow meow meow meow meow meow meow. Meow meow meow meow meow meow meow meow. Meow meow meow meow meow meow meow meow meow meow meow meow meow, meow meow meow meow meow meow meow. Meow meow meow meow meow, meow meow meow meow meow, meow meow meow meow meow meow meow meow meow meow meow. Meow meow meow meow meow meow meow meow meow meow meow. Meow meow meow meow. Meow meow meow meow meow meow meow.

Meow meow meow meow meow meow meow meow meow, meow meow meow meow meow, meow meow meow meow meow meow meow meow meow meow meow. Meow meow meow Meow meow meow, meow meow meow meow meow meow meow meow meow meow, meow Meow meow meow meow meow meow meow meow, meow meow meow meow meow meow meow meow meow meow meow, meow meow meow meow meow. Meow meow meow.

Meow meow meow meow meow meow meow meow meow, meow meow meow meow meow meow meow meow. Meow meow meow meow meow. Meow meow meow Meow meow meow, meow meow meow. Meow meow meow meow, meow meow meow meow meow meow meow. Meow meow meow meow.

Meow meow meow meow meow meow meow, meow meow meow, meow meow meow meow meow, meow meow meow meow meow meow. Meow meow meow meow meow meow meow meow meow meow meow, meow meow meow meow meow meow meow. Meow meow meow meow meow meow meow meow, meow meow meow meow meow. Meow meow meow meow meow, meow meow meow meow meow meow, meow meow meow meow meow meow meow meow. Meow meow meow meow meow meow meow meow meow meow meow meow meow meow. Meow meow meow meow meow meow, meow meow meow meow meow, meow meow meow meow meow. Meow meow meow meow meow meow meow meow meow meow.

Meow meow meow meow meow meow, meow meow meow. Meow meow meow-meow meow. Meow meow meow meow meow, meow meow meow meow. meow meow meow meow meow meow meow, meow meow meow meow meow. Meow meow meow meow meow meow meow meow. Meow meow meow meow meow meow meow, meow meow meow meow meow meow meow. Meow meow meow meow meow meow. Meow meow meow meow meow meow meow meow. Meow meow meow meow meow meow meow meow meow meow meow meow meow meow meow meow meow. Meow meow meow meow meow. Meow meow meow meow meow meow meow. Meow meow meow meow meow, meow meow meow, meow meow meow meow meow. Meow meow meow meow

meow meow meow meow meow meow meow meow meow meow. Meow meow meow meow meow meow.

Meow meow meow meow meow meow, meow meow meow meow meow meow meow meow meow meow meow meow. Meow meow meow meow meow, meow meow, meow meow meow meow meow meow meow meow meow. Meow meow meow meow meow, meow meow meow meow meow meow meow. Meow meow meow meow, meow meow meow meow. Meow meow meow meow meow. Meow meow meow meow meow meow meow meow meow meow meow. Meow meow meow meow, meow meow meow meow meow, meow meow meow meow. Meow meow meow, meow meow meow.

Meow meow meow meow meow meow meow, meow meow meow, meow meow meow meow meow, meow meow meow meow meow. Meow meow meow meow meow meow. Meow meow meow meow meow. Meow meow meow meow meow meow meow, meow meow meow meow. Meow meow meow meow meow. Meow meow meow meow meow meow meow meow meow meow, meow meow meow meow meow meow meow meow meow meow meow meow meow meow meow meow meow. Meow meow meow meow meow. Meow meow meow meow meow meow meow meow meow meow meow meow. Meow meow meow meow meow meow meow, meow meow meow meow meow meow meow meow meow meow meow.

Meow. Meow meow meow meow meow meow meow meow.

Meow meow meow meow meow meow meow meow meow meow meow meow meow meow. Meow meow meow meow. Meow meow meow meow meow meow meow meow meow meow meow meow, meow meow meow, meow meow meow meow meow meow.

"Meow Meow, meow meow," meow meow meow meow meow meow meow meow meow. Meow meow meow meow

meow meow meow meow meow meow meow meow meow meow meow meow.

"Meow meow meow. Meow meow meow meow meow meow meow. Meow meow meow meow meow." Meow meow meow meow meow meow meow meow meow meow. Meow meow meow Meow, meow meow meow meow meow meow meow meow meow meow. Meow meow meow meow, meow meow meow meow meow meow meow.

Meow meow meow meow meow meow, meow meow meow meow meow meow meow meow, meow meow meow meow meow meow meow. Meow meow meow meow meow. Meow meow meow meow meow. Meow meow meow meow meow meow meow meow. Meow meow meow meow meow meow meow meow. Meow meow meow meow meow meow meow meow meow meow meow meow meow meow meow meow meow meow. Meow meow meow meow, meow meow meow meow. Meow meow meow meow meow meow meow meow meow meow meow meow meow meow meow.

"Meow, meow Meow meow?" meow meow. Meow meow meow meow. Meow meow meow meow Meow meow meow meow meow meow meow, meow meow meow meow meow meow. Meow meow meow meow meow meow meow. Meow meow meow, meow meow meow meow. Meow meow meow. Meow meow meow meow meow meow meow meow meow meow. Meow meow mcow meow meow, meow meow meow meow meow meow, meow meow meow meow meow meow meow, meow meow meow meow meow meow meow meow.

Meow meow meow meow meow meow meow, meow meow meow meow meow meow meow. Meow meow meow meow meow meow meow meow meow. Meow meow meow meow meow meow, meow meow meow meow meow meow meow. Meow meow meow meow meow meow meow Meow meow.

Meow meow meow meow meow meow. Meow meow meow meow meow meow. Meow meow meow meow meow. Meow meow meow meow meow meow meow Meow meow Meow meow Meow meow meow meow. meow meow meow meow meow meow meow meow meow meow meow, meow meow meow meow meow meow meow meow meow meow.

Meow meow meow meow, meow meow-meow, meow meow meow meow meow. meow meow meow meow meow meow. Meow meow meow meow. Meow meow meow meow meow, meow meow meow meow meow meow meow meow. Meow meow, meow meow meow meow. Meow meow meow meow meow meow meow meow meow meow meow meow meow meow meow meow meow meow meow meow meow meow meow meow meow meow meow meow meow meow.

Meow meow meow meow meow meow meow meow meow meow meow meow meow meow meow meow meow, meow meow meow meow meow meow meow. Meow meow meow meow meow meow meow, meow meow meow meow meow meow meow, meow meow meow. Meow meow meow meow meow meow, meow meow meow meow meow meow meow meow.

Meow, meow meow meow meow meow meow. Meow meow meow Meow meow meow meow. Meow meow meow meow meow meow meow meow. Meow meow meow meow meow meow meow meow. Meow meow meow meow meow, meow meow meow meow, meow meow meow. Meow meow meow meow meow meow meow meow. Meow meow meow meow meow meow meow meow, meow meow meow meow, meow meow meow meow Meow meow meow, meow meow meow meow meow meow meow meow meow meow meow meow meow meow.

Meow meow meow meow meow meow meow Meow meow Meow meow meow meow meow meow meow meow. Meow

meow meow meow meow meow meow. Meow meow meow meow meow, meow meow meow meow meow meow meow. Meow meow meow meow meow meow, meow meow Meow meow meow, meow meow meow meow meow meow. Meow meow meow meow meow meow meow meow Meow. Meow meow meow meow meow meow, meow meow. Meow meow meow meow meow meow meow. Meow meow meow meow meow meow meow meow.

Meow meow meow meow meow meow meow meow meow meow meow meow meow meow meow meow. Meow meow meow meow meow meow meow meow meow meow meow meow meow meow meow, meow meow Meow meow meow meow, meow meow meow meow meow meow meow. Meow meow meow meow.

Meow meow meow meow meow meow meow, meow meow meow meow meow meow meow meow, meow meow meow meow meow meow meow meow, meow meow meow meow meow meow meow meow, meow meow meow meow meow meow meow meow meow. Meow meow meow meow meow meow meow. Meow meow meow meow meow, meow meow meow meow meow meow meow meow.

Meow meow meow, meow meow meow, meow meow. Meow meow meow meow meow meow meow meow meow. Meow meow meow meow meow meow meow meow meow meow meow meow meow. Meow meow meow meow meow meow meow meow meow meow meow meow meow, meow meow meow meow meow meow. Meow meow meow meow meow meow meow meow. Meow meow meow meow meow meow meow meow meow meow meow meow, meow meow meow meow meow meow meow meow meow meow meow meow meow meow meow. Meow meow "Meow, meow meow meow meow meow meow meow meow."

Meow meow meow meow meow meow. Meow meow meow meow meow meow meow meow meow, meow meow meow meow meow meow meow meow meow meow meow, meow meow, meow meow meow meow meow meow meow meow meow.

"Meow," meow meow, meow meow meow meow meow meow meow meow, meow meow meow meow meow meow meow meow meow, "meow meow Meow," meow meow meow meow meow meow meow, "Meow meow meow meow meow meow meow. Meow meow meow. Meow meow meow meow meow meow meow meow."

Meow meow meow meow meow. Meow meow meow meow meow. Meow meow meow meow meow meow. Meow meow. Meow meow meow meow meow meow. Meow meow meow meow meow meow meow meow meow meow meow meow meow meow meow meow meow meow. meow meow meow meow meow meow meow meow. Meow meow meow meow meow meow meow. Meow meow meow meow meow meow meow meow. Meow meow meow meow meow meow meow, meow meow meow meow meow meow meow. Meow meow meow meow meow meow meow meow, meow meow meow meow meow meow meow meow meow, meow meow meow meow meow meow meow meow meow. Meow meow meow meow meow meow meow meow meow meow meow meow meow meow meow meow.

Meow meow meow, meow meow meow, meow meow meow meow meow, meow meow meow meow meow meow meow. Meow meow meow meow meow meow. Meow meow meow meow meow meow meow meow meow meow meow meow meow meow meow. Meow meow meow meow meow meow meow meow meow meow. Meow meow meow meow meow meow. Meow Meow meow meow, meow meow meow meow meow meow. Meow meow meow meow meow meow meow meow meow, meow meow

Meow meow Meow meow meow meow meow meow meow meow meow meow meow meow meow meow meow.

Meow meow meow meow meow meow. Meow meow meow meow meow. Meow meow meow, meow meow meow meow meow meow meow meow meow meow meow. Meow meow meow meow meow meow meow meow meow meow meow meow, meow meow meow meow meow meow meow meow meow. Meow meow meow meow meow meow, meow meow meow meow meow meow Meow, meow meow meow meow meow meow meow meow meow meow meow meow meow. Meow meow meow meow meow meow Meow meow meow meow meow meow meow meow meow meow meow meow meow. Meow meow meow Meow meow meow meow meow meow meow meow, meow meow meow meow meow meow meow meow, meow meow meow meow meow meow meow, meow meow meow meow meow meow meow.

"Meow meow meow meow meow, meow meow meow meow meow meow meow?" meow meow meow meow meow meow meow meow meow meow meow meow meow meow meow meow, meow meow meow meow meow meow meow meow.

"Meow, meow meow meow meow meow meow meow meow."

Meow meow meow meow meow meow meow meow, meow meow meow meow meow meow meow meow. Meow meow meow meow meow meow. Meow meow meow meow meow meow, meow meow meow meow meow. Meow meow meow, meow meow meow meow meow meow meow meow. Meow meow meow meow meow meow meow meow, meow meow meow meow meow meow, meow meow meow meow meow meow meow meow meow meow. Meow meow meow meow meow meow meow meow meow meow, meow meow meow meow meow meow meow meow meow meow meow. Meow meow meow meow meow

meow meow Meow, meow meow meow meow meow. Meow meow meow meow meow meow meow meow meow meow meow, meow meow meow meow meow meow meow meow meow meow meow meow meow meow meow.

Meow meow meow meow meow meow meow meow meow meow, Meow meow Meow, meow meow meow meow. Meow meow meow meow meow meow meow meow, meow meow meow meow meow meow meow, meow meow meow. Meow meow meow meow meow meow meow meow meow. Meow meow Meow meow meow meow meow meow meow meow meow meow meow meow meow meow meow. Meow meow meow meow meow meow meow meow meow. Meow meow meow meow meow meow meow meow meow meow.

Meow meow Meow meow meow, meow Meow meow. Meow meow meow meow meow meow meow meow meow meow meow meow meow meow, meow meow meow meow, meow meow meow meow meow meow meow meow meow meow. Meow meow meow meow meow meow meow meow meow, meow meow meow meow meow meow meow meow meow meow meow meow, meow meow meow meow meow meow meow meow. Meow meow meow meow meow meow meow meow meow. Meow meow meow meow meow meow meow meow meow meow meow meow meow meow meow. Meow meow meow meow meow, meow meow meow meow meow meow Meow meow meow meow meow meow meow meow meow. Meow meow meow meow meow meow meow, meow meow meow meow meow meow meow meow meow.

Meow meow meow meow meow meow meow meow meow, meow meow meow meow meow Meow meow meow meow meow meow, meow meow meow meow meow. Meow meow

meow meow meow meow meow meow meow meow, meow meow meow meow meow, meow meow meow meow meow. Meow meow meow meow meow meow meow meow meow meow meow meow meow, meow meow meow meow meow. Meow meow meow meow meow meow meow meow. Meow meow meow meow meow. Meow meow meow meow meow meow meow meow meow.

Meow meow meow meow, meow meow Meow meow meow meow meow meow meow meow meow, meow meow meow meow meow meow meow. Meow meow meow meow meow meow, meow meow meow meow meow meow meow meow meow meow. Meow meow meow meow meow meow meow meow meow meow meow meow meow meow. Meow meow meow meow meow meow meow meow meow meow meow meow, meow meow meow meow meow meow meow meow meow meow.

Meow meow meow meow meow meow meow meow, meow meow meow meow meow meow meow meow meow meow, meow meow meow meow meow meow meow meow meow meow. Moew meow meow meow meow meow, meow meow meow meow meow meow meow meow meow meow. Meow meow meow meow, meow meow meow meow meow meow meow meow. Meow meow meow meow meow meow. Meow meow meow meow meow meow meow, meow meow meow meow meow meow meow meow mcow, meow meow meow meow meow meow.

Meow meow meow meow meow meow meow, meow meow meow meow meow meow meow meow, meow meow meow meow meow. Meow meow meow meow meow, meow meow meow meow meow meow, meow meow meow, meow meow meow meow meow meow meow. Meow meow meow meow. Meow meow meow meow meow meow meow meow. Meow meow meow

meow meow meow meow. Meow Meow meow meow meow meow meow. Meow meow meow meow meow meow, meow meow meow meow meow meow meow meow meow meow meow.

Meow meow meow meow meow. Meow meow meow meow meow meow meow, meow meow meow meow meow, meow meow meow meow. Meow meow meow meow meow. Meow meow meow meow meow, meow meow meow meow meow meow meow meow, meow meow meow meow meow, meow meow meow meow meow.

"Meow Meow, meow meow meow meow meow meow meow meow meow meow? Meow meow meow meow meow."

Meow meow meow meow meow meow meow meow meow meow, meow meow meow meow meow meow. Meow meow meow meow, meow meow meow meow, meow meow meow meow meow meow meow. Meow meow meow meow meow meow meow meow meow meow meow meow meow meow meow. Meow meow meow meow meow meow meow, meow meow meow, meow meow meow meow meow meow meow meow. Meow meow meow. Meow meow meow meow meow meow meow meow meow meow meow meow meow meow.

Meow meow meow meow meow meow meow. Meow meow meow meow meow meow meow meow meow meow. Meow meow meow meow meow meow meow meow meow meow meow. Meow meow meow meow meow meow meow meow meow meow meow, meow meow meow meow meow. Meow meow meow. Meow meow meow meow meow. Meow meow, meow meow meow, meow meow meow meow meow meow meow meow meow, meow meow meow meow meow. Meow Meow meow meow meow, meow meow Meow meow meow meow meow, meow meow meow meow meow meow Meow.

"Meow meow meow, Meow? Meow, meow meow meow...."

"M'eow Meow, meow meow, meow meow meow meow," Meow meow.

"Meow meow, Meow, meow meow meow meow meow meow, meow meow meow meow meow meow meow," meow meow meow meow meow meow meow meow meow.

"Meow meow, Meow," Meow meow.

"Meow meow, Meow. Meow meow meow. Meow meow meow meow meow. Meow meow meow."

Meow meow meow meow meow meow meow meow meow meow meow. Meow meow meow meow meow meow meow, meow meow meow meow meow meow meow. Meow meow meow meow meow meow, meow meow meow meow meow meow meow, meow meow meow meow meow meow meow meow.

Meow meow meow meow meow meow meow meow meow meow meow meow meow, meow meow meow meow meow meow meow, meow meow meow meow meow, meow meow meow meow meow meow meow. Meow meow meow meow meow, meow meow meow, meow meow meow meow. Meow meow meow. Meow meow meow meow, meow meow meow, meow meow meow Meow. Meow meow meow meow meow meow meow, meow meow meow meow meow.

Meow meow meow meow meow meow, meow meow meow meow meow meow meow meow meow meow meow, meow meow meow meow meow meow meow. Meow meow meow meow meow. Meow meow meow meow. Meow meow meow meow meow meow meow meow. Meow meow meow meow meow. Meow meow meow meow meow meow meow meow meow meow. Meow meow meow meow meow meow meow meow, meow meow meow meow meow.

Meow meow.

Meow meow meow meow meow meow meow, meow meow meow meow. Meow meow meow meow meow meow, meow

meow, meow meow meow meow. Meow meow meow meow meow meow meow meow. Meow meow meow meow meow, meow meow meow meow meow meow. Meow meow meow meow meow meow meow meow meow meow, meow meow meow meow meow.

Meow meow. Meow meow meow.

Meow meow meow meow meow meow meow meow, meow meow meow meow meow meow meow meow meow meow meow meow meow meow meow. Meow meow meow meow. Meow meow meow meow meow, meow meow meow meow meow meow. Meow meow meow meow meow meow Meow meow meow meow meow meow meow meow meow Meow.

"Meow meow, meow meow meow meow meow meow meow meow," meow meow meow. Meow meow meow meow meow meow meow, meow meow meow meow meow meow meow meow, meow meow meow meow meow meow meow meow meow meow meow meow. Meow meow meow meow, meow Meow meow meow meow meow meow meow.

"Meow," meow meow. Meow meow meow meow meow meow meow meow meow meow, meow meow meow meow meow.

Meow meow meow meow meow meow meow meow meow, meow meow meow meow meow meow meow meow, meow meow meow meow meow meow, meow meow meow meow meow meow meow meow meow meow, meow meow meow meow. Meow meow meow meow, meow meow meow meow meow meow meow. Meow meow meow meow meow meow meow meow, meow meow Meow. Meow meow meow meow meow meow meow meow meow, meow meow meow meow meow meow. Meow meow meow meow, meow meow meow meow meow meow meow meow meow meow.

Meow meow meow meow meow meow meow meow, meow meow meow meow. Meow meow meow meow meow meow. Meow meow meow meow meow meow, meow meow meow meow. Meow meow meow meow meow meow. Meow meow meow meow meow meow meow meow, meow meow meow meow meow meow meow meow.

"Meow, meow meow meow meow meow Meow," meow meow meow meow meow meow meow meow meow.

Meow meow meow meow, meow meow "Meow meow meow, Meow."

Meow meow meow meow meow meow meow. Meow meow meow meow meow meow meow meow meow meow. Meow meow meow meow meow meow meow meow meow meow meow meow meow meow, meow meow meow meow meow meow meow. Meow meow meow meow meow. Meow meow meow meow meow meow meow.

Meow meow meow. Meow meow meow meow, meow meow meow meow meow meow meow meow meow meow, meow meow meow meow meow meow meow meow meow. Meow meow meow meow meow meow. Meow meow meow meow meow meow meow meow meow, meow meow meow meow.

Meow meow meow meow meow meow meow meow meow meow meow meow.

Meow meow meow meow. Meow meow meow meow meow meow meow meow. Meow meow meow meow meow. Meow meow meow meow, meow meow meow meow meow meow meow meow. Meow meow meow meow meow, meow meow meow meow meow. Meow meow meow meow meow meow meow meow meow meow meow meow meow.

Meow meow meow, meow meow meow meow meow. Meow meow meow Meow meow meow. Meow meow meow meow meow. Meow meow meow meow meow meow meow meow

meow. Meow meow meow meow meow meow meow. Meow meow meow meow meow, meow meow meow meow meow meow meow meow meow meow meow ^{Meow} meow meow, meow meow meow meow meow meow. Meow meow meow meow meow meow meow meow meow meow Meow meow. Meow meow, meow meow meow meow meow meow meow, meow meow meow meow meow meow meow. Meow meow meow meow meow meow meow.

Meow meow meow meow meow meow, meow meow meow meow. Meow meow meow meow meow meow meow meow, meow meow meow meow meow meow meow meow meow meow meow meow meow meow meow. Meow meow meow meow meow meow meow meow. Meow meow meow, meow meow meow meow meow, meow meow meow meow meow meow.

Meow meow meow meow meow meow meow meow meow meow meow. Meow meow meow meow meow. Meow meow meow meow meow meow meow meow meow meow meow Meow meow meow meow meow meow.

Meow meow meow meow meow, meow meow meow Meow meow meow meow. Meow meow meow meow meow meow meow meow. Meow meow meow meow meow.

"Meow meow meow meow meow meow meow meow meow meow."

MEOW MEOW MEOW MEOW MEOW

Meow meow meow meow meow, meow meow meow meow meow meow meow meow meow meow. Meow meow meow meow meow meow meow, meow meow meow meow meow meow meow meow meow meow meow meow meow. Meow meow meow meow meow.

Meow meow meow meow meow meow meow meow meow. Meow meow meow meow, meow meow meow meow meow meow meow meow meow meow. Meow, meow meow meow meow meow meow meow, meow meow meow meow meow. Meow meow meow meow meow meow, meow meow meow meow meow meow meow meow meow meow meow. Meow meow meow meow. Meow meow meow meow meow meow meow meow meow. Meow meow meow meow. Meow meow meow meow meow meow. Meow meow meow meow meow meow meow meow meow, meow meow meow meow meow meow meow meow meow. Meow meow meow meow meow meow meow, meow meow meow meow meow meow meow, meow meow meow meow meow meow meow meow.

Meow meow meow meow meow meow meow, meow meow meow meow meow meow meow meow meow meow meow meow meow meow meow. Meow meow meow meow

meow meow meow meow meow, meow meow meow meow
meow meow meow meow meow, meow meow meow meow
meow meow meow. Meow meow meow meow meow meow
meow meow meow meow meow meow meow. Meow meow
meow meow meow meow. Meow meow meow, meow meow
meow meow meow meow meow meow meow meow.

Meow meow meow meow meow meow meow meow meow
meow. Meow meow meow meow meow meow. Meow meow
meow meow meow meow. Meow meow meow meow, meow
meow meow meow meow meow meow meow meow. Meow
meow meow meow meow meow. Meow meow meow meow
meow meow, meow meow, meow meow meow meow meow
meow meow. Meow meow. Meow meow meow meow meow
meow meow meow meow meow meow meow, meow
meow meow meow. Meow meow meow meow.

Meow meow meow meow meow meow meow meow, meow
meow meow meow meow meow meow, meow meow meow
meow meow meow meow meow. Meow meow meow meow
meow meow meow meow, meow meow meow meow meow
meow meow meow meow meow meow meow meow meow
meow meow. Meow meow meow meow meow meow, meow
meow meow meow meow meow meow meow. Meow meow
meow meow. Meow meow meow meow meow meow meow,
meow meow meow meow meow meow meow meow meow
meow, meow meow meow meow meow meow meow meow
meow meow meow. Meow meow meow meow meow meow
meow meow meow.

Meow, meow meow meow meow meow meow meow meow,
meow meow meow meow meow meow. Meow meow meow
meow meow meow meow meow meow meow meow, meow meow
meow meow meow meow, meow meow meow meow meow.
Meow meow meow meow. Meow meow meow meow meow

meow, meow meow meow meow meow meow meow. Meow meow meow meow meow meow meow. Meow meow meow meow meow meow meow meow meow meow meow, meow meow meow meow meow meow meow, meow meow meow meow meow meow meow.

Meow meow meow meow, meow meow meow meow meow meow. Meow meow meow meow meow meow meow meow meow, meow. Meow meow meow meow meow meow meow meow meow meow meow meow meow, meow meow meow meow. Meow meow meow meow meow meow meow meow.

Meow meow meow, meow meow meow meow meow meow meow meow meow, meow meow meow. Meow meow meow meow meow meow meow meow. Meow meow meow meow meow meow meow meow meow, meow meow meow meow meow meow meow, meow meow meow meow meow meow.

Meow meow meow meow, meow. Meow meow meow meow meow meow Meow. Meow meow meow meow meow meow meow meow. Meow meow meow meow meow meow meow meow meow meow meow meow, meow meow meow meow meow meow meow meow, meow meow meow meow meow meow. Meow meow meow meow meow meow meow meow. Meow meow meow meow meow meow meow meow, meow meow meow meow meow meow meow meow, meow meow meow meow meow meow meow meow meow. Meow meow meow meow meow meow. Meow meow meow.

Meow meow meow meow, meow meow meow meow meow meow meow meow. Meow meow meow meow, meow meow. Meow meow meow meow meow meow-meow meow meow meow meow. Meow meow meow meow meow meow meow, meow meow meow meow meow meow meow meow. Meow meow meow meow, meow meow meow meow meow. Meow meow meow meow meow meow meow meow, meow meow meow

meow meow meow. Meow meow meow meow, meow meow meow meow meow meow meow.

"Meow, meow, meow meow meow meow meow? Meow meow meow meow."

Meow meow meow meow. Meow meow meow meow meow. Meow meow meow meow meow meow meow meow meow meow meow meow meow meow. Meow meow, meow meow meow meow.

"Meow meow meow meow meow," meow meow meow meow meow meow meow meow.

"Meow meow meow meow meow meow meow meow meow meow meow meow meow," meow meow meow.

Meow meow, meow meow. Meow meow meow meow meow meow meow meow meow meow meow meow meow. Meow meow meow meow meow meow meow meow, meow meow meow meow meow, meow meow meow meow meow meow meow meow meow, meow meow meow meow meow meow meow meow. Meow meow meow meow meow meow. Meow, meow meow meow meow meow meow meow, meow meow meow meow. Meow meow meow meow, meow meow. Meow meow meow. Meow meow meow meow meow meow. Meow meow meow meow meow meow, meow meow meow meow meow meow meow meow.

Meow meow meow meow meow meow meow.

* * * * * * *

Meow meow meow meow meow meow, meow meow meow meow meow. Meow meow meow meow meow meow meow meow, meow meow meow meow meow meow, meow meow meow meow meow meow. Meow meow meow meow meow meow meow meow meow meow meow meow meow, meow meow meow meow meow

meow meow meow meow meow. Meow meow meow meow, meow meow meow meow meow, meow meow meow meow meow meow meow meow meow meow meow meow, meow meow meow meow meow meow. Meow meow meow meow meow meow meow meow meow meow meow meow, meow meow meow meow meow meow meow meow meow.

Meow meow meow meow meow meow, meow meow meow meow. Meow meow meow meow meow meow meow. Meow meow meow meow meow meow meow meow meow meow meow meow meow meow. Meow meow meow meow meow meow meow meow meow meow meow, meow meow meow meow meow, meow meow meow meow meow, meow meow meow meow.

Meow meow meow meow meow meow meow, meow meow meow meow meow meow meow, meow meow meow meow meow meow, meow meow meow. Meow meow meow meow meow. Meow meow meow meow meow meow meow meow. meow meow meow meow meow meow meow meow meow meow meow meow. Meow meow meow meow meow. Meow meow meow meow meow meow meow meow meow meow meow meow meow meow. Meow meow meow meow meow meow. meow meow meow meow meow, meow meow meow meow meow. Meow meow meow meow meow meow.

Meow meow meow, meow meow meow meow meow, meow meow meow meow meow meow meow meow meow meow. Meow meow, meow meow meow meow meow meow meow meow, meow meow meow meow meow meow meow meow meow meow meow meow meow meow meow. Meow meow meow meow, meow meow, meow meow meow meow, meow meow meow meow meow, meow meow meow meow meow meow meow meow meow meow meow. Meow meow meow meow meow meow meow meow meow meow meow meow meow.

Meow meow meow meow, meow meow meow meow meow meow meow meow meow meow, meow meow meow meow meow meow meow, meow meow meow meow meow. Meow meow meow meow meow meow meow, meow meow meow meow meow meow. Meow meow meow meow meow, meow meow meow meow meow meow meow, meow meow meow meow meow meow meow meow. Meow meow meow meow meow. meow meow meow meow meow meow meow meow meow meow meow. Meow meow, meow meow meow meow. Meow meow, meow-meow meow meow meow meow meow meow meow. meow meow meow meow meow meow meow meow meow meow meow, meow meow meow meow, meow meow meow meow meow meow meow meow meow meow.

Meow meow meow meow meow meow meow meow meow, meow meow, meow meow meow meow meow meow meow, meow meow meow. Meow meow meow meow meow, meow meow meow meow meow meow. meow meow meow meow meow, meow meow meow meow meow meow meow meow meow meow. Meow meow meow meow, meow meow meow meow, meow meow meow meow meow meow meow meow, meow meow meow meow meow meow meow meow meow meow meow meow meow, meow meow meow meow meow meow meow meow meow meow. Meow meow meow meow meow meow meow, meow meow. meow meow meow meow meow meow meow meow meow.

Meow meow meow meow meow meow meow meow meow meow. Meow meow meow meow meow. Meow meow meow meow meow meow meow meow meow meow meow, meow meow meow meow meow meow meow meow meow meow meow, meow meow meow meow-meow meow, meow meow meow meow. Meow meow meow meow meow meow meow meow, meow meow meow meow.

Meow meow meow meow meow meow meow meow, meow meow meow. Meow meow meow. Meow meow meow. Meow meow meow meow meow meow. Meow meow meow meow meow meow meow meow meow, meow meow meow. Meow meow meow. Meow meow meow meow meow meow meow meow meow meow meow meow meow meow meow, meow meow meow meow. Meow meow meow meow meow meow, meow meow meow meow meow meow meow. Meow meow meow meow, meow meow meow meow meow meow, meow meow. Meow meow meow meow. Meow meow meow meow meow meow, meow meow meow meow meow-meow meow.

Meow, meow meow. Meow meow meow meow meow. Meow meow meow meow meow meow meow meow meow meow meow, meow meow meow meow meow meow meow meow meow meow meow meow meow meow meow meow meow. Meow meow meow meow meow, meow meow meow, meow meow meow meow meow meow meow meow. Meow meow meow meow meow meow meow meow meow meow meow meow. Meow meow meow meow meow meow meow meow meow meow.

Meow meow meow meow meow meow, meow meow meow meow meow meow meow, meow meow meow meow. Meow meow meow meow meow meow, meow meow meow meow meow meow. Meow meow meow meow meow meow, meow meow meow, meow meow meow meow meow meow meow meow meow meow meow meow. Meow meow meow, meow meow meow. Meow meow meow meow meow meow meow.

"Meow meow, meow meow meow meow meow! Meow meow meow meow meow meow," meow meow meow meow meow meow meow meow meow meow meow meow. Meow meow meow meow meow meow meow meow meow meow meow, meow meow meow.

"Meow, Meow. Meow meow meow meow meow meow meow meow meow meow meow meow. Meow meow meow meow." Meow meow meow meow meow meow meow meow meow meow, meow meow meow meow meow meow. meow meow meow meow meow meow meow meow, meow meow meow meow meow meow meow.

"Meow meow meow meow, meow. Meow meow meow meow meow meow," meow meow meow. Meow meow.

"Meow meow, meow meow meow. Meow meow meow. Meow meow meow meow meow meow," Meow meow.

"Meow meow meow meow meow meow. Meow meow meow meow meow."

Meow meow. Meow meow meow meow meow meow meow meow, meow meow meow meow meow. Meow meow, meow meow, meow meow. Meow meow meow meow meow meow. Meow meow meow meow meow meow, meow. Meow meow meow meow meow meow meow meow meow meow meow meow. Meow meow meow meow. Meow meow meow meow meow, meow meow. Meow meow meow meow meow meow meow meow, meow meow meow meow meow, meow meow meow meow meow meow meow meow.

Meow meow meow meow meow meow meow, meow meow meow meow meow. Meow meow meow meow, meow meow meow meow meow meow meow meow meow meow meow. Meow meow meow meow meow meow meow, meow meow meow, meow meow meow meow meow meow meow, meow meow meow meow meow meow, meow meow meow meow meow meow meow meow.

Meow meow meow, meow meow meow, meow meow meow meow meow-meow meow. Meow meow meow meow meow meow meow meow meow meow meow meow meow meow meow meow meow meow meow meow. Meow meow meow meow meow

meow meow meow. Meow meow meow meow meow meow, meow meow meow meow, meow meow meow meow meow: meow, meow meow meow meow meow meow meow meow.

Meow meow meow meow meow, meow meow meow meow meow meow meow meow meow meow meow meow meow, meow meow meow meow meow meow meow meow meow, meow meow meow meow. Meow meow meow meow meow meow meow meow meow meow meow meow meow. Meow meow meow meow meow meow meow, meow meow meow meow meow meow meow, meow meow meow meow meow meow meow meow meow meow meow meow meow, meow meow meow meow meow meow meow meow meow. Meow, meow meow meow meow meow meow meow meow meow, meow meow meow meow meow meow meow meow meow meow meow meow meow.

Meow meow meow meow meow, meow. Meow meow meow meow meow meow meow meow meow meow meow, meow meow meow meow meow meow meow meow meow meow meow meow.

Meow meow meow meow meow, meow meow meow meow meow meow meow, meow meow meow meow meow meow meow meow meow meow, meow meow meow meow meow meow meow meow meow meow. Meow meow meow meow meow meow meow meow meow meow meow meow. Meow meow, meow meow meow meow mcow meow meow meow meow. Meow meow. Meow meow meow meow meow meow.

"Meow meow meow meow?" meow meow, meow meow meow meow meow meow, meow meow meow meow meow meow meow meow meow meow meow meow meow meow meow. Meow meow meow meow meow meow meow meow, meow meow meow meow, meow meow meow meow meow meow meow meow meow meow. Meow meow meow meow meow

meow meow meow, meow meow meow meow meow, meow meow meow meow meow meow. Meow meow meow meow meow meow meow meow meow meow. Meow meow meow meow meow meow meow. Meow meow meow meow meow meow meow meow meow meow meow meow meow, meow meow meow meow meow. Meow meow meow, meow meow meow meow. Meow meow meow meow meow meow meow meow meow meow meow meow meow meow meow meow meow meow meow meow meow meow meow meow meow meow, meow meow meow meow meow.

Meow meow meow meow meow meow meow meow. Meow meow meow meow meow meow, meow meow meow meow. Meow meow meow meow meow meow meow meow meow meow, meow meow meow meow. Meow meow meow meow meow meow meow meow meow meow meow meow meow meow, meow meow meow meow meow meow meow. Meow meow meow meow, meow meow meow meow meow meow meow meow, meow meow meow meow meow meow: meow meow meow meow meow, meow meow, meow. Meow meow meow meow meow meow. Meow meow meow meow meow meow meow meow meow, meow meow meow meow meow meow meow.

Meow meow meow meow meow meow meow meow meow meow meow, meow meow meow meow meow meow meow meow, meow meow meow meow meow meow meow meow. Meow meow meow meow meow. Meow meow meow. Meow meow meow meow meow, meow meow. Meow meow meow meow meow meow meow meow meow meow meow.

Meow meow meow meow meow meow meow meow meow. Meow meow meow meow meow, meow meow meow meow meow meow meow meow meow meow meow meow. Meow

meow meow. Meow meow meow meow meow meow meow meow meow.

Meow meow meow meow meow meow meow meow, meow meow meow meow meow. Meow meow meow meow meow meow meow. Meow meow meow meow meow meow meow, meow meow meow meow. Meow meow meow meow meow meow meow meow. Meow meow meow meow meow meow meow meow meow, meow meow meow meow meow meow meow meow meow meow meow meow meow meow meow meow.

Meow meow meow meow meow, meow meow, meow meow meow meow meow meow meow meow meow. Meow meow meow meow meow, meow meow meow meow meow meow meow meow meow meow meow meow meow. Meow meow meow meow meow meow meow. Meow meow meow meow meow meow meow meow. Meow meow meow meow meow meow meow meow meow. Meow meow meow meow meow meow meow meow, meow meow meow meow meow meow meow meow meow meow. Meow meow meow meow meow meow meow meow meow. Meow meow meow meow meow meow meow meow meow meow meow meow. Meow meow meow meow meow, meow meow meow meow meow.

Meow meow meow meow meow meow meow meow meow meow. Meow meow meow meow, meow meow meow meow meow meow meow meow meow meow meow meow, meow meow meow meow meow meow meow meow meow, meow meow meow meow meow meow. Meow meow meow meow meow meow meow meow meow meow. Meow meow meow meow, meow meow meow. Meow meow meow meow meow meow meow meow. Meow meow meow meow meow meow meow. Meow meow meow meow meow. Meow meow meow meow meow meow meow meow meow, meow meow

meow meow meow meow meow meow meow meow meow.
Meow meow meow meow meow meow meow meow meow
meow meow meow meow meow meow meow meow.

Meow meow meow meow meow meow meow meow meow
meow. Meow meow meow meow meow meow meow meow
meow. Meow meow meow meow, meow meow meow meow
meow, meow meow meow meow. Meow meow meow meow,
meow meow meow meow meow meow meow. Meow meow
meow meow meow meow meow meow meow. Meow meow
meow meow meow meow meow. Meow meow meow meow
meow. Meow meow meow meow meow meow meow meow
meow meow meow meow meow meow, meow meow meow
meow meow meow meow meow meow. Meow meow meow,
meow meow meow meow meow meow meow meow meow.
Meow meow meow meow, meow. Meow meow meow meow
meow meow.

Meow meow meow meow meow meow meow meow meow
meow meow meow meow meow meow meow meow meow meow
meow meow. Meow meow meow meow meow meow meow
meow meow meow meow meow meow meow meow meow meow
meow meow, meow meow meow meow meow, meow meow
meow meow meow. Meow meow meow meow meow meow
meow meow meow, meow meow meow meow meow meow
meow. Meow meow meow meow meow meow meow meow
meow meow, meow meow meow meow meow meow meow
meow meow. Meow meow meow meow, meow meow meow
meow, meow meow meow meow meow meow meow meow, meow
meow meow meow meow meow meow meow meow, meow meow
meow meow meow meow meow meow meow meow meow.

Meow meow meow meow meow meow meow. Meow meow
meow meow meow meow meow meow, meow meow meow
meow meow meow meow meow. Meow meow meow meow

meow meow meow meow: meow meow meow meow meow. Meow meow meow meow meow. Meow meow meow.

Meow meow meow meow. Meow meow meow, meow meow meow meow meow meow meow meow meow, meow meow meow meow meow meow meow meow. Meow meow meow meow meow meow meow meow meow meow meow meow meow, meow meow meow meow meow meow meow meow meow meow meow, meow meow meow meow meow meow meow meow meow meow meow meow. Meow meow meow meow meow meow meow meow meow meow meow meow meow. Meow meow meow meow meow meow meow, meow meow meow meow meow meow meow, meow meow meow meow meow meow. Meow meow meow meow meow meow meow meow meow meow meow meow meow meow meow meow meow meow meow meow meow. Meow meow meow meow meow, meow meow meow meow meow. Meow meow meow meow, meow meow meow meow meow.

Meow meow meow meow, meow meow meow meow meow meow meow meow meow meow. Meow meow meow meow meow meow meow meow meow meow meow meow meow. Meow meow meow meow meow meow meow meow meow. Meow meow meow meow meow meow meow meow meow meow meow, meow meow meow meow meow.

"Meow meow meow meow meow meow?" meow meow meow. Meow meow meow meow, meow meow meow meow meow meow meow meow, meow meow meow meow. Meow meow meow meow meow meow meow.

"Meow meow meow meow. Meow meow meow. Meow meow meow meow meow meow meow meow meow meow meow."

Meow meow meow meow meow meow meow meow meow meow meow meow meow meow, meow meow meow meow

meow, meow meow meow meow meow meow meow meow
meow, meow meow meow meow meow. Meow meow meow
meow meow meow meow meow, meow meow meow meow
meow. Meow meow meow meow meow meow meow. Meow
meow meow meow meow.

Meow meow meow meow meow, meow meow meow meow
meow meow meow meow. Meow meow meow meow meow
meow meow meow meow. Meow meow meow meow meow
meow meow meow. Meow meow meow meow meow meow.
Meow meow meow meow meow meow meow meow meow
meow, meow meow meow meow. Meow meow meow meow
meow meow meow meow meow. Meow meow meow meow.
Meow meow meow meow meow meow.

Meow meow meow meow meow meow meow meow, meow
meow meow meow meow. Meow meow meow meow. Meow
meow meow meow meow meow meow meow meow. Meow
meow meow meow meow meow meow meow. Meow meow
meow meow meow meow meow meow meow meow, meow
meow meow meow meow. Meow meow meow meow meow
meow. Meow meow meow meow meow. Meow meow meow
meow meow meow meow. Meow meow meow meow
meow meow, meow meow meow meow. Meow meow meow
meow meow meow meow meow.

Meow meow meow meow meow meow meow meow. Meow
meow meow, meow meow meow meow meow meow. Meow
meow meow meow meow meow meow meow meow meow,
meow meow meow meow meow, meow meow meow meow
meow meow meow meow meow meow. Meow meow meow
meow meow meow.

Meow meow meow meow meow meow meow. Meow meow
meow meow meow meow. Meow meow meow meow, meow
meow meow meow, meow meow meow meow meow meow

meow. Meow meow meow meow meow meow meow, meow meow meow meow meow meow meow meow meow meow. Meow meow meow meow meow, meow meow meow meow meow meow, meow meow meow meow meow meow meow meow meow meow meow, meow meow meow meow meow. Meow meow meow meow meow, meow meow meow meow meow meow. Meow meow meow, meow meow meow meow meow meow meow.

MEOW MEOW MEOW MEOW

Meow meow meow meow meow meow meow meow meow meow meow, meow meow meow meow meow meow meow. Meow meow meow meow meow meow meow meow meow meow, meow meow meow meow meow meow-meow meow meow. Meow meow meow, meow meow meow meow meow meow meow meow meow. Meow meow meow meow meow meow meow meow meow meow meow meow meow meow meow meow. Meow meow meow meow meow meow meow meow meow meow meow. Meow meow meow meow meow meow meow meow. Meow meow meow meow meow meow meow, meow meow meow meow meow meow meow meow meow.

Meow meow meow meow meow meow. Meow meow meow meow, meow meow meow meow meow meow meow. Meow meow meow meow meow meow meow meow meow meow. Meow meow meow meow meow, meow meow meow meow meow meow meow. Meow meow meow meow meow meow meow meow meow meow, meow meow. Meow meow meow meow meow meow meow meow meow meow. Meow meow meow meow meow meow, meow meow meow meow meow meow meow. Meow meow meow meow. Meow meow meow meow meow, meow meow meow meow meow meow.

Meow meow meow meow meow meow, meow meow meow meow meow meow meow. Meow meow meow meow meow meow, meow meow meow meow meow meow meow. Meow meow. Meow meow meow meow meow, meow meow meow meow meow meow. Meow meow meow meow meow meow. Meow meow meow meow meow meow, meow meow meow meow meow meow meow meow, meow meow meow meow meow meow meow, meow meow meow meow meow meow meow meow. Meow meow meow meow meow meow meow meow meow meow meow, meow meow meow meow meow meow, meow meow meow meow meow meow. Meow meow meow meow, meow meow meow meow, meow meow meow meow meow meow meow meow meow meow meow meow meow meow, meow meow meow meow meow meow meow.

Meow meow meow meow meow meow meow meow meow meow meow meow, meow meow meow meow meow meow meow meow meow meow meow meow, meow meow meow meow meow meow meow meow meow meow, meow meow meow meow meow meow meow meow, meow meow meow meow meow meow meow. Meow meow meow meow. Meow meow meow meow meow meow meow meow meow meow meow.

****

Meow meow meow meow meow meow, meow meow meow meow Meow. Meow meow meow meow meow meow meow meow. Meow meow meow meow meow meow meow meow. Meow meow meow meow meow meow meow meow meow. Meow meow meow meow, meow meow.

Meow meow meow meow.

Meow meow meow meow meow meow meow meow meow meow meow meow meow. Meow meow meow meow, meow

meow meow. Meow meow, meow meow meow meow meow meow meow meow meow meow meow. Meow meow meow meow meow meow. Meow meow meow meow meow meow meow meow meow. Meow meow meow meow meow meow meow meow, meow meow meow meow, meow meow meow meow meow meow meow meow meow meow. Meow meow meow meow meow meow meow, meow meow meow meow meow meow meow meow meow meow meow. Meow meow meow meow meow meow meow meow meow, meow meow meow meow meow, meow meow meow meow meow meow meow. Meow meow meow meow meow meow meow meow. Meow meow meow meow meow meow meow meow, meow meow meow, meow meow meow meow meow.

Meow meow meow meow meow meow meow meow meow meow meow meow meow meow meow meow. Meow meow meow meow, meow meow meow meow meow meow. Meow meow meow meow, meow meow meow meow. Meow meow meow meow meow meow meow meow meow meow meow meow. Meow meow meow meow, meow meow meow. Meow meow meow meow meow meow meow meow. Meow meow meow meow meow meow. Meow meow meow meow, meow meow meow meow meow meow meow meow meow meow. Meow meow meow. Meow meow. Meow meow meow meow meow meow meow meow meow meow.

Meow meow meow, meow meow meow, meow meow meow meow meow meow meow: meow meow meow meow meow meow. Meow meow meow meow, meow meow meow meow meow. Meow meow meow meow Meow meow meow meow meow meow, meow meow meow meow meow meow meow meow.

Meow meow meow meow meow meow meow, meow meow meow meow meow meow meow meow meow meow, meow meow

meow meow meow meow meow meow meow. Meow meow meow meow meow meow meow meow meow meow. Meow meow meow meow meow meow meow meow meow meow meow meow, meow meow meow meow meow meow meow meow meow meow. Meow meow meow meow meow meow meow meow meow, meow meow meow meow meow meow meow, meow meow meow meow meow meow meow, meow meow meow meow meow meow meow meow. Meow meow meow meow meow meow meow, meow meow meow meow meow meow. Meow meow meow meow meow meow, meow meow meow meow meow meow meow meow meow meow meow meow. Meow meow meow meow meow meow. Meow meow meow meow meow, meow meow meow meow meow.

Meow meow meow meow meow meow, meow meow meow meow, meow meow meow meow meow meow meow meow, meow meow meow meow meow meow meow meow meow meow, meow meow meow meow meow meow meow. Meow meow meow meow meow meow meow. Meow meow meow meow meow meow meow.

Meow meow meow meow meow meow, meow meow. Meow meow meow meow meow meow meow meow meow meow meow. Meow meow meow meow meow meow meow meow meow meow meow-meow meow-meow. Meow meow meow meow meow meow meow. Meow meow meow meow. Meow meow, meow meow meow meow meow meow meow. Meow meow mcow meow meow meow meow meow meow, meow. Meow meow meow meow meow meow meow meow meow, meow meow meow meow meow meow meow meow meow meow meow, meow meow meow meow meow meow meow. Meow meow meow meow, meow meow meow meow meow. Meow meow meow meow. Meow,

meow meow meow meow, meow meow. Meow meow meow meow meow meow meow meow meow meow meow meow meow. Meow meow meow, meow meow meow meow meow meow meow.

Meow meow meow meow meow meow meow meow meow meow meow meow. Meow meow meow meow meow meow meow meow meow meow meow meow? Meow meow meow meow meow meow meow meow meow, meow meow meow meow meow meow meow meow meow meow. Meow meow.

* * * * * * *

Meow meow meow meow meow meow meow. Meow meow meow meow meow, meow meow meow. Meow meow meow meow meow meow meow meow meow meow, meow meow meow meow meow meow meow meow meow. Meow meow meow meow meow meow meow, meow meow meow meow meow meow. Meow, meow meow meow meow meow. Meow meow Meow meow meow meow. Meow meow meow meow meow meow meow. Meow meow meow meow meow meow meow meow meow meow meow meow meow. Meow meow meow meow meow meow meow, meow meow meow meow meow meow meow meow meow meow.

Meow meow meow meow meow meow, meow meow meow meow meow meow, meow meow meow meow meow meow meow meow meow. Meow meow meow meow meow meow, meow meow meow meow meow meow meow. Meow meow meow meow meow meow meow meow.

"Meow meow meow meow meow meow meow? Meow meow meow meow meow meow meow meow," meow meow meow meow. Meow meow meow meow meow meow meow meow meow meow meow. Meow meow meow meow meow

meow meow meow. "Meow meow meow meow me', meow meow meow meow."

Meow meow meow meow meow meow. Meow meow meow meow meow, meow meow meow meow meow meow meow meow meow. Meow meow meow meow meow meow meow meow meow meow meow meow meow meow. Meow meow meow meow meow meow meow, meow meow meow meow meow meow meow meow. Meow meow meow meow meow meow meow meow meow, meow meow meow meow meow meow meow meow, meow meow meow meow meow. Meow meow meow meow meow meow meow meow meow meow, meow meow meow, meow meow meow meow meow meow meow meow, meow meow meow meow meow meow meow meow meow meow meow meow, meow meow meow, meow meow meow meow.

Meow meow meow meow meow. Meow meow meow meow meow meow meow meow meow. Meow meow meow meow meow meow meow meow meow meow meow, meow meow meow meow meow meow, meow meow meow meow, meow meow meow meow meow meow meow meow meow meow. Meow meow meow meow meow meow meow meow, meow meow meow meow. Meow meow meow meow meow meow meow. Meow meow meow meow meow, meow meow meow meow meow. Meow meow meow meow meow meow meow meow meow. Meow meow meow meow meow meow meow meow meow.

Meow meow meow meow. Meow meow meow meow meow, meow meow meow meow meow meow meow meow meow meow meow. Meow meow meow meow meow meow meow meow meow meow meow meow. Meow meow meow meow. Meow meow meow meow meow meow meow. Meow meow meow meow meow, meow meow meow meow, meow meow meow meow meow meow meow. Meow meow

meow meow meow meow meow meow meow meow meow meow meow, meow meow meow meow. Meow meow meow meow meow, meow meow meow meow meow meow meow meow meow. Meow meow meow meow meow meow meow meow. Meow meow meow-meow-meow. Meow meow meow meow meow meow meow meow meow.

Meow meow meow meow meow meow meow, meow meow meow meow meow meow. Meow meow meow meow meow meow meow meow meow. Meow meow meow meow meow, meow meow meow meow meow meow. Meow meow meow meow meow meow meow meow meow. Meow meow meow meow meow, meow meow meow meow meow. Meow meow meow meow meow meow meow meow meow meow meow. Meow meow meow meow meow. Meow meow meow meow meow meow meow, meow meow meow, meow meow meow meow. Meow meow meow meow meow meow meow, meow meow meow meow meow, meow meow meow. Meow meow meow meow meow meow meow meow.

Meow meow meow meow meow meow meow meow, meow meow meow meow meow, meow meow meow meow meow meow meow, meow meow meow meow meow meow, meow meow meow meow meow meow. Meow meow meow meow meow meow, meow meow meow meow meow meow, meow meow meow meow meow, meow meow meow meow meow meow, meow meow meow meow, meow meow meow. Meow meow meow meow meow meow meow meow meow, meow meow meow meow meow meow meow. Meow meow meow. Meow meow meow meow. Meow meow meow meow meow meow meow meow. Meow meow meow meow meow, meow meow meow meow meow meow meow meow. Meow meow meow, meow meow, meow meow meow meow meow meow. Meow meow meow meow meow, meow meow

meow, meow meow meow meow meow meow, meow meow
meow meow meow. Meow meow meow meow, meow meow
meow meow meow, meow meow meow meow meow meow
meow meow, meow meow meow meow meow meow meow,
meow meow meow meow meow, meow meow meow meow.

Meow meow meow meow meow meow-meow meow meow
meow meow: meow meow meow meow meow meow meow
meow meow. Meow meow meow meow meow meow meow
meow meow, meow meow meow meow.

Meow meow meow meow meow meow meow meow, meow
meow meow meow. Meow meow meow meow meow meow,
meow meow meow meow meow meow. Meow meow meow
meow meow meow meow meow meow meow, meow meow meow
meow, meow meow meow meow meow meow meow. Meow
meow meow meow meow meow meow, meow meow meow
meow meow meow meow meow. Meow meow meow meow
meow meow-meow meow meow meow, meow meow meow
meow meow meow. Meow meow meow meow meow meow
meow meow meow.

Meow meow meow meow meow meow meow meow meow.
Meow meow meow meow meow meow, meow meow meow
meow meow, meow meow meow meow, meow meow meow
meow. Meow meow meow meow meow meow meow meow
meow meow meow. Meow meow meow meow meow, meow
meow meow meow meow meow meow meow.

Meow meow meow meow meow. "Meow meow," meow
meow meow meow. "Meow meow meow meow meow meow
meow meow meow?"

Meow meow meow meow meow, meow meow meow meow
MEOW, meow meow meow meow meow meow meow meow.
Meow meow meow meow, meow meow meow meow meow
meow. Meow meow MEOW meow meow meow meow meow

meow. Meow meow meow meow. Meow meow meow meow meow meow meow meow meow meow meow meow meow. Meow meow meow meow.

Meow meow meow meow meow meow meow meow, meow meow meow meow, meow meow meow meow meow meow meow meow meow meow meow. Meow meow meow meow meow meow meow meow meow meow meow meow meow. Meow meow meow meow meow, meow meow meow meow, meow meow meow meow, meow meow meow meow meow meow meow. Meow meow meow meow meow meow, meow meow meow meow meow meow meow meow meow meow, meow meow meow, meow meow meow meow meow meow meow, meow meow meow meow meow: meow meow meow meow meow meow?

Meow meow meow meow meow meow meow meow, meow meow meow meow meow meow meow, meow meow meow meow meow. Meow meow meow meow meow meow. Meow meow meow meow meow, meow meow meow meow, meow meow meow meow meow meow. Meow meow meow meow meow meow meow. Meow meow meow meow meow meow meow meow, meow meow meow meow, meow meow meow meow meow meow meow meow meow meow meow, meow meow meow, meow meow meow meow meow meow meow meow meow meow meow meow meow meow meow meow meow meow meow.

Meow meow meow meow meow meow meow, meow meow meow meow meow meow meow, meow meow meow meow meow meow, meow meow meow meow meow meow meow. Meow meow, meow meow.

Meow meow meow meow meow meow meow MEOW meow meow meow meow, meow meow meow meow meow meow meow meow meow meow, meow meow meow meow meow meow meow meow meow meow meow, meow meow meow meow meow meow

meow meow meow, meow meow meow meow meow. Meow
meow meow meow meow meow meow, meow meow meow
meow meow meow meow meow meow. Meow meow meow
meow meow, meow meow meow meow meow meow meow
meow meow meow meow meow. Meow meow meow meow
meow meow meow meow meow meow, meow meow meow,
meow meow meow meow meow meow, meow meow meow
meow meow meow meow meow meow meow, meow meow
meow meow meow meow. Meow meow meow meow meow
meow meow meow meow meow.

Meow meow meow, meow, meow meow. Meow meow meow
meow meow meow meow meow meow. Meow meow meow
meow meow meow meow, meow meow meow meow meow
meow meow meow meow. Meow meow meow meow meow
meow meow meow meow. Meow meow meow meow meow
meow meow meow meow, meow meow meow. Meow meow
meow meow. Mewo meow meow meow meow meow meow,
meow meow meow meow meow meow meow meow meow
meow meow, meow meow meow. Meow meow meow meow
meow meow, meow meow meow meow meow meow.

Meow meow. Meow meow meow meow meow meow. Meow
meow meow meow meow meow meow meow, meow meow?
Meow meow meow meow meow? Meow meow meow meow?
Meow meow meow meow meow meow meow meow meow
meow meow, meow meow meow meow meow meow meow
meow meow? Meow meow meow meow meow meow. Meow
meow meow meow meow, meow meow.

Meow meow meow, meow meow meow meow meow, meow
meow meow meow meow meow meow meow meow. Meow
meow meow meow. Meow meow. Meow meow. Meow meow
meow meow meow meow meow meow meow meow, meow
meow meow meow meow meow. Meow meow meow meow

meow meow meow meow, meow meow meow meow meow. Meow meow meow meow meow, meow meow meow. Meow meow meow meow meow, meow meow. Meow meow, meow meow meow meow meow meow meow meow. Meow meow meow meow meow meow meow.

Meow meow meow meow meow meow meow meow meow meow meow. Meow meow meow meow meow meow meow, meow meow meow. Meow meow. Meow meow meow meow meow. Meow meow meow meow meow meow meow, meow meow meow meow meow. Meow meow meow meow meow meow Meow meow Meow. Meow meow meow meow, meow meow meow meow meow. Meow meow meow meow meow meow, meow meow meow meow meow, meow meow meow meow. Meow meow meow meow meow meow. Meow meow meow meow meow meow, meow meow meow meow, meow meow meow, meow, meow meow. Meow meow meow meow meow meow meow meow meow meow, meow meow meow meow, meow meow meow meow meow meow meow meow.

Meow meow meow meow meow meow meow. Meow meow meow meow meow meow meow meow meow meow meow meow. Meow meow meow meow meow meow meow meow meow meow, meow meow, meow meow meow. Meow meow meow meow meow meow meow, meow meow meow, meow meow meow meow meow meow, meow meow meow meow. Meow meow meow meow meow meow meow meow meow, meow meow meow meow meow meow meow, meow meow meow meow meow meow meow.

Meow meow meow meow meow meow meow. Meow meow meow meow meow meow meow meow meow. Meow meow meow meow meow meow meow meow meow meow. Meow meow meow meow meow meow. Meow meow meow meow. Meow meow meow meow, meow meow meow, meow meow meow meow meow meow meow meow meow.

MEOW, MEOW, MEOW

Meow meow meow meow meow meow, meow meow meow meow. Meow meow meow meow meow meow, meow meow meow meow meow meow meow meow meow meow meow meow meow meow. Meow meow meow meow, meow meow, meow meow meow meow meow meow, meow meow meow meow meow meow meow meow meow. Meow meow meow meow meow. Meow meow meow meow meow meow meow meow meow meow, meow meow meow meow meow meow meow, meow meow meow meow. Meow meow meow meow meow meow meow meow meow, meow meow meow meow meow meow. Meow meow meow meow meow meow meow, meow meow meow. Meow meow meow meow meow-meow meow meow meow meow meow, meow, meow meow meow meow meow meow meow meow, meow. Meow meow meow meow meow meow meow.

Meow meow meow meow meow meow meow meow meow meow? Meow meow meow meow meow meow meow meow meow meow, meow meow meow meow meow meow meow, meow meow meow meow meow meow meow meow. Meow meow meow meow meow meow, meow meow meow, meow meow meow, meow meow meow meow. Meow meow meow meow meow meow meow, meow meow meow meow meow meow meow. Meow meow meow meow meow, meow meow meow meow meow meow.

Meow meow meow, meow meow meow meow meow meow meow meow meow meow meow. Meow meow meow meow meow, meow meow meow meow meow meow meow. Meow meow meow meow. Meow meow meow meow meow meow meow meow meow, meow meow meow. Meow meow meow meow meow meow meow. Meow meow meow meow meow meow meow meow. Meow meow meow meow meow, meow meow meow meow meow meow meow meow. Meow meow meow meow meow meow meow meow meow meow meow meow meow meow meow, meow meow meow, meow Meow meow meow meow meow meow meow meow.

Meow meow meow meow meow meow meow. Meow meow meow meow meow meow meow meow. Meow meow meow meow meow meow meow, meow meow meow meow meow meow meow meow. Meow meow meow meow meow meow meow, meow meow meow meow meow. Meow meow meow meow meow meow meow meow, meow meow meow meow meow meow, meow meow Meow meow meow meow meow meow meow meow meow meow meow meow, meow meow meow meow, meow meow meow meow.

Meow meow meow meow meow meow meow meow meow meow meow meow meow meow meow meow meow meow meow, meow meow meow meow meow meow meow meow meow meow meow, meow meow meow meow meow meow meow meow meow meow meow. Meow meow meow meow, meow meow meow meow, meow meow meow meow meow meow. Meow meow meow meow meow meow meow meow, meow meow meow meow meow meow meow, meow meow. Meow meow meow meow meow meow meow meow, meow meow meow meow meow meow.

Meow meow meow meow meow meow meow meow meow meow meow, meow meow meow meow meow meow meow

meow. Meow meow meow meow, meow meow meow meow meow meow meow meow meow meow meow. Meow meow meow meow meow meow meow meow meow meow meow, meow meow meow meow meow meow meow meow meow meow meow meow meow meow meow meow meow, meow meow meow meow-meow meow meow meow meow meow meow meow. Meow meow meow meow, meow meow meow meow meow meow meow meow. Meow meow meow meow meow meow meow meow meow meow meow meow meow meow. Meow meow meow meow meow meow, meow meow meow meow meow, meow meow meow meow meow meow meow meow meow meow meow. Meow meow meow meow meow meow, meow meow meow meow meow meow-meow meow meow meow meow, meow meow meow meow meow meow meow meow. Meow meow meow meow meow meow meow meow meow meow meow.

Meow meow meow, meow meow meow, meow meow meow meow meow meow meow meow meow meow. Meow. Meow meow meow. Meow meow meow meow meow meow meow meow meow meow MEOW, meow meow meow meow meow meow meow meow meow. Meow meow meow meow meow meow Meow meow meow meow meow meow, meow meow, meow meow meow meow meow meow meow meow, meow meow meow meow meow meow, meow meow meow meow meow meow meow meow, meow meow meow meow meow meow Meow Meow.

Meow meow meow meow meow meow, meow meow, meow. Meow meow meow meow meow meow meow meow, meow meow meow meow meow meow meow meow meow, meow meow meow. Meow meow meow meow meow meow meow meow, meow meow meow meow meow meow meow meow meow, meow meow meow meow meow meow meow. Meow meow meow meow meow meow meow meow meow meow. Meow

meow meow meow meow meow meow, meow meow meow meow meow meow meow? Meow meow meow meow meow meow meow meow meow, meow meow meow meow meow meow meow meow meow.

Meow meow meow meow meow meow meow meow meow meow, meow meow meow meow meow. Meow meow meow meow meow meow, meow meow meow meow meow meow meow meow. Meow meow meow meow meow meow meow meow meow meow meow meow meow meow, meow meow meow meow meow. Meow meow meow meow meow meow, meow meow meow meow meow meow meow meow meow meow, meow meow meow meow, meow meow meow meow meow. Meow meow meow meow, meow meow meow meow meow. Meow meow, meow meow meow meow meow meow meow. Meow meow meow meow meow meow meow meow meow.

Meow meow meow, meow meow meow meow meow meow meow meow meow meow meow. Meow meow meow meow meow-meow meow meow meow meow meow meow meow meow meow, meow meow meow meow meow meow meow meow meow. Meow meow meow meow meow meow meow meow meow, meow meow, meow meow meow meow meow meow. Meow meow meow meow meow meow meow meow. Meow meow meow meow meow meow meow, meow meow meow meow, meow meow meow meow meow meow meow meow meow meow.

Meow meow meow meow meow meow meow meow meow meow meow meow. Meow meow meow meow meow, meow meow meow meow meow meow meow meow. Meow meow meow meow meow meow meow meow meow meow meow, meow meow meow meow meow meow meow. Meow meow meow, meow meow meow meow meow meow, meow meow meow meow meow. Meow meow meow meow meow meow meow meow

meow meow, meow meow meow meow meow. Meow meow meow meow meow meow meow meow, meow meow meow meow meow meow meow meow. Meow meow meow meow meow, meow meow meow meow meow meow.

****

Meow meow meow meow meow meow, meow meow meow meow meow, meow meow meow meow meow meow. Meow meow meow meow meow meow meow? Meow meow meow meow meow meow meow meow meow meow meow meow, meow meow meow meow meow meow meow. Meow meow meow meow meow meow meow meow meow meow. Meow meow meow meow meow meow meow meow meow meow, meow meow meow meow meow meow meow meow meow meow meow meow meow meow meow meow meow meow meow meow meow meow meow.

Meow meow, meow meow meow meow meow meow meow meow. Meow meow meow, meow meow. Meow meow meow meow meow meow meow? Meow meow meow meow meow meow meow meow meow meow. Meow meow.

Meow meow meow meow meow meow meow meow meow meow meow meow meow. Meow meow meow meow meow. Meow meow meow meow meow meow meow meow, meow meow meow meow meow meow meow meow meow meow meow meow meow. Meow meow meow meow meow, meow meow meow meow meow meow meow meow. Meow meow meow meow meow meow, meow. Meow meow meow meow meow. Meow meow meow meow meow meow meow. Meow meow meow meow meow meow, meow meow meow meow meow meow. Meow meow meow Meow meow meow meow meow meow meow meow meow meow.

MEow meow meow meow meow meow meow meow meow. Meow meow meow. Meow meow meow meow meow meow meow meow, meow meow meow meow meow meow meow meow meow meow meow meow, meow meow meow meow. Meow meow meow meow meow meow meow meow meow meow meow meow meow meow meow meow meow. Meow meow meow meow. Meow meow meow meow meow meow meow meow meow meow.

Meow meow meow meow meow meow meow meow Meow Meow meow meow meow meow meow meow meow meow, meow meow meow meow meow meow meow Meow Meow, meow meow meow meow meow meow meow, meow meow meow meow meow meow meow meow. Meow meow meow meow meow meow meow meow meow meow meow. Meow meow meow meow meow meow. Meow meow meow meow meow meow, meow meow meow meow meow. Meow meow meow meow meow meow meow meow, meow meow meow meow meow. Meow meow meow meow meow meow meow meow meow meow meow. Meow meow meow meow meow meow, meow meow meow.

"Meow, meow meow meow meow?" meow meow. Meow meow meow meow meow, meow meow meow meow meow meow meow meow meow meow meow meow meow meow meow meow meow meow meow, meow meow meow meow. Meow meow meow meow meow. Meow meow meow, meow meow meow meow meow meow meow, meow meow meow meow meow meow meow meow meow meow meow meow meow meow, meow meow meow meow meow meow meow meow meow. Meow meow meow, meow meow meow meow meow, meow meow meow meow meow meow meow, meow meow meow meow meow meow meow. Meow meow. Meow meow meow, meow meow meow meow meow meow meow meow meow meow meow meow meow.

Meow meow meow meow meow meow. Meow meow meow meow meow. Meow meow meow meow meow meow meow meow meow meow. Meow meow meow meow meow meow meow meow meow. Meow meow meow meow meow meow, meow meow meow meow meow meow meow, meow meow meow meow meow meow meow meow meow meow, meow meow meow meow meow, meow meow meow meow meow meow meow meow meow. Meow meow meow meow meow meow meow, meow meow meow meow meow meow meow meow meow meow. Meow meow meow meow meow meow meow meow *meow* meow.

Meow meow meow meow, meow meow meow meow meow meow meow, meow meow meow meow meow meow meow. Meow meow Meow. Meow meow meow meow meow meow meow. Meow meow meow meow meow. Meow meow meow meow meow meow meow meow. Meow meow meow meow meow meow, meow meow meow meow, meow meow meow meow meow meow meow. Meow meow meow meow meow meow meow: meow, meow meow meow meow meow meow meow.

Meow meow meow meow meow meow meow meow meow meow meow meow meow meow meow meow, meow meow. Meow meow meow meow meow meow. Meow meow meow meow meow meow meow meow. Meow meow meow meow. Meow meow meow meow meow meow meow meow meow meow meow meow meow meow meow meow meow meow meow. Meow meow meow meow meow meow, meow meow meow meow meow, meow meow meow meow meow meow meow meow meow meow. Meow meow meow meow meow meow meow meow meow, meow meow meow meow meow meow meow meow meow.

Meow meow meow meow meow, meow meow meow meow meow meow meow meow. Meow meow meow, meow meow

meow meow meow meow meow meow meow meow meow meow meow. Meow meow meow meow, meow meow meow meow. Meow meow meow meow meow meow meow, meow meow meow meow meow, meow meow meow meow meow meow meow meow meow meow meow.

Meow meow meow meow meow meow meow, meow meow meow meow meow, meow meow meow meow meow meow meow meow meow meow, meow meow meow, meow meow meow meow meow meow meow meow meow meow meow meow meow meow meow, meow meow meow meow meow. Meow meow meow meow, meow meow meow meow meow meow, meow meow meow meow meow, meow meow meow meow meow meow meow meow, meow meow meow meow meow meow. Meow meow meow meow meow meow meow meow meow meow meow, meow meow meow meow meow meow meow meow meow meow meow meow.

Meow meow meow meow meow meow. Meow meow meow meow meow meow meow meow meow meow meow meow meow meow meow meow meow, meow meow meow meow meow meow meow meow meow meow. Meow meow meow meow meow meow. Meow meow meow meow meow meow. Meow meow meow meow meow meow meow meow meow, meow meow meow meow meow meow meow meow meow meow meow meow meow, meow meow meow, meow meow meow meow meow meow meow meow. Meow meow meow meow meow meow meow meow.

Meow meow meow meow. Meow meow meow meow meow meow meow meow meow. meow meow meow meow meow meow meow. Meow meow meow meow meow meow, meow meow meow meow meow meow meow meow meow meow, meow meow.

* * * * * * *

Meow meow meow meow meow meow. Meow meow meow meow meow meow meow meow meow. Meow meow meow meow meow meow meow meow meow. Meow meow meow meow meow, meow meow meow, meow meow meow meow meow meow meow meow meow, meow meow meow meow meow meow meow meow. Meow meow meow meow meow meow meow meow meow meow meow. Meow meow meow meow meow meow meow meow meow, meow meow meow meow meow meow meow meow meow, meow meow meow meow. Meow meow meow meow meow meow meow meow, meow meow meow meow meow meow, meow meow, meow. Meow meow meow meow meow meow meow meow meow meow meow, meow meow meow meow meow meow meow meow. Meow meow meow meow meow meow. Meow meow meow meow meow meow, meow meow meow meow meow meow. Meow meow meow meow meow meow, meow meow meow meow meow meow. Meow meow meow meow meow.

Meow meow meow meow meow meow. Meow meow meow meow meow. Meow meow meow meow meow meow meow meow meow meow meow meow. Meow meow meow meow meow, meow meow meow meow meow meow, meow meow meow meow meow meow. Meow meow meow meow meow meow, meow meow meow meow meow meow meow meow, meow meow meow meow meow meow meow, meow meow meow meow meow meow meow. Meow meow meow meow meow meow, meow meow meow meow meow meow meow meow meow meow meow.

"Meow, Meow Meow," meow meow meow, "meow meow meow. Meow meow meow meow meow meow meow meow meow meow meow meow meow meow."

Meow meow meow meow meow meow meow meow meow meow meow meow meow meow. Meow meow meow meow

meow, meow meow meow meow meow meow meow meow meow. Meow meow meow meow meow meow meow, meow meow meow meow meow meow, meow meow, meow meow meow meow meow meow meow meow meow meow meow meow. Meow meow meow meow meow, meow, meow meow meow meow meow meow meow meow meow meow. Meow meow meow meow meow meow meow meow meow meow, meow meow meow meow meow meow. Meow meow meow meow meow, meow meow meow meow meow meow meow meow meow meow meow meow.

"Meow meow meow meow meow?"

"Meow Meow."

"Meow meow?"

"Meow meow meow."

"Meow meow meow meow?"

"Meow meow meow meow meow."

"Meow meow meow meow meow."

"Meow meow."

Meow meow meow meow, meow meow meow meow meow, meow meow meow.

Meow meow meow meow meow meow meow meow meow meow, meow meow meow meow meow meow meow. Meow meow meow. Meow meow meow meow. Meow meow meow meow meow meow meow meow meow meow. Meow meow meow meow meow meow meow, meow meow meow meow meow meow meow meow. Meow meow meow meow meow, meow meow meow meow meow, meow meow meow meow, meow meow meow meow meow meow meow, meow meow meow meow meow meow meow meow, meow meow meow meow meow. Meow meow meow meow. Meow meow meow.

Meow meow meow meow meow meow meow meow meow meow meow meow meow meow meow. Meow meow meow

meow meow meow meow, meow meow meow. Meow meow meow meow meow meow meow meow meow meow meow, meow meow meow meow meow meow meow. Meow meow meow meow, meow meow meow meow.

Meow meow meow meow. meow meow meow meow meow meow meow meow meow meow meow. Meow meow meow meow meow meow meow meow meow, meow meow meow. meow meow meow meow meow meow meow, meow meow meow meow meow meow meow meow meow meow.

Meow meow meow meow meow meow meow meow, meow meow meow, meow meow meow meow meow meow, meow meow meow meow, meow meow meow meow meow, meow meow meow meow meow meow meow, meow meow meow meow meow. Meow meow meow meow. Meow meow. Meow meow meow meow meow meow meow meow meow meow.

MEOW!

Meow meow meow meow meow, meow meow, meow meow meow meow meow. Meow meow meow meow meow meow meow meow meow. Meow meow meow meow meow meow meow meow meow. Meow meow meow meow meow meow meow meow meow meow meow meow meow. Meow meow meow meow. Meow meow meow meow meow, Meow meow meow meow meow meow meow. Meow meow meow meow meow meow meow meow meow meow meow meow meow meow meow meow meow meow meow meow meow meow meow. Meow meow meow meow meow meow meow meow meow, meow meow meow meow meow.

Meow meow meow meow meow, meow meow meow, meow meow meow meow meow. Meow meow meow meow meow meow meow meow meow meow, meow meow meow meow meow meow meow meow. Meow meow meow meow meow, meow meow meow meow meow meow meow meow meow meow. Meow meow meow meow meow meow, meow Meow meow meow meow meow meow meow meow meow, meow meow meow meow meow meow meow meow. Meow meow, meow meow meow, meow, meow Meow meow meow, meow meow meow meow meow meow, meow meow meow meow meow meow meow meow. Meow meow meow meow meow meow meow meow meow meow meow meow. Meow meow meow meow meow meow meow meow meow meow meow meow meow.

Meow meow meow meow, meow meow meow meow meow meow meow meow meow. Meow meow meow meow meow meow meow meow, meow meow meow meow meow, meow meow meow meow meow meow meow meow. Meow meow, meow meow meow meow meow meow meow meow meow meow, meow meow meow meow meow meow meow meow meow meow meow meow meow, meow meow meow meow meow meow meow meow meow meow meow.

"Meow meow meow meow meow," Meow meow. "Meow meow meow meow meow meow meow meow," meow meow.

"Meow?" meow meow, meow meow meow meow meow. Meow meow meow meow meow meow meow meow meow. Meow meow meow meow meow, meow meow meow meow meow meow meow meow.

"Meow, meow meow meow meow meow meow." Meow meow meow meow meow meow meow meow, meow meow meow meow meow meow meow meow meow meow meow meow meow meow meow meow meow, meow meow meow meow meow meow meow meow meow meow meow meow meow. Meow meow meow meow meow, meow meow meow meow meow. Meow meow meow meow meow meow meow meow Meow meow. Meow meow meow meow meow meow meow meow meow meow meow meow meow. Meow meow meow meow meow meow meow meow. Meow meow meow, meow meow.

Meow meow meow meow meow, Meow meow meow meow meow meow, meow meow meow meow meow meow meow meow meow meow meow meow meow meow meow meow meow, meow meow meow. Meow meow meow meow meow meow meow meow. Meow meow meow meow meow meow meow meow meow. Meow meow meow meow meow meow meow meow meow meow meow meow meow meow meow meow. Meow meow meow meow meow meow meow meow meow, meow

meow meow, meow meow meow meow meow meow meow, meow meow meow meow meow. Meow meow meow meow meow meow meow meow, meow meow meow meow meow meow meow meow meow.

Meow meow meow meow meow meow meow meow. Meow meow meow meow meow meow meow meow, meow meow meow meow meow, meow meow meow meow. Meow meow meow meow meow meow meow meow. Meow meow meow meow meow meow meow meow. Meow meow meow meow meow meow meow meow, meow meow meow meow meow meow meow meow meow meow meow. Meow meow meow meow meow meow meow meow meow meow meow meow meow meow meow meow.

Meow meow meow meow meow meow, meow meow meow meow meow meow meow meow meow meow meow meow. Meow meow meow meow meow meow meow meow meow meow meow meow meow, meow meow meow meow meow meow meow meow meow meow, meow meow meow meow meow meow meow meow meow meow meow. Meow meow meow meow meow meow meow meow meow meow meow meow meow meow meow, meow meow meow meow, meow meow meow meow meow, meow. Meow meow meow meow meow. Meow meow meow meow meow meow meow, meow meow meow meow.

Meow meow meow meow meow meow meow meow meow meow meow meow meow meow meow meow meow meow meow meow meow. Meow meow meow meow meow meow meow meow meow, meow meow meow meow meow meow meow meow meow meow. Meow meow meow, meow meow meow meow meow meow meow meow meow meow meow. Meow meow. Meow meow meow meow meow. Meow meow meow meow meow meow meow meow meow meow meow meow meow meow meow, meow meow meow meow meow.

Meow meow meow meow, meow meow meow meow meow meow meow meow meow meow, Meow meow meow meow meow meow. Meow meow meow meow meow. Meow meow meow, meow meow meow meow meow meow meow meow meow meow meow meow. Meow meow meow meow meow meow, meow meow meow meow. Meow meow, meow meow meow meow meow meow meow meow. Meow meow meow meow meow meow meow meow meow, meow meow meow meow meow meow meow meow meow meow meow meow meow.

Meow meow meow meow meow meow meow meow meow meow meow meow meow meow meow. Meow Meow meow meow meow meow meow meow meow meow meow. Meow meow meow Meow. Meow meow meow meow meow meow meow meow meow meow.

Meow meow meow meow meow meow meow meow meow. Meow meow meow meow meow meow meow meow meow meow meow meow meow meow. Meow meow meow meow meow meow meow meow meow meow meow meow meow meow meow meow. Meow meow meow meow meow meow meow meow meow meow meow. Meow meow meow meow meow meow meow meow meow meow meow meow meow meow meow meow. Meow meow meow Meow meow Meow meow meow meow meow meow meow. Meow meow meow meow meow, meow meow meow meow meow meow meow meow meow meow meow meow meow meow. Meow meow meow mcow meow meow meow meow meow meow meow meow meow meow.

Meow meow meow meow meow meow meow meow meow meow meow meow meow. Meow meow meow meow meow meow meow meow meow meow, meow meow meow meow meow meow meow meow meow meow meow meow meow meow meow meow. Meow meow meow meow.

Meow meow meow meow meow meow meow meow, meow meow Meow meow meow meow meow meow meow meow meow meow meow meow meow meow meow. Meow meow meow meow meow meow. Meow meow, meow meow. Meow meow meow meow meow meow. Meow meow meow meow meow meow meow meow meow. Meow meow meow meow meow meow meow meow. Meow meow meow meow meow meow, meow meow meow meow meow, meow meow meow meow meow meow meow, meow meow meow meow meow, meow meow meow meow meow meow meow. Meow meow meow meow meow meow meow meow meow meow meow meow. Meow meow meow meow meow meow meow meow meow meow meow meow. Meow meow meow meow meow meow meow meow meow meow meow, meow meow meow meow meow meow meow meow meow meow meow meow meow meow Meow MEOW. Meow meow meow meow meow meow, meow meow meow meow meow meow meow meow Meow.

Meow meow meow meow meow meow meow meow meow meow meow meow, meow meow meow meow meow meow meow meow meow, meow. Meow meow meow meow meow meow meow meow meow, meow meow meow meow meow meow meow meow meow meow meow, meow meow meow, meow meow meow meow meow meow. Meow meow meow meow meow meow meow meow meow. Meow meow meow meow meow, meow meow meow meow meow meow. Meow meow meow meow meow meow meow meow meow meow meow meow meow meow, meow meow meow Meow Meow. Meow meow meow meow meow, meow meow meow meow meow.

Meow meow meow meow meow, meow meow meow meow meow meow meow meow meow meow meow meow meow meow

meow, meow meow meow meow meow meow meow meow. Meow meow meow meow meow meow meow. Meow meow meow meow, meow meow meow meow meow meow meow meow meow meow. Meow meow meow meow, Meow, meow meow meow. Meow meow meow meow meow, meow meow meow meow meow meow meow meow. Meow meow meow meow, meow meow meow. Meow meow meow meow meow meow meow meow, meow meow meow meow meow meow meow meow meow meow meow meow, meow meow meow meow meow meow.

Meow meow meow meow, meow meow meow. Meow meow meow meow meow meow meow meow meow meow meow meow. Meow meow meow meow meow meow meow meow meow meow meow meow meow meow meow meow meow. Meow meow, meow meow meow meow meow meow meow meow meow, meow meow meow meow meow, meow meow meow meow meow meow meow, meow meow. Meow meow meow meow meow meow meow meow meow meow. Meow meow meow meow meow meow.

Meow meow meow meow meow meow meow meow meow meow meow meow. Meow meow meow meow meow meow meow meow, meow meow meow meow meow meow meow. Meow meow meow meow-meow meow meow meow meow meow meow meow meow meow meow meow. Meow meow meow meow meow meow meow. Meow meow meow meow meow meow meow meow meow meow meow meow meow meow meow. Meow meow meow meow meow Meow meow meow meow meow meow meow. Meow meow meow meow meow meow meow meow meow meow meow. Meow meow meow meow meow. Meow meow meow meow meow meow meow. Meow meow meow meow meow meow

meow meow. Meow meow meow meow meow meow meow meow meow meow meow meow meow meow.

Meow meow Meow meow meow meow meow meow. Meow meow meow meow meow meow meow meow meow meow meow meow meow, meow meow meow meow meow meow meow meow meow meow. Meow meow meow meow, meow meow meow meow meow meow meow meow meow. meow meow meow meow meow meow meow meow meow meow. Meow meow meow meow meow meow meow meow meow meow. Meow meow meow meow meow meow. Meow meow meow meow meow meow, Meow meow meow meow.

"Meow meow, Meow," meow meow. "Meow meow meow meow meow meow meow meow, meow meow meow meow. Meow meow meow meow meow."

Meow meow meow meow, meow meow meow. Meow meow meow Meow meow meow meow meow meow meow, meow meow meow meow meow meow meow meow meow meow meow meow meow. Meow meow meow meow meow meow meow, meow meow meow meow, meow meow meow meow meow meow meow meow meow meow meow, meow meow meow meow, meow meow meow meow. Meow meow meow meow meow. Meow meow meow meow meow meow meow, meow meow meow meow meow meow meow meow. Meow meow meow meow meow meow meow, meow meow meow meow meow, meow meow meow meow meow meow meow meow meow meow meow.

Meow meow meow meow meow meow meow meow meow meow. Meow meow meow meow meow meow, meow meow. Meow meow. Meow meow meow meow meow meow meow, Meow meow meow meow meow meow meow meow meow, meow meow meow meow meow meow meow meow meow. Meow meow.

Meow meow meow, meow meow meow meow meow meow meow meow meow. Meow meow meow meow meow meow, meow meow, meow meow meow meow meow meow meow. Meow meow meow meow meow meow meow meow, meow meow meow meow meow meow meow meow. Meow meow. Meow meow meow meow meow meow, meow meow meow. Meow meow meow meow meow meow meow meow meow meow meow meow. Meow meow meow meow meow meow meow, meow meow meow meow meow meow meow meow.

(MEOW MEOW)

Meow meow meow meow meow meow meow meow. Meow meow meow meow meow meow meow, meow meow meow meow meow meow meow meow meow. Meow meow meow meow meow, meow meow meow meow, meow meow meow meow meow meow meow meow meow meow meow meow meow.

Meow meow meow meow meow meow meow meow meow meow meow meow meow meow meow. Meow meow meow meow meow. Meow meow meow meow meow meow meow meow meow meow meow meow meow meow. Meow meow meow meow meow. Meow meow meow meow meow meow meow meow meow, meow meow meow meow meow, meow meow meow meow.

Meow meow meow, meow meow meow meow meow meow meow. Meow meow meow meow meow meow meow meow. Meow meow-meow meow meow meow meow meow meow meow meow meow meow meow meow meow meow meow, meow meow meow meow. Meow meow meow meow meow meow meow meow. Meow meow. Meow meow meow meow meow meow meow meow. Meow meow meow meow meow meow meow meow meow meow, meow meow meow meow. Meow meow meow meow meow meow, meow meow meow meow meow, meow meow meow meow meow, meow meow meow meow meow meow. Meow meow meow meow meow meow meow meow meow meow meow. Meow meow meow meow

187

meow meow meow Meow, meow meow meow meow. Meow meow meow meow meow meow meow. Meow meow meow meow meow, meow meow meow, meow meow meow meow meow meow meow meow meow meow meow meow.

Meow meow meow meow meow meow. Meow meow meow meow meow meow. Meow meow meow meow meow meow meow meow meow meow. Meow meow meow meow meow meow meow meow meow meow, meow meow meow meow meow meow. Meow meow meow meow meow meow. Meow meow meow, meow meow. Meow meow meow meow meow meow meow, meow meow meow meow meow meow.

Meow meow meow meow, meow meow meow meow meow meow meow meow meow meow. Meow meow meow meow meow meow meow meow meow meow, meow meow meow meow meow meow meow meow meow meow meow meow meow meow meow. Meow meow meow meow meow meow meow, meow meow meow meow meow meow meow meow meow. Meow meow meow meow meow meow meow meow meow. Meow meow meow. Meow meow meow, meow meow meow, meow meow meow meow meow meow, meow meow meow meow meow, meow meow meow meow meow meow meow meow meow meow meow.

Meow meow meow meow meow meow meow. Meow meow meow meow meow meow, meow meow meow meow meow meow meow meow meow meow. Meow meow meow meow meow, meow meow meow meow meow, meow meow, meow, meow meow meow. Meow meow meow meow, meow meow meow meow meow meow meow meow meow meow meow meow meow. Meow meow meow. Meow meow meow meow meow meow meow meow meow meow. Meow meow meow meow meow meow meow meow meow meow meow, meow meow meow meow meow meow, meow meow meow meow. Meow

meow meow meow meow meow meow meow, meow meow meow meow. Meow meow meow meow meow meow meow meow meow meow meow, meow meow meow meow meow meow meow meow meow meow meow meow meow meow meow.

Meow meow meow meow meow meow meow meow meow. Meow meow meow meow meow meow. Meow meow meow meow meow, meow meow meow meow meow meow meow meow. Meow meow meow meow meow meow meow, meow meow meow, meow meow. Meow meow meow meow meow meow meow meow, meow meow meow meow meow meow meow meow. Meow meow meow meow, meow meow meow meow meow meow meow, meow meow. Meow meow meow meow meow meow meow meow meow meow. Meow meow meow meow meow meow meow meow meow meow meow meow meow, meow meow meow meow meow, meow meow meow meow meow meow meow meow-meow. Meow meow meow meow meow meow meow, meow meow meow meow meow meow meow. Meow meow meow meow meow meow meow meow meow. Meow meow meow meow meow, meow meow meow meow. meow meow meow meow meow meow meow meow meow meow meow meow meow. Meow meow meow meow meow meow, meow meow, meow meow. Meow meow meow meow meow meow meow, meow meow meow meow.

Meow meow meow meow meow meow meow meow, meow meow meow meow meow meow meow meow, meow meow meow meow meow meow meow. Meow meow meow meow meow meow meow meow meow meow meow meow meow meow meow meow meow meow meow meow meow meow meow meow, meow meow meow meow meow meow, meow meow meow meow meow meow meow meow meow. Meow meow meow meow meow meow meow meow. Meow meow meow

meow meow meow meow meow. Meow meow meow meow
meow, meow meow meow meow meow meow, meow meow
meow meow meow meow, meow meow meow meow meow
meow meow meow meow meow meow. Meow meow meow
meow meow meow, meow. Meow meow meow meow meow
meow meow meow meow meow meow meow meow meow
meow meow, meow meow meow meow meow meow meow
meow meow, meow meow meow meow meow meow meow.

Meow meow meow meow meow. Meow meow meow meow
meow meow meow meow meow meow meow meow meow
meow meow, meow meow meow meow meow meow. Meow
meow meow meow meow meow meow meow meow.
meow meow meow meow meow meow, meow meow. Meow
meow meow meow meow. meow meow meow meow meow
meow meow meow meow meow. Meow meow meow meow
meow meow meow. Meow meow meow meow meow meow
meow meow. Meow meow meow meow meow meow meow
meow meow meow meow meow, meow meow meow meow
meow meow meow meow.

Meow meow meow meow meow meow. Meow, meow meow.
Meow meow meow meow meow meow meow meow meow
meow meow meow, meow meow meow meow meow, meow
meow meow meow meow meow meow meow.

Meow meow meow meow meow, meow meow meow meow.
Meow meow meow meow meow meow meow meow meow
meow meow. Meow meow meow meow meow meow meow
meow. Meow meow meow, meow meow meow meow meow
meow meow, meow meow meow meow meow meow meow.
Meow meow meow meow meow meow meow, meow meow
meow meow meow meow meow meow meow meow meow.
Meow meow meow meow meow meow meow meow. Meow
meow meow meow meow meow meow meow meow meow

meow meow, meow meow meow meow meow meow meow meow meow.

Meow meow meow meow meow meow, meow meow meow. Meow meow meow meow meow meow meow meow meow meow meow. Meow meow meow meow meow meow meow meow meow meow meow meow. Meow meow meow meow meow, meow meow meow meow: meow meow, meow meow. Meow meow. Meow meow meow meow meow meow meow meow meow meow meow. Meow meow meow meow meow, meow meow meow meow meow. Meow meow meow meow meow, meow meow meow meow meow meow meow meow meow meow meow meow meow. Meow meow meow meow. Meow meow meow meow meow meow, meow meow meow meow meow meow meow meow meow.

Meow meow meow, meow meow meow meow meow meow meow meow. Meow meow meow meow. Meow meow meow meow meow meow meow meow meow meow meow, meow meow meow meow meow meow, meow meow meow meow meow, meow meow meow meow meow meow meow meow meow meow meow. Meow meow meow meow meow meow meow meow meow meow meow. Meow meow meow meow meow meow meow. Meow meow meow meow meow meow. Meow meow, meow meow meow meow meow meow meow meow meow meow meow. Meow meow meow meow meow meow meow, meow meow meow meow meow meow meow meow meow meow.

"Meow, meow meow meow meow meow meow?" meow meow meow. Meow meow meow meow, meow meow meow. Meow meow meow meow meow meow meow meow meow meow. Meow meow meow meow, meow meow meow meow meow meow meow meow. meow meow meow. Meow meow meow meow, meow meow meow meow meow meow meow meow

meow meow meow, meow meow meow meow meow meow. Meow meow meow meow meow meow meow meow meow meow meow meow, meow meow meow meow meow meow, meow meow meow meow meow, meow meow meow meow.

"Meow meow meow meow meow meow meow meow?" meow meow meow, meow meow meow meow meow meow meow meow meow meow meow meow meow meow meow meow meow meow meow meow meow meow meow meow meow meow meow meow meow. Meow meow meow meow meow meow meow meow meow.

"Meow meow meow meow meow meow meow," meow meow meow, meow meow meow meow meow meow meow meow meow. Meow meow meow meow meow. Meow meow meow meow meow meow meow meow, meow meow meow meow meow meow meow. Meow meow meow meow meow, meow meow meow meow meow meow meow, meow meow meow meow meow meow meow meow meow meow. Meow meow meow meow meow meow meow meow meow meow meow meow, meow meow meow meow meow meow.

Meow meow meow, meow meow meow, meow meow meow meow meow. Meow meow meow meow meow meow meow meow, meow meow meow meow meow meow meow, meow meow meow meow meow, meow meow meow meow meow meow meow meow, meow meow meow meow meow meow meow meow. Meow meow meow meow meow meow meow meow. Meow meow meow meow meow meow meow meow meow meow meow meow meow meow meow meow meow, meow meow meow meow meow meow. Meow meow meow meow meow meow meow meow meow meow. Meow meow meow meow. meow meow meow meow.

"Meow meow meow meow meow meow meow meow," meow meow meow, meow meow meow meow meow meow

meow meow meow meow meow, meow meow meow meow meow meow meow meow meow. Meow meow meow meow meow meow meow meow meow meow.

Meow meow meow meow, meow meow meow meow meow meow meow meow meow meow meow meow. meow meow meow meow meow meow meow meow meow meow meow meow meow meow, meow meow meow meow meow meow meow meow, meow meow meow meow meow meow meow meow.

"Meow meow meow, meow meow meow meow. Meow meow meow meow meow meow meow meow," meow meow meow meow meow meow meow meow meow meow meow meow.

Meow meow meow meow meow meow meow, meow meow meow meow meow, meow meow meow meow meow meow meow meow meow meow meow meow meow meow. Meow meow meow meow. Meow meow meow. Meow meow meow meow meow, meow meow meow meow meow meow meow meow meow meow. Meow meow meow meow meow meow meow meow, meow meow meow meow: Meow Meow meow meow meow meow. Meow meow meow meow. Meow meow meow meow meow.

Meow meow meow meow meow meow meow meow, meow meow meow meow. Meow meow meow meow meow "meow." Meow meow meow "meow meow meow" meow "meow meow meow," meow meow meow meow meow. Meow meow meow meow meow meow meow meow meow meow meow meow meow meow, meow meow meow meow, meow meow meow meow meow meow meow meow meow, meow meow meow meow meow meow meow meow meow meow meow meow meow meow meow, meow meow meow meow meow. Meow meow meow meow meow meow, "Meow meow meow meow meow meow-meow meow meow meow meow

meow meow meow meow meow meow, meow meow meow meow meow meow meow."

Meow meow meow meow meow meow meow meow meow, meow meow meow meow. Meow meow meow meow meow meow meow meow meow meow meow meow meow meow, meow meow meow meow meow meow meow meow meow meow meow meow:

"Meow meow meow meow meow."

Meow meow meow meow meow meow meow meow meow meow, meow meow meow meow. Meow meow meow meow meow meow meow meow, meow meow meow meow, meow meow meow meow, meow meow meow meow meow meow meow meow meow meow meow meow meow meow meow. Meow meow meow meow meow meow meow meow, meow meow meow meow meow meow meow meow meow. Meow meow meow meow meow meow meow, meow meow meow meow meow meow meow meow meow meow meow meow meow, meow meow meow meow meow meow meow. Meow meow meow meow meow meow meow meow meow, meow meow meow meow meow meow meow meow meow. Meow meow meow, meow meow. Meow meow meow meow meow meow meow, meow meow meow meow meow. Meow meow meow meow meow.

Meow meow meow meow meow meow meow, meow meow meow meow meow meow meow, meow meow meow meow meow meow meow meow meow meow meow meow. Meow meow meow meow meow meow meow, meow, meow meow meow. Meow meow, meow meow meow meow meow meow meow meow meow meow, meow meow meow meow meow meow.

Meow meow meow meow meow, meow meow meow meow. Meow meow meow meow meow meow meow meow meow

meow meow, meow meow meow meow meow meow meow
meow meow meow meow. Meow meow meow meow, meow
meow meow meow. Meow meow. Meow meow meow meow
meow meow, meow meow meow meow meow meow meow
meow meow meow. Meow meow meow meow meow meow
meow, meow meow meow meow, meow meow meow meow
meow meow meow meow meow. Meow meow meow meow
meow meow meow meow meow meow meow, meow meow
meow meow meow meow meow meow meow meow meow
meow meow. Meow meow meow meow meow, meow meow
meow meow meow meow meow meow. Meow meow meow
meow meow meow meow meow meow meow meow, meow
meow meow meow meow meow meow meow meow meow
meow.

"Meow meow meow meow, meow meow?" meow meow
meow meow meow meow meow. "Meow meow meow meow
meow meow meow meow meow meow meow meow."

Meow meow meow meow meow meow meow meow meow,
meow meow meow meow meow meow, meow meow meow
meow. Meow meow meow. Meow meow meow meow meow
meow meow. Meow meow meow meow, meow meow meow
meow meow meow meow meow meow meow meow. Meow
meow meow meow meow meow, meow meow meow meow
meow meow, meow meow meow meow meow meow meow
meow meow meow meow.

"Meow meow meow meow meow meow, Meow," meow
meow meow meow. Meow meow meow meow meow meow
meow meow meow. Meow meow meow meow meow meow,
meow meow meow meow meow meow meow. Meow meow
meow meow meow meow. Meow meow meow meow meow
meow meow meow, meow meow meow meow meow meow
meow meow meow meow meow meow, meow meow meow

meow meow meow, meow meow meow meow meow meow, meow meow meow meow meow meow meow. Meow meow meow meow meow, meow meow meow meow meow meow meow. Meow meow meow meow, meow meow meow meow meow meow meow meow. Meow meow meow meow meow meow, meow meow meow meow meow meow meow meow meow meow meow meow, meow meow meow meow meow meow meow.

Meow meow meow meow meow meow meow meow, meow meow meow meow, meow meow meow meow meow meow. Meow meow meow meow meow meow meow meow meow. Meow meow meow meow meow meow meow meow meow meow meow meow meow, meow meow meow meow meow meow meow meow, meow meow meow meow meow meow meow. Meow meow meow.

Meow meow meow meow meow meow meow meow, meow meow meow meow meow meow meow meow meow meow meow meow, meow meow meow meow meow meow meow meow meow meow meow meow meow meow meow, meow meow meow meow meow meow meow meow meow. Meow meow meow meow meow meow meow meow meow meow meow meow meow meow meow. Meow meow meow meow meow meow meow. Meow meow meow meow meow meow meow. Meow meow meow meow meow. Meow meow meow meow meow meow. Meow meow meow meow meow meow.

Meow meow meow meow meow meow. Meow meow meow meow, meow meow meow meow meow meow. Meow meow meow meow, meow meow meow meow meow meow meow meow, meow meow meow meow meow meow meow, meow meow. Meow meow meow meow meow meow, meow meow meow meow, meow meow meow meow meow meow meow

meow meow meow, meow meow meow meow meow. Meow meow meow meow meow meow meow meow meow meow, meow meow meow meow meow meow meow meow meow meow meow-meow meow.

Meow meow meow meow, meow meow. Meow meow meow meow meow meow meow meow. Meow meow meow meow meow meow meow meow meow meow meow meow meow. Meow meow meow meow meow meow, meow meow meow meow meow meow meow meow meow méow, meow meow meow. Meow meow meow meow, meow meow meow meow, meow meow meow meow meow meow meow meow. Meow meow meow meow meow meow meow. Meow meow meow meow meow meow meow meow, meow-meow. Meow meow meow meow meow meow, meow meow meow meow meow meow meow meow meow meow.

Meow meow meow meow meow meow, meow meow meow, meow meow meow meow meow meow meow meow meow meow meow meow meow meow meow meow. Meow meow meow meow. Meow meow meow meow meow, meow meow meow meow meow. Meow meow meow, meow meow meow meow meow meow. Meow meow meow meow meow meow meow meow meow. Meow meow meow meow meow meow, meow meow meow meow meow meow meow meow meow meow. Meow-meow meow meow meow meow meow. Meow meow meow meow meow meow meow meow meow meow meow, meow meow meow meow. Meow meow meow meow meow. Meow meow meow, meow meow meow meow meow. Meow meow meow meow meow, meow meow meow meow meow meow meow.

Meow meow meow meow meow meow meow meow meow. Meow meow meow meow meow meow meow meow meow, meow meow meow meow meow meow meow. Meow meow

meow meow meow meow meow meow meow meow meow
meow meow meow meow meow, meow meow meow meow
meow meow meow meow. Meow meow meow meow meow
meow meow, meow meow meow meow, meow meow meow
meow meow. Meow meow meow meow meow meow meow
meow meow meow. Meow meow meow meow meow meow.

Meow meow meow meow meow meow meow meow meow
meow. Meow meow meow meow meow meow meow meow
meow meow meow meow, meow meow. Meow meow meow
meow meow meow meow, meow meow meow meow meow
meow. Meow meow meow, meow meow meow meow meow
meow.

"Meow meow meow meow?" meow meow.

"Meow," meow meow meow.

"Meow meow meow meow?"

Meow meow meow meow meow meow, meow meow meow
meow, meow meow meow meow meow meow meow meow,
meow meow meow meow meow meow meow meow meow
meow. Meow meow meow meow meow meow meow, meow
meow meow meow meow meow meow meow meow. Meow
meow meow meow meow meow, meow meow meow meow
meow meow, meow meow meow meow meow meow. Meow
meow meow meow meow meow. Meow meow meow. Meow
meow meow meow meow meow, meow meow meow meow
meow meow. Meow meow meow meow meow meow meow
meow meow meow meow. Meow meow meow meow meow
meow. Meow meow meow meow meow meow meow meow
meow meow meow meow meow meow meow meow meow.
Meow meow meow meow meow meow meow meow meow
meow meow meow. Meow meow. Meow meow meow.

Meow meow meow meow meow meow meow meow meow,
meow meow meow meow meow. Meow meow meow meow

meow meow meow meow meow meow meow meow, meow meow meow meow meow meow. Meow meow meow meow meow? Meow meow, meow. Meow meow meow meow meow meow meow meow meow.

MEOW

Meow meow meow meow meow meow meow meow meow meow meow. Meow meow meow meow meow meow meow meow meow meow meow, meow meow meow meow meow meow meow-meow meow, meow meow meow meow meow meow-meow meow meow meow. Meow meow meow meow meow meow, meow meow meow. Meow meow meow meow meow. Meow meow meow meow meow meow meow, meow meow, meow meow meow meow meow. Meow meow meow meow meow, meow meow meow meow meow meow meow meow meow meow meow meow meow.

Meow meow meow meow meow, meow meow meow meow meow meow meow meow meow meow. Meow meow meow meow meow meow, meow meow meow meow meow meow. Meow meow meow meow meow meow, meow meow. Meow meow meow meow meow. Meow meow meow meow meow meow meow meow meow.

Meow meow meow meow meow meow. Meow meow meow meow, meow meow meow meow, meow meow meow meow meow meow meow meow meow meow meow meow meow meow. Meow meow meow meow, meow meow meow meow meow meow meow, meow meow meow meow meow meow.

Meow meow meow meow meow meow meow meow meow, meow meow meow meow meow meow meow, meow meow meow meow meow meow meow meow meow meow meow meow.

Meow meow meow meow, meow meow meow meow meow meow meow meow meow. Meow meow meow meow meow meow, meow meow, meow meow meow meow meow, meow meow meow meow meow meow meow meow. Meow meow meow meow. Meow meow meow meow meow meow meow meow meow meow meow. Meow meow meow meow meow meow meow meow meow meow, meow meow meow meow meow meow meow meow. Meow meow meow meow meow.

Meow meow meow, meow meow meow meow meow meow meow meow, meow meow meow meow meow meow meow, meow meow meow meow meow meow. Meow meow meow meow meow meow, meow meow meow meow meow meow. Meow meow meow meow meow, meow meow meow meow meow meow meow meow meow meow meow meow. Meow meow meow, meow meow meow meow meow meow meow meow meow. Meow meow meow meow meow, meow meow meow meow meow meow meow meow meow meow meow meow, meow meow meow meow meow meow meow meow meow meow, meow meow meow meow meow meow meow. Meow meow meow meow meow meow meow meow meow meow meow meow meow meow meow meow meow meow meow meow meow. Meow meow meow meow meow meow meow meow meow meow meow meow, meow meow meow meow meow meow meow meow, meow meow meow meow meow meow meow. Meow meow meow meow meow meow meow meow meow meow meow, meow meow meow meow meow meow, meow meow meow meow meow meow meow meow. Meow meow Meow meow meow meow, meow meow meow meow meow meow meow meow meow, meow meow meow meow Meow meow meow meow meow meow meow meow meow.

Meow meow meow meow meow meow meow meow, meow. Meow meow meow meow meow meow meow meow meow,

meow meow meow meow. Meow meow meow meow meow meow meow meow meow meow meow meow meow. Meow meow meow meow meow meow, meow meow meow meow meow meow, meow meow meow meow meow meow meow meow meow meow, meow meow meow meow meow meow. Meow meow meow meow meow meow meow meow meow meow. Meow meow meow meow meow meow meow meow meow. Meow meow, meow meow meow meow meow. Meow meow meow meow meow meow meow meow. Meow meow meow meow meow meow. Meow meow meow, meow meow meow meow meow meow meow. Meow meow meow meow meow, meow meow meow meow, meow meow meow meow meow, meow meow meow meow meow meow meow, meow meow meow meow, meow meow meow meow meow meow meow meow meow meow meow.

Meow meow meow meow meow meow meow meow meow, Meow, meow meow meow meow meow. Meow meow meow meow meow. Meow meow meow meow meow meow meow meow meow meow meow meow meow meow meow meow meow, meow meow meow meow meow meow meow meow, meow meow meow meow meow meow meow, meow meow meow meow meow. Meow meow meow meow meow meow meow meow, meow meow meow meow meow meow, meow meow meow meow meow meow meow meow meow meow meow. Meow meow meow meow meow meow. Meow meow. Meow meow meow meow meow meow. Meow meow meow.

Meow meow meow meow meow, meow meow meow meow meow. Meow meow meow meow meow. Meow meow meow meow meow meow meow meow meow meow meow meow meow meow, meow meow. Meow meow meow meow meow meow meow meow meow meow meow meow meow meow meow

meow? Meow meow meow meow, meow meow meow meow meow meow. Meow meow meow meow, meow meow meow meow meow meow meow meow meow, meow meow meow meow, meow meow meow meow meow meow, meow meow meow-meow meow. Meow meow meow meow meow meow meow meow meow meow meow meow, meow meow meow meow meow meow meow meow meow meow meow meow, meow meow meow, meow meow meow meow meow meow.

Meow meow meow meow meow meow meow meow meow meow meow meow, meow meow meow meow meow meow meow. Meow meow meow meow meow, meow meow meow meow. Meow meow meow meow, meow meow meow meow. Meow meow meow meow meow, meow meow meow meow. Meow meow meow meow meow meow meow meow meow meow-meow, meow meow meow meow meow meow meow meow, meow meow meow meow meow meow meow meow, meow meow meow meow meow meow meow meow, meow meow meow meow meow meow. Meow meow meow meow meow meow meow meow.

Meow meow meow meow meow meow, meow meow meow meow meow meow meow meow meow meow. Meow meow meow. Meow meow meow meow meow meow meow. Meow meow meow meow meow meow meow meow, meow meow meow meow meow meow meow meow, meow meow. Meow meow meow meow meow meow meow meow meow?

Meow meow meow meow, meow meow meow meow meow meow meow meow meow. Meow meow meow meow meow meow meow meow meow meow meow, meow meow meow meow meow meow meow meow meow, meow meow meow meow meow meow. Meow meow meow meow, meow meow meow. Meow meow meow meow, meow meow meow meow meow meow, meow meow meow meow meow meow meow meow. Meow

meow meow meow meow meow meow meow meow meow
meow meow meow meow meow meow meow meow meow,
meow meow meow, meow meow meow, meow meow meow
meow meow meow meow meow, meow meow meow meow
meow. Meow meow meow meow meow meow meow meow
meow meow meow, meow meow meow meow meow meow
meow meow, meow meow meow meow meow, meow meow
meow meow meow meow meow meow meow meow, meow
meow meow-meow meow. Meow meow meow meow meow
meow, meow meow meow meow meow meow meow meow
meow meow meow meow meow meow meow meow, meow
meow meow meow meow meow meow meow, meow meow
meow meow meow meow meow meow meow. Meow meow
meow meow meow meow meow meow meow, meow meow
meow meow meow meow meow meow, meow meow meow
meow meow meow meow meow meow. Meow meow meow
meow meow meow meow meow meow meow meow meow.
Meow meow meow meow meow meow meow meow meow
meow meow meow. Meow meow meow, meow meow meow
meow meow meow meow meow meow, meow meow meow
meow meow meow meow meow meow meow meow meow.
Meow meow meow meow meow meow meow Meow, meow
meow meow meow meow meow meow.

Meow meow meow meow. Meow meow meow meow meow
meow. Meow meow meow meow meow meow meow. Meow
meow meow meow meow meow, meow meow meow meow
meow meow meow, meow meow meow meow meow. Meow
meow meow meow meow meow meow meow.

Meow meow meow meow meow meow meow meow meow
meow meow meow meow meow meow meow, meow meow
meow, meow meow meow meow meow meow meow meow
meow meow meow meow, meow meow meow. Meow meow

meow meow meow meow meow meow meow meow, meow
meow meow meow meow meow. meow meow meow meow
meow meow, meow meow meow meow meow meow
meow meow. Meow meow meow meow meow meow meow,
meow meow meow meow meow meow meow meow meow
meow meow meow meow, meow meow meow meow meow
meow, meow meow meow meow meow meow, meow meow
meow meow meow meow meow meow meow meow meow
meow, meow meow meow meow, meow meow meow. Meow
meow meow meow meow meow meow meow meow meow
meow. Meow meow meow meow meow meow meow meow
meow meow meow meow meow meow, meow meow meow
meow meow meow, meow meow meow meow meow meow
meow.

Meow meow meow meow meow meow meow, meow meow.
Meow meow meow meow meow meow meow meow meow
meow. Meow meow meow meow meow meow meow meow
meow meow meow meow. Meow meow, meow meow meow
meow meow meow meow meow meow meow meow, meow
meow meow meow meow meow. Meow meow meow meow,
meow meow meow meow meow meow meow meow. Meow
meow meow meow meow meow, meow meow meow
meow meow meow meow, meow meow meow meow meow
meow meow meow meow meow. Meow meow meow meow,
meow meow meow meow meow meow meow meow, meow
meow meow meow meow meow meow meow. Meow meow meow
meow meow meow meow meow meow meow meow meow.
Meow meow meow meow meow meow meow meow. Meow
meow meow meow meow, meow meow meow meow meow
meow meow meow meow meow meow meow. Meow meow
meow meow meow meow meow meow. Meow meow meow.
Meow meow meow meow meow meow meow?

Meow meow meow meow meow meow meow meow. Meow meow meow meow meow meow meow meow meow meow meow meow meow meow. Meow meow meow meow meow meow meow meow meow meow, meow meow meow meow meow meow meow meow. Meow meow meow meow meow, meow meow meow meow meow meow meow meow meow meow meow, meow meow. Meow meow meow meow meow, meow meow meow meow. Meow meow meow meow meow meow meow, meow meow meow, meow meow meow meow meow meow meow meow. Meow meow meow meow meow meow meow meow meow meow meow meow meow meow meow meow?

Meow meow meow meow meow meow meow, meow meow meow meow meow meow meow meow meow. Meow meow meow meow meow meow. Meow meow meow, meow meow meow meow meow meow meow meow meow meow meow. Meow meow meow meow meow meow meow meow meow meow meow meow, meow meow meow. Meow meow meow meow meow meow meow meow meow meow meow meow meow meow. Meow meow meow meow meow meow meow meow meow meow meow, meow meow meow meow meow meow meow meow meow meow.

"Meow meow meow meow meow meow meow meow?" meow meow meow.

Meow meow meow meow meow meow meow meow meow, meow meow meow meow meow meow meow meow meow meow meow meow meow meow, meow meow meow meow meow meow meow meow meow meow meow meow meow. Meow meow meow meow meow meow meow meow meow meow meow, meow meow meow meow meow meow meow meow meow meow. Meow meow meow meow meow meow meow meow

meow meow meow meow meow. Meow meow meow, meow, meow meow meow meow meow meow meow meow, meow meow meow meow meow meow meow meow meow meow meow.

Meow meow meow meow, meow meow meow meow meow meow meow meow meow meow meow meow meow meow meow meow. Meow meow meow meow, meow meow, meow meow meow meow meow meow meow. Meow meow meow meow meow, meow meow meow, meow meow meow, meow meow meow meow meow meow meow, meow meow meow meow meow meow meow.

Meow meow meow meow meow meow, meow meow meow meow meow meow meow meow meow meow, meow meow meow. Meow meow meow meow meow meow meow meow. Meow meow meow meow meow meow, meow meow meow meow meow meow meow meow meow meow meow meow, meow meow meow, meow meow meow meow meow. Meow meow meow meow meow meow meow meow meow, meow meow meow meow. Meow meow meow meow. Meow meow meow meow meow, meow meow meow meow meow, meow meow meow. Meow meow meow meow meow meow meow meow meow meow meow meow meow meow. Meow meow meow meow meow meow meow meow meow meow.

Meow meow meow meow. Meow meow meow meow meow meow meow meow meow. Meow meow meow meow. Meow meow meow meow meow, meow meow meow meow. Meow meow meow meow meow meow, meow meow meow meow meow meow meow meow meow meow meow, meow meow meow meow meow meow. Meow meow meow meow meow. Meow meow meow meow meow meow meow meow meow. Meow meow meow meow meow meow, meow meow meow meow meow meow meow.

Meow meow meow meow meow meow meow meow, meow meow meow, meow meow meow meow, meow meow meow. Meow meow meow meow meow meow meow meow. Meow meow meow. Meow meow meow meow meow meow meow meow meow meow meow meow meow. Meow meow meow meow meow meow meow, meow meow meow meow meow, meow meow meow meow meow meow meow meow meow meow meow meow meow meow. Meow meow meow meow meow meow, meow meow meow meow meow meow. Meow meow meow meow. Meow meow, meow meow meow meow.

Meow meow meow meow meow meow meow meow meow meow, meow meow meow meow meow meow. Meow meow meow meow meow meow meow meow meow, meow meow meow meow meow meow meow. Meow meow meow meow meow meow meow. Meow meow meow meow meow meow meow, meow meow meow meow meow meow meow meow meow, meow meow meow meow meow meow meow meow meow meow meow meow meow. Meow meow meow meow meow meow meow meow meow. Meow meow meow meow meow meow meow meow meow meow meow meow meow meow meow meow meow meow meow. Meow, meow meow meow meow meow meow meow meow meow meow meow meow meow meow. Meow meow meow meow meow meow meow meow meow, meow meow meow meow meow meow meow meow meow.

Meow meow meow meow. Meow meow meow meow meow meow meow meow, meow meow meow meow meow meow meow meow meow, meow meow meow meow. Meow meow meow meow meow meow meow meow, meow meow meow meow meow meow meow meow. Meow meow meow, Meow, meow meow meow. Meow meow meow. Moew meow meow. Meow meow meow. Meow meow meow. Meow meow. Meow meow meow meow meow meow. Meow meow meow, meow meow meow meow meow?

Meow meow meow meow meow meow meow. Meow meow meow. Meow meow meow. Meow meow meow meow meow meow meow meow, meow meow meow meow meow meow meow.

MEOW MEOW, MEOW

Meow meow meow meow meow meow meow. Meow meow. Meow meow meow meow meow meow meow meow meow meow, meow meow meow meow meow meow meow, meow meow meow meow meow meow meow meow meow meow meow meow. Meow meow meow meow meow meow meow meow meow meow meow meow, meow meow meow meow meow meow meow meow, meow meow meow meow meow meow meow meow. Meow meow meow meow meow meow, meow meow meow meow meow meow meow meow.

Meow meow meow meow meow meow meow meow meow meow meow meow meow. Meow meow meow meow. Meow meow meow meow meow meow meow meow meow meow, meow meow meow meow meow meow meow meow meow meow. Meow meow meow meow meow, meow meow meow meow, meow meow meow, meow meow meow meow meow meow meow meow. Meow meow meow meow meow meow meow meow meow meow. Meow meow meow meow, meow meow meow meow meow, meow meow meow meow meow meow meow meow meow meow meow meow meow meow meow meow meow meow, meow meow meow meow meow, meow meow meow meow. Meow meow meow meow meow meow meow meow, meow meow meow meow meow meow, meow meow meow meow meow meow meow meow meow, meow meow meow meow meow meow meow meow meow meow meow meow meow meow meow meow meow meow.

Meow meow meow meow meow meow meow, meow meow meow meow meow. Meow meow meow meow meow meow, meow meow meow meow meow meow meow meow meow-meow meow, meow meow meow meow meow meow-meow-meow. Meow meow meow, meow meow meow meow, meow meow meow. Meow meow meow, meow meow meow meow meow meow meow. Meow meow meow meow meow meow, meow meow meow meow meow. Meow meow meow meow meow meow meow meow meow.

Meow meow meow meow, meow meow meow meow meow meow meow, meow meow meow meow meow meow, meow meow meow meow meow meow meow-meow meow. Meow meow meow meow meow meow meow meow meow meow meow meow. Meow meow meow meow meow, meow meow meow meow meow meow meow meow meow meow meow, meow meow meow meow meow meow. Meow meow meow, meow meow meow meow meow-meow meow meow meow meow meow. Meow meow meow meow meow meow meow meow meow meow, meow meow meow meow meow meow meow meow meow meow meow, meow meow meow meow meow. Meow meow meow meow meow, meow meow meow meow meow.

Meow meow meow meow-meow meow meow meow meow, meow meow meow meow meow meow meow meow meow meow meow meow meow. Meow meow, meow meow meow, meow meow meow meow meow meow meow meow meow meow meow meow meow meow. Meow meow meow meow meow meow. Meow meow meow meow meow meow meow meow, meow meow meow meow meow meow meow meow. Meow meow meow meow meow meow meow meow meow. Meow Meow meow meow.

"Meow meow," meow meow, "Meow meow meow. Meow meow meow meow meow meow meow meow meow meow meow meow meow. Meow meow meow meow meow meow."

Meow meow meow meow. Meow meow meow meow meow meow meow. Meow meow meow meow, meow meow meow meow meow meow meow. Meow meow meow meow. meow meow meow meow meow meow meow meow, meow meow. Meow meow meow meow meow meow meow meow meow, meow meow meow meow, meow meow meow meow meow, meow meow meow meow meow meow meow meow. Meow meow meow. Meow meow meow, meow meow meow meow.

Meow meow, meow meow meow, meow meow meow meow meow meow meow. Meow meow meow meow meow meow meow meow, meow meow meow meow meow meow meow, meow meow meow meow meow meow meow meow. Meow meow meow meow meow meow meow meow meow meow meow, meow meow meow. Meow meow meow meow meow. Meow meow meow meow meow meow meow meow meow. Meow meow meow meow. Meow meow meow meow meow meow meow. Meow meow meow meow meow meow meow meow meow. Meow meow meow meow meow meow meow meow meow. Meow meow meow meow meow, meow, meow meow meow meow meow meow meow. Meow meow meow Meow meow Meow meow meow meow meow meow meow meow meow meow, meow meow meow meow meow. Meow meow meow meow meow meow meow meow meow meow meow.

Meow meow meow meow meow meow meow meow meow. Meow meow meow meow meow meow meow meow meow. Meow meow meow meow meow meow meow meow meow meow. Meow meow meow meow meow meow meow meow meow. Meow meow meow meow meow. Meow meow meow

meow meow meow meow, meow meow meow meow meow meow meow meow meow meow meow meow meow meow, meow meow meow meow meow, meow meow meow meow meow.

Meow meow meow meow meow meow meow meow meow meow. Meow meow meow meow meow meow meow meow meow meow.

Meow meow meow meow meow meow meow meow meow meow. Meow meow meow meow meow meow meow, meow meow meow meow meow meow meow. Meow meow meow meow meow. meow meow meow meow meow meow meow meow meow meow meow meow meow meow. Meow meow. Meow meow meow meow meow meow meow meow meow meow. Meow meow meow meow, meow meow meow meow meow meow meow meow meow meow meow meow meow, meow meow meow meow meow meow meow. Meow meow meow meow meow meow meow meow meow. Meow meow meow meow meow meow meow meow, meow, meow. Meow meow meow meow meow meow meow meow meow.

Meow meow meow, meow meow Meow meow meow meow meow meow meow meow meow meow meow meow meow. Meow meow, meow meow meow. Meow meow meow meow meow meow meow meow meow, meow meow meow, meow meow meow meow meow meow, meow meow meow meow meow meow meow meow meow meow meow meow meow. Meow meow meow meow meow meow meow meow meow meow meow. Meow meow meow meow Meow meow Meow. Meow meow meow meow meow meow meow meow. Meow meow meow meow meow meow, meow meow meow meow meow meow meow meow meow meow meow meow meow meow, meow meow meow meow meow meow meow meow meow.

Meow meow meow meow, meow meow meow meow meow meow meow meow meow meow meow meow meow meow meow, meow meow meow meow meow Meow meow meow meow meow meow. Meow meow meow meow meow meow, meow meow meow. Meow meow meow meow meow meow meow meow meow meow, meow meow meow. Meow meow meow meow meow meow, meow meow meow meow meow meow meow meow meow meow meow meow meow meow meow meow. Meow meow meow meow meow, meow meow meow meow meow meow meow meow meow meow meow, meow meow meow meow meow meow. Meow meow meow meow meow meow meow meow meow meow meow meow meow meow meow meow.

Meow meow meow meow meow meow meow meow meow, meow meow meow meow meow meow, meow meow meow meow meow meow meow meow meow. Meow meow meow meow, meow meow meow meow: meow meow meow. Meow meow meow meow meow meow meow meow meow. Meow meow meow-meow meow, meow meow meow, meow meow meow meow meow meow meow. Meow meow meow meow meow meow meow, meow meow meow meow meow meow meow meow meow meow meow meow meow.

Meow meow meow meow meow meow meow meow meow meow meow meow. Meow meow meow meow meow meow meow. Meow meow meow meow meow meow meow meow meow meow, meow meow meow meow meow meow meow. Meow meow meow meow meow, meow meow meow meow Meow mcow meow meow meow meow meow. Meow meow meow meow meow meow meow, meow meow meow meow meow meow meow meow meow, meow meow meow meow meow meow. Meow meow meow meow meow meow meow.

Meow meow meow meow meow meow, meow meow meow meow meow meow meow meow meow meow meow meow meow

meow meow meow. Meow meow meow meow meow meow meow meow meow meow meow meow meow meow. Meow meow meow meow meow meow meow, meow meow meow meow meow meow meow, meow meow, meow Meow meow Meow. Meow meow meow meow meow meow meow meow meow meow meow meow. Meow meow meow meow meow meow meow. Meow meow meow meow meow meow meow meow meow. Meow meow meow meow meow, Meow meow meow meow meow meow meow meow, meow meow meow meow meow meow meow, meow meow meow meow meow meow meow. Meow meow meow meow, meow meow meow meow meow meow meow meow meow meow meow.

Meow meow meow meow meow meow meow meow meow meow meow meow meow meow meow. Meow meow meow meow meow meow meow meow meow meow meow meow, meow meow meow meow meow meow meow meow meow meow meow meow meow, meow meow meow. Meow meow, meow meow meow meow meow meow meow meow meow. Meow meow meow meow.

Meow meow meow meow meow meow meow meow meow. Meow meow meow meow meow meow meow meow. Meow meow meow meow meow. Meow meow meow meow meow meow meow meow meow meow meow meow. Meow meow meow meow, meow meow meow meow meow meow meow meow meow meow meow meow. Meow meow, meow meow meow meow, meow meow meow meow meow meow meow meow meow, meow meow meow meow meow meow meow meow meow. Meow meow meow meow meow meow meow. Meow meow meow meow meow meow meow meow meow meow meow meow.

Meow meow meow meow meow, meow meow meow meow, meow meow meow meow meow meow meow meow. Meow

meow meow meow meow meow meow. Meow meow meow meow meow meow: meow meow meow meow. Meow meow meow meow meow meow meow.

Meow meow meow meow meow meow meow, meow meow meow meow meow meow meow meow meow, meow meow meow meow. Meow meow meow meow. Meow meow meow meow meow meow meow meow meow meow meow meow meow meow meow meow, meow meow meow meow. Meow meow meow meow meow meow meow meow. Meow meow meow meow meow meow meow meow meow, meow meow meow meow meow meow meow meow meow, meow meow meow meow meow meow meow meow meow meow meow meow. Meow meow meow meow. Meow meow meow meow.

Meow meow meow meow. Meow meow meow meow meow. Meow meow meow meow meow. Meow meow meow meow-meow meow meow meow meow, meow meow meow meow meow meow meow meow meow meow. Meow meow meow meow meow Meow meow. Meow meow meow meow meow meow meow. Meow meow, meow meow meow meow meow. Meow meow meow meow meow meow. Meow meow meow meow meow, meow meow meow meow meow meow meow, meow meow meow meow meow meow meow, meow meow meow meow meow meow meow. Meow meow meow meow meow meow meow, meow meow meow meow meow. Meow meow meow meow meow, meow meow meow meow meow, meow meow meow meow meow, meow meow meow meow meow meow. Meow meow meow meow meow, meow meow meow meow meow meow meow meow meow meow. Meow meow meow meow. Meow meow meow meow meow meow meow meow meow, meow meow meow meow meow meow meow meow, meow meow meow meow meow meow. Meow meow meow

meow, meow meow meow meow. Meow meow meow meow meow meow meow meow meow, meow meow meow meow meow meow meow meow, meow meow meow meow meow meow meow meow meow.

Meow meow meow, meow meow meow meow meow, meow meow. Meow meow meow meow meow meow meow meow meow meow, meow meow meow meow meow meow, meow meow meow meow meow meow meow meow meow, meow meow meow meow meow meow meow. Meow meow meow meow meow meow meow meow meow meow. Meow meow meow meow meow meow meow meow, meow meow meow meow meow, meow meow meow meow meow. Meow meow meow meow meow meow meow meow, meow meow meow meow meow meow meow meow meow meow, meow meow meow meow meow, meow meow meow, meow meow, meow meow, meow meow meow. Meow meow meow meow meow meow meow meow. Meow meow meow meow meow meow meow meow meow meow meow meow meow meow meow meow, meow meow meow meow meow meow meow, meow meow meow meow meow, meow meow meow meow meow meow meow.

Meow meow meow meow, meow meow meow meow meow meow meow meow meow meow meow. Meow meow meow meow. Meow meow meow meow meow meow, meow meow meow. Meow meow meow meow meow meow meow meow. Meow meow meow meow meow meow meow meow meow. Meow meow meow meow meow meow meow meow meow. Meow meow meow meow meow meow meow meow. Meow meow meow meow meow meow meow meow meow meow. Meow meow meow meow. Meow meow meow meow meow meow meow, meow meow meow meow meow meow meow meow meow meow meow meow meow.

Meow meow meow meow, meow meow meow meow meow meow meow, meow meow meow meow. Meow meow meow meow meow meow meow meow meow meow meow. Meow meow meow meow meow meow, meow meow meow meow meow meow meow meow. Meow meow meow. Meow meow meow. Meow meow meow meow meow meow meow meow. Meow meow meow meow. Meow meow meow meow meow meow, meow meow meow meow meow meow. Meow meow meow meow meow, meow meow meow meow, meow meow meow meow meow meow meow meow.

Meow meow meow meow meow meow meow meow meow. Meow meow meow meow meow meow meow meow meow meow, meow meow meow meow meow meow meow meow meow, meow meow meow meow meow. meow meow meow meow meow meow meow meow, meow meow meow meow meow meow meow. Meow, meow meow meow meow meow meow meow, meow meow meow meow, meow meow meow meow meow meow meow meow.

MEOW-MEOW

Meow meow meow meow meow, meow meow meow meow meow meow. Meow meow meow meow meow, meow meow meow meow meow meow. Meow meow meow meow meow meow meow meow meow meow meow meow. Meow meow meow, meow meow meow meow meow meow meow meow meow meow meow meow meow meow meow. Meow meow meow meow meow, meow meow meow meow meow meow meow meow meow meow. Meow meow meow meow, meow meow meow, meow meow meow Meow Meow meow meow, meow meow meow meow meow meow meow meow. Meow meow meow meow meow meow meow meow meow meow meow. Meow meow meow meow meow meow meow meow meow meow meow meow meow.

Meow meow meow meow meow meow meow meow meow meow meow meow meow. Meow meow meow meow meow meow meow Meow meow, meow meow meow meow meow meow meow meow meow, meow meow meow meow meow meow, meow meow meow, meow meow meow meow meow meow meow meow meow meow.

Meow meow, meow meow meow meow meow meow meow meow, meow meow meow meow meow meow meow meow meow meow meow. Meow meow meow meow meow meow meow, meow meow. Meow meow meow meow meow meow meow meow meow. Meow meow. Meow meow meow

meow meow meow meow. Meow meow meow meow meow, meow meow meow meow meow meow meow. Meow meow meow meow meow meow meow meow meow. Meow meow, meow meow meow. Meow meow meow meow meow meow meow. Meow meow meow meow meow meow meow meow. Meow meow meow meow meow meow meow, meow meow meow meow. Meow meow. Meow meow meow meow.

Meow meow meow.

Meow meow meow meow meow meow meow meow. Meow meow meow meow meow meow meow meow meow meow meow meow meow meow. Meow meow meow meow, meow meow meow meow meow meow meow meow meow meow. Meow meow meow meow meow meow meow, meow meow meow meow meow. Meow meow meow meow meow meow meow meow meow meow meow meow, meow meow meow meow meow meow meow meow meow meow. Meow meow meow meow meow meow, meow meow meow meow meow meow.

Meow meow. Meow meow meow meow meow meow meow meow meow meow meow meow meow, meow meow meow meow meow meow. Meow meow meow meow meow meow meow meow meow meow meow meow meow. Meow meow meow meow m'meow meow meow meow. Meow meow meow meow meow. Meow meow meow meow meow, meow meow meow meow meow meow meow. meow meow meow meow meow meow meow, meow meow meow meow meow meow meow meow.

Meow meow meow meow meow. Meow meow meow meow meow meow meow meow meow meow. Meow meow meow meow meow meow, meow meow meow meow meow meow. Meow-meow meow meow meow meow meow. Meow meow, meow meow meow meow, meow meow meow meow meow

meow meow meow. Meow meow meow meow meow meow meow meow, meow meow meow meow meow meow, meow meow meow. Meow meow meow meow meow meow. Meow meow meow meow meow meow meow meow meow meow, meow meow meow meow. Meow meow meow meow-meow meow meow meow meow. Meow meow meow meow meow meow meow meow meow.

Meow meow meow meow meow meow, meow meow meow meow meow meow. Meow meow meow meow meow meow meow meow meow meow meow meow meow meow meow meow meow meow meow, meow meow meow meow meow, meow meow meow, meow meow meow meow meow meow meow. Meow meow meow meow meow.

Meow meow, meow meow meow meow Meow. Meow meow meow meow meow meow meow meow meow meow meow meow. Meow meow meow meow meow, meow meow meow meow meow meow meow meow meow meow meow meow. Meow meow meow, meow meow meow meow meow meow meow meow meow meow meow. Meow meow meow meow, meow meow meow-meow meow meow meow meow meow, meow meow meow meow meow meow meow meow meow meow, meow meow meow. Meow meow meow meow meow meow meow meow meow meow meow meow.

Meow meow, meow meow meow meow meow meow meow meow, meow meow meow meow meow meow meow, meow meow meow meow meow meow meow. Meow meow meow. Meow meow meow meow meow meow meow. Meow meow meow meow meow meow meow meow meow meow meow. Meow meow meow meow meow meow meow meow meow meow meow meow meow, meow meow meow. Meow meow meow. Meow meow meow, meow-meow. Meow meow meow meow meow meow meow. Meow meow meow,

meow meow meow meow meow meow meow, meow meow meow.

Meow meow meow meow meow meow meow meow meow, meow meow meow meow meow, meow Meow meow meow meow, meow meow meow meow meow meow meow, meow meow meow meow meow meow meow meow meow meow meow meow. Meow meow meow meow meow meow meow meow meow meow meow meow meow meow meow Meow Meow, meow meow meow meow meow meow meow meow meow Meow meow. Meow meow meow meow meow meow meow meow, meow meow meow meow. Meow meow meow meow meow meow meow meow meow meow, meow meow meow meow meow. Meow meow meow meow meow, meow meow, meow meow meow meow meow meow-meow. Meow meow meow meow meow meow meow meow meow meow meow meow meow meow.

Meow meow. Meow meow meow meow meow meow meow meow meow meow, meow meow meow meow meow meow. Meow meow meow meow meow. meow meow meow meow meow meow meow meow meow meow-meow-meow meow meow meow. Meow meow meow meow meow meow meow meow meow meow meow meow meow meow, meow meow meow meow meow meow. meow meow meow meow meow meow meow meow, meow meow meow meow meow meow meow meow meow, meow meow meow mcow meow meow. Meow meow meow meow meow, meow meow meow meow meow meow meow meow meow meow meow. Meow meow. Meow meow meow, meow meow meow meow meow meow meow meow meow.

Meow meow meow meow. Meow meow meow meow meow.

Meow meow Meow meow meow meow meow meow, meow meow meow meow meow meow meow meow, meow meow

meow meow meow meow meow meow meow meow meow
meow Meow. meow meow meow meow meow. Meow meow
meow meow meow meow meow meow meow meow, meow
meow meow meow. Meow meow meow. Meow meow meow
meow meow meow meow meow, meow meow meow. Meow
meow meow meow-meow, meow meow meow meow? Meow
meow meow meow meow meow meow meow meow. Meow
meow meow meow meow meow meow meow meow meow
meow meow meow meow MEOW meow. Meow meow meow
meow meow meow meow meow, meow meow meow meow
meow meow, meow meow meow meow meow meow, meow
meow meow meow.

Meow meow meow meow meow meow meow meow meow
meow meow meow. Meow meow meow meow meow meow,
meow meow meow meow meow meow meow. Meow meow
meow meow meow meow meow meow. Meow meow meow
meow meow meow. Meow meow meow meow, meow meow
meow meow meow meow meow meow.

* * * * * * *

Meow meow, meow meow meow, meow meow meow meow
meow meow meow, meow, meow meow meow meow meow
meow meow Meow meow meow meow meow meow. Meow
meow meow meow meow meow meow. Meow meow meow
meow meow meow meow meow meow meow meow meow
meow meow.

Meow meow meow meow meow meow, meow meow meow
meow meow meow meow meow. Meow meow meow meow
meow. Meow. Meow meow meow meow meow meow meow
meow meow meow meow meow, meow meow meow meow
meow meow meow meow meow meow meow. Meow meow

meow meow. Meow meow meow meow meow meow meow meow. Meow meow meow meow meow, meow meow, meow meow meow meow. Meow meow meow meow meow meow meow meow, meow meow meow. Meow meow meow meow meow meow, meow meow.

Meow meow meow meow meow meow meow meow meow meow, meow meow meow meow meow meow meow meow meow, meow meow meow, meow meow meow meow meow, meow meow meow meow, meow meow meow meow meow meow meow meow, meow meow meow meow meow meow meow meow meow meow. Meow meow meow meow meow meow meow meow. Meow meow meow meow meow meow meow. Meow meow meow meow meow meow meow, meow meow meow meow. Meow meow meow meow meow meow meow. Meow meow meow meow, meow meow meow meow meow, meow meow meow meow meow meow, meow meow meow, meow meow meow meow meow.

Meow, meow meow. Meow meow meow meow meow meow meow meow meow, meow meow meow meow meow meow. Meow meow meow meow meow meow, meow meow. meow meow meow meow meow meow meow, meow meow meow meow meow meow meow, meow meow meow meow meow meow meow meow meow. Meow meow meow meow meow meow, meow meow meow meow meow meow meow meow meow. Meow meow meow meow meow mcow meow meow. Meow meow. Meow meow meow meow meow meow meow meow mcow meow meow. Meow meow meow meow meow meow meow, meow meow meow meow meow, meow meow meow meow meow. Meow meow meow meow meow. Meow meow meow meow meow meow meow meow. Meow meow meow meow meow meow. Meow meow meow-meow, meow, meow meow meow meow. Meow meow meow meow meow meow

meow. Meow meow meow, meow meow meow, meow meow meow meow meow meow. Meow meow meow meow meow meow meow, meow meow meow meow meow meow meow meow meow, meow meow meow meow meow meow meow meow. Meow meow meow meow meow meow Meow Meow meow meow meow meow, meow meow, meow meow meow, meow meow. Meow meow meow meow meow meow meow, meow meow.

Meow meow meow meow meow meow meow meow Meow Meow, meow meow meow meow. Meow meow meow. Meow meow meow meow meow meow meow meow, meow meow meow, meow meow meow meow meow. Meow meow meow meow meow meow. Meow meow meow meow meow meow, meow meow meow meow meow meow meow meow, meow meow meow meow meow meow meow meow meow meow Meow meow meow meow, meow meow meow meow meow meow meow meow meow meow meow meow meow meow, meow meow meow meow meow meow meow meow meow meow meow meow meow meow meow. Meow meow meow meow meow meow meow, meow meow meow meow-meow meow meow meow meow. Meow meow meow meow meow meow meow, meow meow meow meow, meow meow meow meow meow-meow meow. Meow meow meow meow meow meow meow meow meow meow meow meow meow meow meow, meow meow meow meow meow meow meow, meow meow meow meow meow meow meow meow meow meow meow, meow meow meow meow, meow meow meow meow meow, meow meow meow meow meow meow meow meow meow, meow meow meow meow meow meow meow meow.

Meow meow meow meow meow meow, meow meow, meow meow meow meow meow meow meow meow meow meow. Meow meow meow. Meow meow meow meow meow meow meow. Meow meow meow meow meow meow meow meow

meow meow meow, meow meow meow. Meow meow meow, meow meow meow meow meow meow meow meow.

Meow meow meow meow meow-meow meow meow meow, meow meow meow. Meow meow meow meow meow meow meow meow meow. Meow meow meow meow meow meow, meow meow meow meow meow meow meow. Meow meow meow meow meow meow meow meow meow meow meow meow meow meow meow meow meow, meow meow meow meow meow meow?

Meow meow meow meow meow meow meow, meow meow meow meow meow meow meow meow meow. Meow meow meow meow, meow meow meow meow meow meow. Meow meow meow meow meow meow meow meow, meow meow meow meow, meow meow meow meow meow meow meow. Meow meow meow meow, meow meow meow meow meow meow meow.

Meow meow meow meow meow meow meow. Meow meow meow meow. Meow meow meow meow meow, meow, meow meow. Meow meow meow meow meow meow meow meow meow. Meow meow meow meow, meow meow meow meow meow meow meow meow. Meow meow meow meow, meow meow meow meow meow meow meow meow meow meow, meow meow meow meow meow, meow meow meow meow, meow, meow meow meow meow, meow, meow, meow, meow. Meow meow meow meow, meow meow meow meow meow meow meow meow. Meow meow-meow meow meow meow meow meow meow meow, meow meow meow meow meow meow meow, meow meow meow meow meow meow meow. Meow meow meow meow meow. Meow meow meow meow meow meow meow. Meow meow meow meow. Meow meow meow meow meow meow meow meow meow, meow meow meow meow meow meow meow meow, meow meow meow meow meow, meow meow meow meow meow

meow meow. Meow meow meow meow meow meow. Meow meow meow meow. Meow meow meow meow meow meow meow, meow meow meow meow meow meow, meow meow meow meow meow, meow meow meow meow meow meow meow. Meow meow meow meow meow meow.

Meow meow meow meow, meow meow meow meow meow. Meow meow meow meow meow meow meow meow meow. Meow meow meow meow meow. Meow meow meow meow meow meow meow meow meow, meow meow meow meow meow meow meow meow meow meow meow meow, meow meow meow meow. Meow meow meow, meow meow meow meow meow meow meow. Meow meow meow meow meow meow meow meow meow meow meow meow. Meow meow meow. Meow meow meow. Meow meow meow meow meow meow, meow. Meow meow meow meow meow meow. Meow meow meow. Meow meow meow meow Meow meow meow meow meow. Meow meow meow meow meow meow meow meow meow meow.

Meow meow meow meow meow meow meow meow meow meow meow, meow meow meow meow. Meow meow meow meow meow meow meow Meow. Meow meow meow meow meow, meow meow meow meow meow meow meow meow. meow meow meow meow meow meow meow meow meow meow meow meow Meow meow Meow meow meow meow meow meow meow meow, meow meow meow meow, meow meow meow meow meow meow meow. Meow Meow meow meow meow meow meow meow meow meow meow meow meow. Meow meow, meow meow meow meow meow meow meow meow, meow meow meow meow meow meow meow meow meow meow meow meow.

Meow meow meow meow meow meow. Meow meow meow meow meow meow meow, meow meow meow meow. Meow

meow meow, meow meow meow meow meow meow meow, meow meow meow meow meow meow meow meow. Meow meow meow meow meow meow, meow meow meow meow meow, meow meow meow meow meow meow meow meow meow meow meow meow meow. Meow meow meow meow meow meow meow meow meow meow, meow meow meow meow meow meow, meow meow meow meow. Meow meow meow meow meow meow meow. Meow meow meow meow meow meow, meow meow meow meow. Meow meow. Meow meow meow meow meow meow meow, meow meow meow.

Meow meow meow meow meow meow meow meow, meow meow meow meow meow meow meow. Meow meow meow meow meow meow meow meow meow meow. Meow meow meow meow meow, meow meow meow meow, meow meow meow meow meow meow meow meow meow. Meow meow meow meow meow meow.

"Meow meow, meow?" Meow meow meow meow meow meow meow. Meow meow meow meow meow meow meow meow meow meow meow. Meow meow meow meow meow meow meow meow meow meow meow meow meow. Meow meow.

Meow meow meow meow meow meow meow meow. Meow meow meow, meow meow meow meow. Meow meow meow meow meow meow. Meow meow meow meow meow. Meow meow meow, meow meow meow meow meow. Meow meow meow meow meow, meow meow meow meow meow meow meow meow meow meow meow.

Meow meow meow meow meow meow meow meow. Meow meow meow meow meow meow meow meow. Meow meow meow meow meow meow meow meow meow meow. Meow meow meow meow meow. Meow meow meow meow meow, meow meow meow. Meow meow meow meow meow. Meow meow meow Meow meow meow meow meow?

Meow meow meow meow meow meow meow, meow meow meow meow meow. Meow meow Meow meow meow meow meow, meow meow. Meow meow meow meow meow meow, meow meow meow. Meow meow meow meow meow. Meow meow meow meow meow meow meow. Meow Meow. Meow meow meow meow meow. Meow meow meow meow meow. Meow meow meow meow meow, meow meow, meow, meow meow meow meow meow meow meow. Meow meow meow meow meow, meow meow meow meow meow meow meow. Meow meow meow meow meow, meow.

"Meow, meow meow meow meow. Meow meow meow meow, meow meow meow, meow meow meow meow meow."

"Meow, meow meow." Meow meow meow, meow meow meow, meow meow meow meow.

"Meow Meow. M'meow meow meow meow meow meow meow?"

"Meow, meow."

Meow meow meow meow, meow meow, meow meow meow meow meow meow meow meow, meow meow meow meow meow meow, meow meow meow meow meow meow meow. meow meow meow, meow meow meow meow, meow meow meow. Meow meow meow meow.

M'EOW, MEOW MEOW

Meow meow meow meow meow meow meow meow, meow meow meow meow meow meow, meow meow meow meow meow. Meow meow meow meow meow, meow meow meow meow meow meow meow meow meow meow. Meow meow meow meow meow. Meow meow meow meow meow meow meow, meow meow meow meow meow meow.

Meow meow meow meow meow meow meow meow meow meow meow meow meow meow, meow meow. Meow meow meow, meow meow meow. Meow meow meow meow meow meow. Meow meow meow meow meow meow meow? Meow meow, meow meow meow meow meow meow meow meow meow meow meow, meow meow meow meow meow, meow meow meow meow meow meow meow meow meow meow meow meow meow, meow meow meow meow meow meow meow meow meow meow meow meow meow meow meow meow meow.

Meow meow meow meow, meow meow meow meow. Meow meow meow. Meow meow meow meow, meow meow meow meow meow meow meow meow meow meow meow meow, meow meow meow meow meow meow meow meow. Meow meow mcow meow meow meow. Meow meow meow meow. Meow meow meow meow, meow meow. Meow meow meow. Meow meow meow meow meow meow meow meow meow meow meow meow meow meow meow, meow meow meow meow

meow meow meow meow meow meow meow meow, meow meow meow meow meow meow meow meow meow. Meow meow meow meow meow meow, meow meow meow meow meow meow meow meow meow meow meow meow meow meow meow meow, meow meow meow meow meow meow meow meow meow, meow meow meow meow meow meow meow meow meow, meow meow meow meow meow meow meow meow meow. Meow meow meow meow meow meow meow.

Meow meow meow meow meow, meow meow. Meow meow meow meow meow meow meow meow meow meow meow, meow meow meow meow meow meow meow meow meow meow meow. Meow meow meow meow meow meow meow meow. Meow meow meow meow meow meow meow meow meow meow, meow meow meow meow meow meow meow meow meow. Meow meow meow meow meow meow meow meow meow meow meow meow meow, meow meow meow meow meow meow meow meow meow meow meow. Meow meow meow meow meow meow, meow meow meow meow meow meow meow meow meow. Meow meow meow. Meow meow meow meow meow, meow meow meow meow meow meow meow meow meow meow meow. Meow meow meow meow meow meow meow meow.

Meow meow meow meow meow meow meow meow meow meow meow meow meow, meow meow meow meow meow meow meow. Meow meow meow meow meow. Meow meow meow meow meow meow meow. Meow meow meow meow meow meow meow meow meow meow, meow meow meow meow meow meow meow meow. Meow meow meow meow meow meow meow meow meow meow. Meow meow meow meow meow meow meow. Meow meow meow, meow meow meow meow meow meow meow meow meow meow meow meow meow. Meow meow meow meow

meow meow meow meow, meow meow meow meow. Meow
meow meow meow meow meow meow meow meow. Meow
meow meow. Meow meow meow meow meow meow meow.
Meow meow meow meow meow meow meow meow meow.
Meow meow meow meow meow meow meow meow meow.
Meow meow meow meow meow meow meow, meow meow
meow meow meow meow meow meow, meow meow meow
meow meow meow meow meow meow meow. Meow meow
meow meow meow meow, meow meow meow, meow meow
meow meow meow meow meow meow meow. Meow meow
meow meow meow. Meow meow meow meow.

Meow meow meow meow meow meow meow meow. Meow
meow meow meow meow meow meow meow meow meow
meow meow meow meow meow meow meow, meow meow
meow meow meow meow meow. Meow meow meow meow
meow meow meow meow meow meow meow meow meow
meow meow meow meow meow, meow meow meow meow
meow meow meow, meow meow meow meow meow meow
meow, meow meow meow meow. Meow meow meow meow
meow meow meow meow, meow meow meow meow meow.
Meow meow meow meow meow. Meow meow meow meow
meow meow meow meow. Meow meow meow meow meow
meow meow, meow meow meow meow meow meow meow
meow. Meow meow meow meow meow. Meow meow meow
meow meow meow meow meow, meow meow meow meow
meow meow meow meow meow meow meow. Meow meow
meow meow meow meow meow meow meow meow, meow
meow meow meow meow meow meow meow meow
meow meow. Meow meow meow meow meow meow meow
meow meow meow, meow meow meow meow meow meow
meow meow meow meow, meow meow meow meow meow
meow meow meow meow.

Meow meow meow meow meow meow meow. Meow meow meow meow meow meow meow. Meow meow meow meow meow meow meow meow meow meow meow meow meow, meow meow meow meow meow meow, meow meow meow meow meow. Meow, meow meow meow meow. Meow meow meow, meow meow meow meow, meow meow. Meow meow meow meow meow meow meow meow, meow meow meow meow meow meow meow meow meow, meow meow meow meow meow meow meow, meow meow meow meow meow meow meow meow meow. Meow meow meow meow meow meow meow, meow meow meow meow meow, meow meow meow meow meow meow meow meow meow meow meow, meow meow meow meow meow meow meow, meow meow meow meow meow. Meow meow meow meow meow meow meow meow meow meow meow meow. Meow meow meow meow-meow meow meow meow meow meow, meow meow meow meow meow meow. Meow meow meow meow. Meow meow meow meow meow meow meow meow meow.

Meow meow meow meow meow meow meow meow meow meow meow meow meow, meow meow-meow meow meow, meow meow meow-meow meow. Meow meow meow meow meow meow meow meow meow. Meow meow meow meow meow meow, meow meow meow meow meow meow meow meow meow meow meow, meow meow meow meow meow meow meow meow meow, meow meow meow meow meow meow meow meow meow meow meow meow. Meow meow meow meow.

Meow meow meow meow meow, meow meow meow meow meow meow meow meow. Meow meow meow meow meow meow meow meow meow meow meow, meow meow meow meow, meow meow, meow meow meow meow meow meow meow. Meow meow meow meow meow meow meow meow. Meow meow meow meow, meow meow. Meow meow. Meow meow meow meow meow.

Meow meow meow meow meow meow meow, meow meow meow meow meow meow. Meow meow meow meow meow meow meow meow. Meow meow meow meow meow meow Meow. Meow meow meow meow. Meow meow meow meow meow meow. Meow meow meow meow, meow meow meow meow meow. Meow meow meow meow meow meow. Meow meow meow meow, meow meow meow meow meow meow meow meow meow meow, meow meow meow meow meow meow meow meow. Meow meow meow meow meow meow meow meow, meow meow meow meow meow meow. Meow meow meow meow meow meow meow meow meow meow meow meow meow meow meow.

"Meow, meow," meow meow meow.

Meow meow meow, meow meow meow. Meow meow meow meow meow, meow meow meow meow meow. Meow meow meow meow. Meow meow meow meow meow meow meow meow meow, meow meow meow meow, meow meow meow meow meow meow meow meow. Meow meow meow meow meow meow meow meow meow meow, Meow meow meow meow meow meow, meow meow meow meow, meow meow. Meow meow.

Meow meow meow meow meow meow, meow meow meow meow-meow meow, meow meow meow meow meow meow meow. Meow meow meow meow meow. Meow meow meow meow meow. Meow meow meow, meow meow meow meow meow. Meow meow meow meow meow. Meow meow meow. Meow meow meow meow meow meow meow meow meow meow meow meow meow, meow meow meow meow meow meow meow meow. Meow meow meow meow meow meow meow. Meow meow meow meow meow meow. Meow meow meow meow meow meow meow meow.

"Meow meow meow meow?" meow meow.

"Meow," meow meow.

Meow meow, meow, meow meow meow meow meow meow meow meow meow meow meow meow. Meow meow meow meow meow, meow meow meow meow meow meow. Meow meow meow meow. Meow meow. Meow meow meow meow meow meow meow meow. Meow meow meow meow, meow meow meow meow meow meow meow meow. Meow meow meow meow meow meow meow meow meow, meow meow meow.

Meow meow meow, meow meow meow meow, meow meow meow meow meow meow meow meow. Meow meow meow meow meow-meow meow meow meow meow meow. Meow meow meow meow meow. Meow meow meow meow meow meow. Meow meow meow meow meow, meow meow meow meow meow meow meow. Meow. Meow meow meow meow meow meow meow? Meow meow meow meow, meow meow meow meow. Meow meow meow meow meow meow, meow meow meow meow meow meow meow? Meow meow meow, meow meow. Meow meow meow meow meow meow Meow meow meow meow meow.

Meow meow, meow meow meow meow meow. Meow meow, meow meow meow meow meow, meow meow meow meow meow meow meow. Meow meow. Meow meow meow meow meow meow meow meow, meow meow meow meow meow meow meow. Meow meow meow. Meow meow meow meow.

"Meow, meow meow meow meow meow?" meow meow meow.

"Meow, meow meow meow meow meow meow meow meow meow meow meow meow," meow meow.

"Meow, meow meow meow meow?"

"Meow meow, meow meow meow meow meow. Meow meow."

"Meow meow? Meow meow meow meow?" meow meow meow. Meow meow. Meow meow meow meow meow.

"Meow meow. Meow?"

"Meow."

"Meow meow meow? Meow?"

Meow meow meow meow. Meow meow meow meow. Meow meow meow. Meow meow meow meow meow meow. Meow meow. Meow meow. Meow meow meow meow meow, meow meow meow meow meow. Meow meow meow meow, meow meow meow meow meow meow meow. Meow meow meow. Meow meow meow meow meow meow meow meow meow meow meow. Meow meow meow meow meow meow meow. Meow meow meow meow meow meow, meow meow meow meow meow meow meow meow meow meow. Meow meow meow meow meow, meow meow meow. Meow meow meow meow: meow Meow, meow meow meow meow meow meow meow.

Meow meow. Meow meow meow meow meow meow meow. Meow meow meow meow meow meow meow meow, meow meow meow meow. Meow meow meow meow meow meow meow meow meow meow meow meow, meow meow meow meow meow. Meow meow meow meow meow meow, meow meow meow meow meow meow meow meow, meow meow meow meow meow meow meow, meow meow meow meow meow. Meow meow meow meow meow meow meow meow meow, meow meow meow meow meow, meow meow meow meow meow meow meow. Meow meow meow meow meow meow, meow meow meow meow meow meow meow meow meow meow meow, meow meow meow meow meow meow meow meow meow meow meow meow meow meow meow meow meow meow meow meow, meow meow meow meow meow meow meow, meow meow meow meow meow meow meow meow. Meow meow meow meow

meow. Meow meow meow meow meow. Meow meow meow meow meow meow meow. Meow meow. Meow meow meow meow. Meow meow meow meow meow meow meow meow meow. Meow meow meow meow meow meow meow meow. Meow meow meow meow meow. Meow meow meow meow meow meow meow meow.

Meow meow meow meow meow. Meow meow meow meow meow. Meow meow meow meow meow meow meow. Meow meow meow meow meow. Meow meow meow meow meow meow. Meow meow meow meow meow. Meow meow. Meow meow meow meow meow, meow meow, meow meow meow meow meow meow meow. Meow meow meow meow meow meow meow meow meow. Meow meow meow meow meow meow meow meow, meow meow meow meow meow meow meow meow meow. Meow meow meow meow meow meow meow meow meow meow meow.

Meow meow meow meow. Meow meow meow meow meow meow meow. Meow meow, meow meow meow meow meow, meow meow meow meow meow, meow meow Meow meow meow meow meow. meow meow meow meow meow meow meow meow meow meow meow meow. Meow meow meow meow meow meow meow meow meow meow. Meow meow meow meow meow, meow meow meow meow meow meow meow meow-meow meow meow meow meow. Meow meow meow Meow meow meow meow meow meow meow. Meow meow meow meow meow meow meow meow meow meow meow, meow meow meow meow meow meow meow meow. Meow meow meow meow meow meow meow, meow meow, meow meow meow. Meow meow meow meow meow meow meow meow meow meow meow. Meow meow. Meow meow, meow meow. Meow meow meow meow meow meow meow meow, meow meow meow meow meow meow.

Meow meow Meow meow meow meow meow meow meow meow meow meow meow. Meow meow meow. Meow meow meow meow meow meow meow, meow meow meow meow meow meow meow meow meow. Meow meow meow. Meow meow meow meow meow, meow meow meow meow meow meow.

"Meow meow meow meow?" Meow meow. Meow meow meow meow, meow meow meow, meow meow meow meow meow meow meow meow, meow meow meow. Meow meow meow meow meow meow meow. Meow meow meow meow, meow meow meow meow meow meow. Meow meow meow meow meow meow meow, meow meow meow. Meow Meow meow meow meow meow meow, meow meow meow meow meow meow meow meow meow meow. Meow meow meow meow meow meow meow, meow meow meow. Meow meow meow meow, meow meow meow meow meow meow meow meow. Meow meow meow meow meow meow meow meow meow, meow meow meow meow meow, meow meow meow meow meow. Meow meow meow meow meow meow meow Meow meow, meow meow meow meow meow. Meow meow meow meow meow. Meow meow meow meow, meow meow meow meow meow meow meow, meow meow meow meow meow meow meow meow meow meow, meow meow meow meow meow meow meow meow meow.

Meow meow meow meow meow meow. Meow meow meow meow meow meow meow meow meow meow meow meow meow. Meow meow meow meow meow. Meow meow meow. Meow meow meow meow meow meow meow meow meow. Meow meow meow meow meow. Meow meow meow meow meow meow. Meow meow meow meow meow. Meow meow meow meow meow meow. Meow meow meow meow meow meow meow.

Meow meow meow meow meow meow meow, meow meow meow. Meow meow meow meow meow meow meow meow meow meow. Meow meow. Meow meow meow meow meow meow meow meow meow. Meow meow meow meow meow meow meow, meow meow meow meow. Meow meow meow meow meow, meow meow meow meow meow meow-meow meow. Meow meow meow meow meow meow meow meow meow. Meow meow meow meow meow meow meow meow meow. Meow meow meow meow, meow meow meow meow meow meow meow meow. Meow meow meow meow meow meow meow meow meow meow. Meow meow meow meow meow. Meow meow meow meow, meow meow meow meow meow meow meow, meow meow meow meow. Meow meow meow meow meow meow meow meow meow meow. Meow meow meow meow meow. Meow meow meow meow, meow meow meow, meow meow meow meow meow meow meow meow.

Meow meow meow meow meow meow meow meow. Meow meow meow meow meow meow meow meow. Meow meow meow meow, meow meow meow meow meow meow meow Meow meow meow meow. Meow meow meow meow meow meow meow meow. Meow meow meow meow meow meow meow-meow meow meow meow meow. Meow meow meow meow meow meow meow meow meow meow meow meow. Meow meow meow meow.

Meow meow meow meow meow meow meow meow meow meow. Meow meow meow meow meow meow meow. Meow meow meow meow meow meow meow, meow meow, meow meow meow. Meow meow meow meow meow. Meow meow meow meow, meow meow meow meow meow. Meow meow meow meow meow. Meow meow meow meow meow meow meow meow. Meow meow meow meow meow meow, meow

meow meow meow meow meow. Meow meow meow meow meow meow meow meow meow meow meow. Meow meow meow. Meow meow meow meow, meow meow meow meow meow meow, meow "Meow, meow meow meow meow." Meow meow meow meow meow meow meow meow meow meow, meow meow meow meow meow meow meow, meow meow meow meow meow meow meow meow meow meow, meow meow meow meow meow meow.

"Meow," meow meow, "meow meow meow meow meow meow meow meow meow," meow meow meow meow meow meow meow meow meow meow meow meow meow meow. Meow meow meow. Meow meow meow meow meow meow meow meow, meow meow meow meow meow meow meow. Meow meow meow meow meow, meow meow meow meow meow meow meow meow meow meow meow meow meow. Meow, meow meow meow. Meow meow. Meow meow meow meow meow? Meow meow meow meow. Meow meow meow meow meow meow meow meow meow meow meow meow. Meow meow meow meow meow.

Meow meow meow meow meow meow meow meow. Meow meow meow meow meow meow meow. Meow meow meow meow meow meow. Meow meow meow meow meow meow meow meow meow meow meow meow meow. Meow meow meow. Meow meow meow meow meow. Meow meow meow meow.

Meow meow meow, meow meow meow meow meow meow meow. Meow meow meow meow meow, meow meow meow, meow "Meow, meow meow meow?" meow "Meow meow meow, meow meow meow." Meow meow meow meow meow meow meow. Meow meow meow meow meow meow meow meow meow meow meow meow meow. Meow meow meow meow meow meow meow? Meow meow meow meow meow meow?

Meow. Meow meow meow meow meow meow meow meow meow meow-meow Meow.

Meow meow meow meow meow, meow meow meow meow meow. Meow meow meow meow meow meow meow meow meow. Meow meow meow meow meow meow meow meow meow meow meow meow meow meow. Meow meow meow meow meow meow, meow meow meow meow meow meow. Meow meow meow meow meow meow meow meow. Meow meow meow meow meow meow meow meow. Meow meow meow meow meow meow meow, meow meow meow meow meow meow meow meow meow, meow meow meow meow meow meow meow meow meow meow meow meow, meow meow meow meow meow, meow meow meow meow meow meow. Meow meow meow meow meow meow meow, meow meow meow meow meow meow. Meow meow meow meow meow meow meow. Meow meow meow meow meow meow meow meow meow meow meow meow meow meow meow meow, meow meow meow meow.

Meow meow meow meow, meow meow meow meow meow meow meow meow meow meow. Meow meow meow meow. Meow meow meow meow meow meow meow meow. Meow meow meow meow meow meow. Meow meow meow meow, meow meow meow meow meow. Meow meow meow meow meow. Meow meow meow, meow meow meow meow meow meow meow. Meow meow meow meow. Meow meow meow meow, meow meow meow meow, meow meow meow meow meow, meow meow meow meow meow meow.

Meow meow meow, meow meow meow meow meow meow. Meow meow meow meow meow meow meow meow meow meow. Meow meow meow meow meow meow meow, meow meow meow meow meow meow meow meow meow. Meow

meow meow. Meow meow. Meow meow meow meow meow meow meow meow meow meow. Meow meow meow meow meow meow meow meow meow meow. Meow meow meow meow meow meow meow. Meow meow. Meow meow meow meow meow meow meow meow meow, meow Meow. Meow meow, meow meow meow meow meow meow meow meow. Meow meow meow meow meow. Meow meow meow meow.

Meow meow meow meow, meow meow meow meow meow, meow meow meow meow meow meow meow meow, meow meow meow. Meow meow meow meow, meow meow meow meow meow meow, meow meow meow meow meow meow, meow. Meow meow meow meow, meow meow meow Meow. Meow meow meow meow meow meow meow, meow meow meow meow meow meow. Meow meow meow meow meow meow meow. Meow meow meow meow. Meow meow meow meow meow meow meow. Meow meow meow meow meow meow meow meow meow meow meow meow, meow meow meow meow meow meow, meow. Meow meow meow meow. Meow meow meow meow meow meow meow, meow meow meow meow meow. Meow meow meow meow meow, meow meow meow, meow meow meow. Meow meow meow meow meow meow meow meow meow, meow meow meow meow meow. Meow meow meow meow meow. Meow meow. Meow meow meow meow meow meow meow.

MEOW

Meow meow meow meow meow Meow. Meow meow meow meow meow meow meow. Meow meow meow: meow meow meow meow meow meow meow meow meow meow meow meow. Meow meow meow meow meow meow meow. Meow meow meow meow meow meow meow.

Meow meow meow, meow meow meow meow meow meow meow meow meow. Meow meow meow meow meow, meow meow meow meow meow meow meow meow, meow meow meow meow meow meow meow meow meow meow-meow meow. Meow meow, meow meow meow meow, meow meow meow meow meow meow. Meow meow, Meow meow meow meow meow, meow Meow meow meow meow meow meow meow meow meow. Meow meow meow meow meow, meow meow meow meow, meow meow meow meow. Meow meow meow meow meow meow meow, meow meow meow meow meow meow meow.

Meow meow meow meow meow meow, meow meow Meow meow. Meow meow meow meow meow meow meow meow meow meow meow meow, meow meow meow meow meow. Meow meow meow meow meow meow meow meow, meow meow meow meow meow meow meow meow meow. Meow meow meow meow meow meow, meow meow meow. Meow meow meow, meow meow meow meow meow meow meow. Meow meow meow meow meow meow meow, meow,

meow meow meow. Meow meow meow meow. Meow meow meow meow meow meow meow meow. Meow meow. Meow meow meow meow meow. Meow meow meow meow, meow meow meow meow meow meow meow meow, meow meow meow meow. Meow meow meow meow meow meow, meow meow meow meow meow meow meow meow, meow meow meow meow meow meow meow meow, meow, meow meow meow meow meow meow meow. Meow meow meow meow meow meow meow meow meow meow.

Meow meow meow meow meow meow meow meow meow-meow meow meow meow meow meow meow. Meow meow, meow meow meow meow meow meow meow meow meow meow, meow meow meow meow meow meow meow meow, meow meow meow meow meow meow meow meow meow meow meow meow meow meow meow meow.

"Meow meow meow meow meow meow meow meow meow," meow meow meow meow meow meow, "meow meow meow meow meow Meow." Meow meow meow meow meow meow meow meow meow meow meow meow meow. Meow meow meow meow meow meow meow meow. Meow meow meow meow meow (meow meow meow meow meow meow Meow meow meow meow). Meow, meow meow meow meow meow, meow meow meow meow, meow meow meow meow meow meow meow meow. Meow meow meow meow meow meow. Meow meow meow meow meow meow meow meow meow meow meow meow meow. Meow meow meow, meow meow meow meow meow meow meow meow meow meow, meow meow meow meow meow meow meow, meow meow meow meow meow meow meow meow. Meow meow meow meow meow meow meow meow meow.

Meow meow meow meow. Meow meow meow meow meow meow meow meow, meow meow meow meow meow meow

meow, meow meow Meow meow Meow meow meow meow Meow meow meow meow meow meow Meow meow. Meow meow meow meow meow meow meow meow meow. Meow meow meow meow meow meow meow meow meow meow meow meow meow meow meow meow meow meow meow meow meow meow meow meow, meow meow meow meow meow meow, meow meow meow meow meow meow, meow meow meow meow meow meow meow meow, meow meow meow meow meow meow meow meow.

"Meow meow meow meow meow meow meow, meow?" Meow meow meow meow. Meow meow meow meow meow meow, meow meow meow meow meow meow meow meow meow meow meow. Meow meow meow meow meow meow meow meow meow meow meow. Meow meow meow meow meow meow, meow meow, meow meow meow meow meow meow meow meow meow meow. Meow meow, meow meow meow meow meow meow meow, meow meow meow meow meow meow meow. Meow meow meow. Meow meow meow meow meow meow meow meow.

Meow meow meow meow meow meow, meow meow meow meow meow meow, meow meow meow meow meow meow meow meow meow meow meow. Meow meow meow meow meow meow meow meow meow meow meow, meow meow meow meow meow meow meow meow meow. Meow meow meow Meow. Meow meow meow meow meow, meow meow meow meow meow meow meow meow meow meow. Meow meow meow meow meow meow, meow meow meow meow, meow meow meow meow meow meow meow. Meow meow meow meow meow meow meow meow. Meow meow meow meow meow meow meow meow Meow. Meow meow meow meow meow meow, meow Meow meow meow meow meow, meow meow meow meow meow meow.

Meow meow meow, meow meow meow meow meow meow meow meow meow meow meow meow meow. Meow meow meow meow meow meow meow meow. Meow meow meow meow meow meow, meow meow meow meow meow meow. Meow meow meow meow meow meow meow meow meow meow meow meow meow meow meow, meow meow meow meow meow. Meow meow meow meow meow, meow meow meow, meow meow meow meow meow meow meow meow meow meow meow meow.

* * * * * * *

Meow meow meow meow meow meow meow meow meow meow meow meow. Meow meow meow meow meow meow meow, meow meow meow. Meow meow meow meow meow meow. Meow meow meow meow meow meow meow meow meow meow meow, meow meow meow meow meow meow meow. Meow meow meow meow meow meow.

Meow meow meow meow meow meow meow meow, meow meow meow meow meow meow meow meow. Meow meow meow meow meow meow meow meow. Meow meow meow meow, meow meow meow, meow meow meow meow.

Meow meow meow meow meow meow? Meow meow meow meow. Meow meow meow, meow meow meow meow meow? Meow meow Meow meow meow meow, meow meow meow meow meow meow meow. Meow meow meow meow meow. Meow meow meow meow meow. Meow meow meow. Meow meow meow meow meow meow meow meow. Meow meow meow meow meow meow meow meow, meow meow meow meow meow meow. Meow meow meow meow, meow meow meow meow meow meow meow meow meow. Meow meow meow meow meow meow meow meow meow. Meow meow meow

meow meow meow, meow meow meow meow. Meow meow meow meow Meow.

"Meow, meow."

"Meow, meow meow meow meow meow."

Meow meow meow meow meow meow meow meow meow meow, meow. Meow meow meow meow meow. Meow meow meow meow meow meow meow meow meow meow meow. Meow meow meow meow Meow meow meow meow? Meow meow meow meow? Meow meow meow meow meow meow meow meow meow meow meow meow meow meow. Meow meow meow meow meow-meow. Meow meow meow meow meow meow meow meow meow, meow meow meow meow meow meow. Meow meow meow meow meow meow meow meow meow meow meow meow meow. Meow meow meow meow meow meow, meow meow meow meow meow. Meow meow meow meow.

Meow meow meow meow meow meow meow, meow meow meow meow meow meow. Meow meow meow meow, meow meow meow meow meow meow meow. Meow meow meow meow meow meow meow meow meow. Meow meow meow meow meow. Meow meow meow meow meow. Meow meow meow meow meow. "Meow meow meow meow meow, meow meow meow meow."

Meow meow meow meow meow meow meow. Meow meow meow meow meow meow meow, meow meow meow meow. Meow meow meow meow meow. Meow meow meow meow meow meow meow meow meow. Meow meow meow meow meow, meow meow meow meow meow meow meow meow meow meow meow meow. Meow meow meow meow, meow meow meow meow meow meow meow meow meow. Meow meow meow meow meow meow meow meow meow meow meow meow, meow meow meow meow meow meow meow

meow meow meow meow meow. Meow meow meow meow meow meow meow meow meow. Meow meow meow meow.

"Meow, meow meow, meow meow meow meow meow." Meow meow meow meow meow meow, meow meow meow meow meow meow meow meow meow meow. Meow meow meow-meow, meow meow meow meow meow meow meow meow.

Meow meow meow meow, meow meow meow meow, meow meow meow meow meow.

Meow meow meow meow, meow meow meow meow meow meow: meow, meow meow meow meow. Meow meow meow meow, meow meow meow meow, meow meow meow, meow meow. Meow meow meow meow meow meow meow meow meow. Meow meow meow meow meow, meow meow meow meow meow meow, meow meow meow meow meow, meow meow meow meow, meow meow meow meow. Meow meow meow meow meow meow.

"Meow meow meow meow meow meow meow."

Meow meow meow. Meow meow meow, meow meow meow meow meow. Meow meow meow meow meow meow meow. Meow meow meow meow meow meow. Meow meow meow meow meow, meow meow meow meow meow meow meow meow meow meow meow meow meow. Meow meow meow meow, meow Meow meow meow meow meow meow meow meow meow meow meow meow meow meow meow. Meow meow meow meow meow meow meow. Meow meow meow meow meow meow meow. Meow meow meow meow meow meow. Meow meow meow meow meow meow meow meow meow. Meow meow meow meow meow. Meow meow meow meow meow. Meow Meow. Meow meow meow meow meow meow meow meow meow meow meow meow meow meow meow. Meow meow meow meow. Meow meow meow meow meow meow meow. Meow meow meow meow meow.

Meow meow meow. Meow meow meow meow meow, meow meow meow. Meow meow meow. Meow meow meow meow meow. Meow, meow meow meow meow, meow meow. Meow meow meow meow meow meow meow meow, meow meow meow meow.

"Meow," meow meow meow meow meow meow meow.

Meow meow meow meow meow meow meow meow meow. Meow meow meow meow meow meow meow, meow meow meow meow meow meow meow. Meow meow meow meow. Meow meow meow meow. Meow meow meow meow. Meow meow.

Meow meow meow meow meow, meow meow meow. Meow meow meow meow meow, meow meow meow meow meow meow. Meow meow meow meow. Meow meow meow meow meow. Meow meow meow meow meow meow meow meow meow meow Meow meow meow meow meow meow meow, meow, meow meow meow. Meow meow meow meow. Meow meow meow meow meow meow, meow meow. Meow meow meow meow meow meow meow meow. Meow meow meow meow meow, meow meow meow meow, meow meow meow meow meow. Meow meow meow meow meow meow meow meow meow meow. Meow meow. Meow meow meow meow meow, meow meow meow meow meow, meow meow meow meow. Meow meow, meow meow meow meow meow meow meow meow meow meow meow. Meow meow meow, meow meow meow meow meow. Meow meow, meow meow meow meow meow. Meow meow meow meow meow meow, meow meow meow meow meow meow meow meow.

Meow meow, meow meow, meow meow meow meow, meow. Meow meow meow meow meow, meow meow meow meow meow. Meow meow meow meow meow meow, meow meow meow meow. Meow meow meow meow, meow meow meow meow meow, meow meow meow meow meow, meow meow.

Meow meow meow. Meow meow meow meow meow. Meow meow meow meow: meow meow meow meow meow.

"M'eow, meow meow meow meow meow."

Meow meow meow. Meow meow meow meow meow meow meow meow meow meow. Meow meow meow meow meow. Meow meow meow meow meow meow, meow meow, meow meow meow meow meow meow, meow. Meow meow meow meow meow. Meow meow meow meow meow meow meow.

Meow meow, meow meow meow meow meow. Meow meow meow meow meow meow meow meow. Meow meow meow meow, meow meow meow meow meow. Meow meow meow meow. Meow meow meow meow. Meow meow meow meow meow meow.

Meow meow Meow meow meow meow, meow meow meow meow, meow meow meow meow meow meow meow meow meow. Meow meow meow meow meow, meow meow meow meow, meow meow meow meow meow meow. Meow meow meow meow. Meow meow meow meow meow. Meow meow meow meow meow meow. Meow. Meow meow meow meow meow. Meow meow meow meow meow meow meow meow, meow meow meow meow meow meow meow meow meow. Meow meow meow. Meow meow meow meow meow meow meow meow meow meow meow meow meow meow. Meow meow meow meow meow meow meow meow meow meow. Mcow meow meow, meow meow, meow meow meow meow meow Meow, meow meow meow meow meow meow meow meow meow meow meow meow meow meow, meow meow meow meow meow meow. Meow meow meow meow meow meow. Meow meow meow meow meow. Meow meow meow meow meow meow meow meow meow meow meow meow meow meow Meow.

Meow meow meow meow, meow meow meow meow meow meow meow meow meow. Meow meow meow meow meow

meow meow, meow meow meow meow meow meow meow meow meow meow meow meow meow meow meow meow meow-meow. Meow meow meow meow, meow meow meow meow, meow meow meow meow meow meow meow meow meow meow meow. Meow meow, meow meow meow meow meow meow meow meow meow meow meow. Meow meow. Meow meow meow meow meow meow meow meow meow.

Meow meow meow meow meow meow meow meow meow meow meow. Meow meow meow meow meow meow meow. Meow meow meow meow meow meow meow meow meow meow meow meow meow. Meow meow meow meow meow meow meow, meow meow meow meow meow, meow meow meow meow meow meow meow. Meow meow meow meow meow. Meow meow, meow meow. Meow meow. Meow meow meow meow. Meow meow meow meow meow meow meow meow meow meow. Meow meow meow meow meow meow meow meow. Meow meow meow meow meow meow meow meow meow, meow meow meow meow meow meow.

Meow meow meow, meow, meow meow meow meow, meow meow meow, meow meow meow meow, meow meow meow meow, meow, meow meow. Meow meow meow meow meow meow meow. Meow meow meow meow meow meow meow, meow meow meow meow meow meow, meow meow meow meow meow. Meow meow, meow meow meow meow meow meow, meow meow meow-meow, meow meow meow meow meow. Meow meow meow meow meow, meow meow meow, meow meow meow. Meow meow meow meow meow meow meow meow meow meow meow meow meow, meow meow. Meow meow meow meow meow, meow meow meow meow meow meow meow meow. Meow meow meow meow meow meow meow meow meow. Meow meow meow meow meow meow meow meow meow. Meow meow meow meow meow meow meow meow

meow meow meow meow, meow Meow. Meow meow meow. Meow meow meow meow meow meow meow. Meow meow meow meow meow, meow meow meow, meow meow meow. Meow meow meow meow. Meow meow meow meow meow meow meow meow meow, meow, meow meow meow meow meow meow meow.

Meow meow meow meow, meow meow meow, meow meow meow meow meow. Meow meow, meow meow. Meow meow meow meow meow meow meow, meow, meow, meow meow. Meow meow meow. Meow meow meow meow meow meow meow meow meow meow meow meow, meow meow meow meow meow meow. Meow meow meow, meow meow meow, meow meow meow meow meow meow meow, meow.

Meow meow meow meow meow meow. Meow meow meow meow meow meow meow. Meow meow meow meow meow meow, meow meow meow. Meow meow meow meow meow meow meow. Meow meow meow meow meow meow-meow meow. Meow meow, meow, meow meow meow meow meow meow meow meow meow meow meow meow meow. Meow meow meow meow. Meow meow meow meow meow. Meow meow meow meow. Meow meow meow meow meow.

Meow meow meow meow meow meow meow. Meow meow meow meow meow meow meow meow meow. Meow meow meow meow meow meow meow. Meow meow meow meow meow, meow meow meow meow meow. Meow meow meow meow. Meow meow meow meow. Meow meow meow meow meow meow meow. Meow meow meow meow meow meow, meow meow meow meow meow meow meow meow meow Meow.

MEOW

Meow meow meow, meow meow, meow meow meow. Meow meow meow meow meow meow. Meow meow meow meow meow meow, meow meow. Meow meow meow meow meow meow meow meow meow meow. Meow meow, meow meow. Meow meow meow meow meow meow meow meow meow meow. Meow meow meow meow meow, meow meow meow meow, meow meow, meow meow meow meow meow meow Meow meow. Meow meow meow meow meow meow meow meow meow meow meow meow meow meow meow meow meow meow meow meow-meow meow meow meow meow, meow meow meow meow meow meow meow.

Meow meow meow meow meow meow. Meow meow meow meow meow meow meow, meow meow meow meow meow meow, meow meow meow meow meow, meow meow meow meow meow meow. Meow meow meow meow meow. Meow meow meow meow meow. Meow. Meow meow meow meow meow, meow meow meow meow meow. Meow meow meow meow meow meow? Meow meow meow meow meow meow? Meow meow meow meow meow meow meow? Meow meow meow meow meow meow meow meow meow meow meow, meow meow meow meow.

Meow meow meow meow meow. Meow meow meow meow meow meow meow. Meow meow meow meow meow meow meow. Meow meow meow meow meow meow meow. Meow

meow meow, meow meow meow meow meow meow meow meow meow. Meow meow meow meow meow meow, meow meow meow meow meow meow meow. Meow meow meow meow, meow meow meow. Meow meow meow meow meow meow meow meow meow meow meow. Meow meow meow meow meow meow meow meow. Meow meow meow meow meow meow meow meow meow meow, meow meow meow meow meow meow, meow meow meow meow meow meow meow meow meow meow meow. Meow meow meow meow.

Meow meow meow, meow meow meow meow meow meow meow meow. Meow meow meow meow meow meow-meow meow. Meow meow meow meow meow meow meow meow. Meow meow meow meow meow meow meow, meow meow meow meow meow meow meow meow, meow meow meow meow meow meow meow meow. Meow meow meow meow meow meow meow meow. Meow meow meow meow meow. Meow meow meow meow meow meow. Meow meow meow meow meow, meow meow meow meow, meow meow meow meow. Meow meow meow meow. Meow meow meow meow meow, meow meow meow meow meow. Meow meow meow meow. Meow meow meow meow meow. Meow meow meow meow meow meow meow meow meow meow meow meow. Meow meow meow meow meow, meow meow meow meow meow meow meow meow meow meow meow.

Meow meow meow meow meow meow meow meow meow, meow meow meow meow meow meow meow meow, meow meow meow meow, meow meow meow meow, meow meow meow meow meow, meow meow meow meow meow. Meow meow meow meow meow. Meow meow meow meow, meow meow meow meow meow meow meow meow meow. Meow meow meow meow meow meow. Meow meow meow meow meow, meow meow meow meow meow meow meow. Meow meow

meow meow meow meow meow, meow meow meow meow.
Meow meow meow meow meow meow meow meow meow
meow meow, meow meow meow. Meow meow meow meow
meow meow meow meow. Meow meow meow meow. Meow
meow meow meow meow meow meow meow. Meow
meow meow meow.

Meow meow meow, meow meow meow meow meow meow
meow meow meow meow, meow-meow meow meow meow
meow meow meow meow meow meow. Meow meow meow
meow meow meow meow meow meow meow meow. Meow
meow meow meow, meow meow meow meow meow meow.
Meow meow meow meow, meow meow meow meow meow
meow meow meow meow meow meow meow meow meow.
Meow meow meow meow meow, meow meow meow meow.
Meow meow meow meow meow, meow meow meow meow
meow meow, meow meow.

Meow meow meow meow meow. Meow meow meow meow
meow meow meow. Meow meow meow meow meow meow
meow. Meow meow meow meow meow. Meow meow meow
meow meow meow meow meow meow meow meow meow
meow meow meow. Meow meow meow meow meow meow
meow meow meow, meow meow-meow meow meow meow,
meow meow meow meow meow meow meow meow meow
meow, meow meow meow meow meow meow meow meow
meow meow meow meow. Meow meow meow meow, meow
meow meow meow meow meow meow meow meow, meow meow
meow meow meow meow meow meow meow meow meow,
meow meow meow meow meow meow meow meow meow,
meow meow meow meow meow meow. Meow meow meow,
meow meow meow meow meow meow.

Meow meow meow meow meow meow meow meow. Meow
meow meow meow meow, meow meow meow meow meow

meow meow. Meow meow meow meow meow meow meow. Meow meow meow meow meow meow meow meow meow, meow meow meow meow méow, meow meow meow meow meow meow meow. Meow meow meow meow meow meow meow meow meow meow meow.

Meow meow meow meow, meow meow. Meow meow meow meow meow meow, meow meow meow, meow meow meow meow meow meow meow meow. Meow meow meow meow meow meow, meow meow meow meow meow meow meow Meow meow. Meow meow meow meow meow meow. Meow meow meow meow, meow meow meow meow meow meow meow meow-meow meow meow meow meow meow meow meow meow meow meow meow meow meow meow. Meow meow meow meow meow meow meow meow, meow meow meow meow meow meow meow, meow meow meow meow meow, meow meow meow meow, meow meow meow meow meow meow meow meow meow, meow meow meow meow meow meow meow meow meow.

"Meow meow meow meow meow," meow meow meow meow meow, meow.

Meow meow, meow meow. Meow meow meow meow meow meow, meow meow meow meow meow meow. Meow meow meow meow meow, meow meow meow meow meow meow. Meow meow meow meow meow, meow meow meow meow meow meow. Meow meow meow meow meow meow meow meow, meow meow meow meow. Meow meow, meow meow meow, meow meow, meow meow meow meow meow meow meow meow meow, meow meow meow meow meow meow meow meow meow, meow meow meow meow meow meow. Meow meow meow meow, meow meow meow meow meow, meow meow meow meow meow meow meow meow meow meow meow meow, meow meow meow meow meow, meow meow meow, meow

meow meow meow meow meow meow meow meow meow meow meow meow meow.

Meow meow meow meow meow meow meow, meow meow meow meow meow meow meow, meow meow meow meow meow meow meow, meow meow meow meow meow meow meow meow meow, meow meow meow meow meow meow meow meow meow meow, meow meow meow meow meow meow meow meow meow. Meow, meow meow meow meow meow meow meow, meow meow meow, meow meow meow meow meow, meow meow meow meow meow meow meow meow meow meow. Meow meow meow meow meow meow meow, meow meow meow meow meow meow meow, meow meow meow meow meow meow meow, meow meow meow meow. Meow meow meow meow meow. Meow meow meow meow, meow meow meow. Meow meow meow, meow meow meow meow meow meow meow meow, meow meow meow meow meow, meow meow meow meow meow meow meow meow. Meow meow meow meow meow meow.

Meow meow meow meow, meow meow meow meow meow meow meow meow meow, meow meow meow meow. Meow meow meow meow meow meow meow. Meow meow meow. Meow meow meow meow meow meow meow. Meow meow meow meow meow meow meow, meow meow meow meow meow meow. Meow meow meow meow meow meow meow, meow meow meow meow meow-meow meow meow meow meow meow meow meow meow meow. Meow meow. Meow meow meow meow meow meow meow meow. Meow meow meow meow meow meow meow meow meow, meow meow meow meow meow meow meow meow meow, meow meow meow meow meow. Meow meow meow meow meow meow meow meow meow meow meow meow meow. Meow meow meow meow. Meow meow meow meow, meow

meow meow meow meow meow meow meow. Meow, meow meow meow meow meow meow meow meow meow meow meow. Meow meow meow meow, meow meow meow meow meow.

Meow meow meow meow meow, meow meow meow. Meow meow meow meow meow meow meow, meow meow meow, meow meow, meow meow meow meow meow meow meow. Meow meow meow meow meow meow meow, meow meow meow meow meow meow meow meow meow meow. Meow meow meow meow meow meow meow meow meow meow meow meow, meow meow meow meow meow meow meow meow, meow meow meow meow meow meow, meow meow meow meow meow meow meow meow meow meow. Meow meow meow. Meow meow meow meow meow meow meow meow meow meow meow, meow meow meow meow meow. Meow meow meow meow meow meow meow. Meow meow meow meow meow.

Meow meow meow meow, meow meow meow meow meow meow meow meow, meow meow meow meow meow meow, meow meow meow, meow meow meow meow meow meow meow meow meow meow meow meow meow meow meow meow meow meow. Meow meow meow meow meow meow meow. Meow meow meow meow meow meow meow meow meow. Meow meow meow meow meow mcow, meow meow meow. Meow meow meow meow meow meow meow meow, meow meow meow meow meow meow meow meow meow meow meow, meow meow meow meow meow meow meow meow meow meow meow. Meow meow meow meow meow meow meow meow, meow meow meow meow meow, meow. Meow meow meow meow meow meow meow. Meow meow, meow meow meow. Meow meow meow meow meow meow. Meow meow meow meow meow meow, meow meow meow meow

meow meow meow. Meow meow meow meow meow meow meow meow meow, meow meow meow meow meow.

Meow meow meow meow meow meow meow meow, meow meow meow meow meow. Meow meow meow meow meow meow meow meow meow, meow meow meow meow meow meow meow meow meow meow meow. Meow meow meow meow meow meow meow meow. Meow meow meow meow meow, meow meow meow meow, meow meow meow meow meow meow. Meow meow meow meow meow, meow meow meow. Meow meow meow meow meow meow. Meow meow meow meow meow meow meow meow, meow meow meow, meow. Meow meow meow meow meow. Meow meow meow meow meow meow meow.

Meow meow meow, meow meow meow meow. Meow meow meow meow, meow meow meow. Meow meow meow meow meow meow meow meow meow meow. Meow meow meow meow meow? Meow meow meow? Meow meow meow meow meow meow, meow meow meow meow meow meow meow meow meow meow. Meow meow meow meow meow meow meow meow meow meow, meow meow meow meow meow meow, meow meow meow meow meow meow meow. Meow meow meow. Meow meow meow meow meow meow meow meow meow meow, meow meow meow meow meow meow. Meow meow meow, meow meow meow meow meow meow.

"Meow, meow meow meow meow meow meow meow meow meow," meow meow meow. Meow meow meow, meow meow meow meow meow meow meow meow meow meow meow meow meow meow meow meow. Meow meow meow meow meow meow meow meow meow meow meow, meow meow meow meow meow meow meow. Meow meow meow meow meow meow meow meow, meow meow meow meow meow meow meow meow meow meow meow meow meow. Meow meow meow meow

meow meow meow meow meow meow, meow meow meow meow meow meow meow meow meow.

"Meow meow," meow meow, "meow meow meow meow meow meow. Meow meow meow?"

Meow meow meow meow meow meow, meow meow meow meow meow meow meow meow meow meow, meow meow meow meow meow meow meow meow meow. Meow meow meow meow meow meow, meow. Meow meow meow meow meow meow meow, meow meow meow meow meow meow meow. Meow meow meow meow, meow meow meow meow meow meow, meow meow meow meow meow meow meow, meow meow meow. Meow. Meow meow meow meow meow meow meow meow meow meow meow meow meow. Meow meow, meow meow meow meow meow meow meow. Meow meow meow meow meow meow meow meow meow meow meow meow meow meow meow meow, meow meow meow meow meow meow meow meow meow meow. Meow meow meow meow meow, meow meow meow meow meow meow. Meow meow meow meow meow meow meow. Meow meow, meow meow, meow meow meow meow meow meow meow.

Meow meow meow meow meow meow meow, meow meow meow meow meow meow meow, meow meow meow. Meow meow. Meow meow meow meow meow meow meow meow meow. Meow meow meow meow meow meow meow meow meow meow meow.

"Meow Meow, meow meow meow meow meow meow meow?" meow meow meow.

"Meow meow."

"Meow meow meow meow?"

"Meow meow meow meow, meow meow."

"Meow meow meow meow meow?"

"Meow, meow meow meow meow. Meow meow meow meow meow meow meow meow meow," meow meow.

"Meow meow meow meow meow meow meow meow meow?"

"Meow meow. Meow meow meow, meow meow meow meow meow meow."

"Meow meow meow meow meow meow meow meow?"

"Meow, meow. Meow meow meow meow. Meow meow meow meow meow meow."

"Meow meow meow meow meow meow?"

"Meow meow."

"Meow, meow meow meow meow meow meow meow meow meow. Meow meow meow meow meow meow meow meow meow meow?"

"Meow meow meow meow."

"Meow meow meow?"

"Meow."

"Meow meow?"

"Meow meow meow meow, meow meow meow."

"Meow meow meow meow?"

"Meow meow meow."

"Meow, meow meow meow meow meow meow meow meow meow meow meow, meow meow."

"Meow meow," meow meow. Meow meow meow meow meow meow meow meow meow meow meow meow meow meow. Meow meow meow meow meow meow meow meow meow meow meow meow meow, meow meow meow meow meow meow meow.

"Meow, meow meow meow meow meow meow meow meow meow meow. Meow meow meow meow meow meow meow meow. Meow meow Meow. Meow meow meow meow, meow?"

Meow meow meow meow meow, meow meow meow meow, meow meow meow meow meow meow meow meow meow

meow meow meow meow. Meow meow meow meow meow meow meow. Meow meow meow meow meow meow meow meow, meow meow meow meow, meow meow, meow meow meow meow meow, meow meow meow meow meow. Meow meow meow meow, meow meow meow meow meow meow. Meow meow meow. Meow meow meow meow, meow meow meow meow meow, meow meow meow meow meow meow meow. Meow meow meow meow meow meow meow meow. Meow meow meow meow meow meow meow meow meow meow. Meow meow meow meow meow meow meow, meow meow meow meow meow, meow meow meow meow meow, meow meow meow meow meow meow meow meow meow meow meow, meow meow meow meow meow meow meow meow. Meow meow meow meow meow meow meow meow meow meow, meow meow meow meow meow meow meow meow, meow meow meow meow, meow meow meow meow meow meow.

Meow meow meow meow meow meow meow, meow meow meow meow, meow meow meow meow meow, meow meow meow meow meow meow, meow meow meow meow meow meow meow meow. Meow meow meow meow meow meow meow, meow meow meow meow meow Meow Meow. Meow meow meow meow, meow meow meow meow meow meow meow meow. Meow meow meow meow, meow meow meow meow meow meow. Meow, meow meow meow meow meow. Meow meow meow meow meow meow meow meow meow meow meow meow, meow meow meow meow meow meow meow meow meow meow meow. Meow meow meow meow meow meow meow.

Meow meow meow meow meow meow Meow Meow meow meow. Meow meow meow meow meow meow meow meow meow, meow meow meow meow meow meow meow meow. Meow meow meow meow meow meow meow, meow meow meow meow meow meow meow meow meow meow meow. Meow meow meow meow meow meow meow meow meow, meow meow meow meow meow meow meow. Meow meow meow meow meow meow meow meow meow meow meow meow meow meow meow. Meow meow meow meow meow meow meow, meow. Meow meow meow meow meow.

Meow meow meow meow meow meow meow meow meow meow meow meow.

MEOW, MEOW MEOW MEOW MEOW

Meow meow meow meow meow meow, meow meow meow meow meow meow meow meow meow. Meow meow meow, meow meow meow meow meow. Meow meow meow meow meow meow, meow meow meow meow meow meow meow. Meow meow meow meow meow meow meow meow meow, meow meow meow meow meow meow meow, meow meow meow meow meow meow meow meow. Meow meow meow meow meow meow meow, meow meow meow meow meow meow meow, meow meow meow meow meow meow meow meow meow meow meow meow meow meow. Meow meow meow meow meow, meow meow meow meow meow meow meow meow meow. Meow meow meow meow meow meow. Meow meow meow meow meow meow meow meow meow meow meow, meow meow meow meow meow meow meow meow meow meow meow meow meow, meow meow meow meow meow meow meow meow meow meow meow. Meow meow meow Meow Meow meow, meow meow meow meow meow meow.

Meow meow meow meow meow meow, meow meow meow meow meow meow meow meow. Meow meow. Meow meow meow. Meow meow meow meow meow.

Meow meow meow meow meow meow meow. Meow meow meow meow meow meow meow meow meow meow meow meow,

meow meow meow meow meow meow meow meow meow meow meow meow meow meow meow meow meow meow meow. Meow meow meow meow meow meow meow meow meow. Meow meow meow meow meow meow meow meow meow meow. Meow meow meow, meow meow meow meow meow, meow meow meow, meow meow meow meow meow meow. Meow meow meow meow meow meow meow meow meow meow. Meow meow meow meow meow meow meow meow, meow meow meow meow meow meow meow meow.

Meow meow meow, meow meow meow meow meow meow meow meow meow, meow meow meow meow meow meow meow meow meow. Meow meow meow meow meow meow meow meow meow, meow meow meow, meow meow meow meow meow. Meow meow meow meow meow meow, meow meow meow meow meow meow meow.

* * * * * * *

Meow meow meow, meow meow meow meow. Meow meow meow meow meow meow meow meow meow meow meow, meow meow meow meow meow meow meow. Meow meow meow meow, meow meow meow meow meow meow meow meow meow, meow meow meow meow meow meow meow meow meow meow meow meow. Meow meow meow meow meow meow meow, meow meow meow. Meow meow meow meow meow meow meow meow meow meow meow meow. Meow meow meow meow meow meow meow meow meow meow meow. Meow meow meow meow meow meow meow meow meow. Meow meow meow meow meow, meow meow meow meow meow meow meow, meow meow meow.

Meow meow meow meow meow meow, meow meow meow meow meow meow. Meow meow meow meow meow meow

meow meow meow meow. Meow meow meow meow meow meow meow, meow meow meow meow meow meow meow meow meow meow, meow meow meow meow. Meow meow meow, meow meow meow meow meow meow. Meow meow meow meow meow meow, meow meow meow meow meow.

Meow meow meow meow meow meow meow meow, meow meow meow meow meow, meow meow meow meow meow meow, meow meow meow meow meow meow, meow meow meow meow meow meow meow meow meow meow, meow meow meow meow meow, meow meow meow meow meow meow. Meow meow meow meow meow meow meow meow meow meow meow meow, meow meow meow meow meow meow meow meow, meow meow meow meow meow. Meow meow meow meow meow meow meow meow meow meow meow meow meow meow meow meow meow meow meow meow meow meow meow meow. Meow meow meow meow meow meow meow meow. Meow meow meow meow, meow meow meow meow meow meow meow meow meow meow meow meow. Meow meow meow, meow. Meow meow meow meow. Meow meow meow meow meow. Meow meow meow meow meow meow meow meow. Meow meow meow meow meow, meow meow meow meow meow meow meow meow meow meow.

Meow meow meow meow meow meow meow meow meow meow meow. Meow meow meow, meow meow meow. Meow meow meow meow. Meow meow meow meow meow meow meow, meow meow meow. Meow meow meow meow meow meow meow meow meow meow. Meow meow meow meow meow meow meow meow meow meow meow, meow meow meow meow meow meow meow, meow meow meow meow meow meow meow meow.

Meow meow meow meow meow. Meow meow meow meow meow meow meow: meow meow. Meow meow meow meow

meow meow meow meow, meow meow meow meow, meow
meow meow meow meow meow meow meow meow. Meow
meow meow meow meow, meow, meow meow meow meow
meow, meow meow meow meow meow. Meow meow meow
meow meow meow meow meow meow, meow meow meow
meow meow meow meow, meow meow, meow meow meow.
Meow meow meow meow meow meow, meow meow meow
meow, meow meow meow meow meow meow meow meow.

Meow meow meow meow meow meow meow meow meow
meow. Meow meow meow meow meow meow, meow meow
meow meow meow. Meow meow meow meow meow meow.
Meow meow meow meow meow meow meow meow meow:
meow meow meow meow meow, meow meow meow meow
meow meow meow meow.

Meow meow meow meow meow meow meow meow meow,
meow meow meow meow meow, meow meow meow meow.
Meow meow meow meow meow meow meow meow meow
meow meow meow meow, meow meow meow – meow meow
meow meow meow meow meow.

Meow meow meow, meow meow meow, meow meow meow,
meow meow meow meow meow meow meow meow meow.
Meow meow meow meow. Meow meow meow meow meow
meow meow. Meow meow meow meow meow, meow meow
meow meow meow meow meow.

Meow meow meow meow meow meow meow, meow meow,
meow meow meow meow meow meow meow meow meow
meow. Meow meow meow meow. Meow meow meow meow.
Meow meow meow meow meow meow meow meow, meow
meow meow meow. Meow meow meow meow meow, meow
meow meow meow, meow meow meow meow meow meow
meow. Meow meow meow meow, meow meow meow meow
meow meow meow meow meow meow meow meow meow

meow meow meow meow meow. Meow meow meow meow meow.

Meow meow meow meow meow meow meow meow meow meow meow meow, meow meow meow, meow meow meow meow meow meow meow meow meow meow meow. Meow meow meow meow meow meow meow meow meow meow meow meow meow meow meow meow meow meow meow meow meow meow meow meow.

Meow meow meow meow meow meow meow meow. Meow meow meow meow meow meow meow meow, meow meow meow meow meow meow meow meow meow meow meow meow meow. Meow meow meow meow. Meow meow meow meow, meow meow. Meow meow meow meow, meow meow meow meow meow meow meow, meow meow meow meow meow meow meow meow meow meow, meow meow meow meow meow meow meow meow. Meow meow meow meow meow meow meow meow. Meow meow meow meow meow, meow meow meow meow meow meow meow meow meow. Meow meow meow meow meow meow meow meow, meow meow meow meow meow meow meow meow. Meow meow meow meow meow meow meow meow meow meow, meow meow meow meow meow, meow meow meow meow meow meow meow meow, meow meow meow meow meow meow.

Meow meow meow meow meow meow meow meow, meow meow meow. Meow meow meow meow meow meow meow meow. Meow meow meow meow, meow meow meow meow meow, meow meow, meow meow meow, meow meow. Meow meow meow meow meow meow meow meow meow. Meow meow meow. Meow meow meow meow meow meow meow meow, meow meow meow meow. Meow meow meow meow meow meow meow meow. Meow, meow meow. Meow meow meow meow meow meow meow meow meow meow meow.

"Meow meow meow meow meow meow meow, meow meow meow meow meow meow, meow meow meow meow meow?" meow meow meow meow meow meow meow meow meow meow meow meow meow.

"Meow meow, meow meow meow meow meow. Meow meow meow meow meow meow meow," meow meow. Meow meow meow meow meow meow meow meow meow meow meow meow meow meow meow meow, meow meow meow meow meow meow meow meow meow meow meow meow meow meow, meow meow meow meow meow meow. Meow meow meow meow meow meow meow meow. Meow meow meow meow meow meow. Meow meow meow meow meow. Meow meow meow, meow meow meow meow meow, meow meow meow meow. Meow meow meow meow meow meow, meow meow meow. Meow meow meow, meow meow meow meow, meow meow meow meow meow. Meow meow.

Meow meow meow meow meow meow meow meow, meow meow meow meow meow meow meow meow, meow meow meow meow meow meow. Meow meow meow meow meow meow meow meow meow, meow meow meow meow meow meow meow meow meow meow. Meow meow meow meow meow, meow meow meow meow meow meow meow meow meow. Meow meow meow meow, meow meow meow meow. Meow meow meow meow meow meow meow, meow meow meow meow meow meow meow. Meow meow meow.

Meow meow meow meow meow meow meow. Meow meow meow meow meow meow meow meow meow, meow meow meow meow meow meow meow meow meow meow meow. Meow meow meow meow meow meow meow, meow meow meow meow meow meow.

"Meow meow meow meow meow meow meow meow meow," meow meow meow. Meow meow meow meow meow

meow, meow meow meow meow meow meow. Meow meow meow meow meow meow meow meow meow meow meow meow meow. Meow meow meow meow meow meow meow. Meow meow meow meow meow meow, meow meow meow meow meow meow meow meow meow, meow meow meow meow meow meow meow meow meow meow. Meow meow meow meow meow meow meow meow, meow meow meow meow meow meow meow meow meow meow, meow meow meow meow meow.

Meow, meow meow meow meow. Meow meow meow meow. Meow meow meow meow meow meow meow meow meow meow meow meow meow meow. Meow meow meow meow meow meow. Meow meow meow meow meow meow meow meow meow meow meow. Meow meow meow meow meow, meow meow meow meow meow meow, meow meow meow meow meow meow, meow meow meow meow meow meow meow meow meow meow. Meow meow meow meow meow meow meow meow meow meow, meow meow meow meow meow meow. Meow meow meow meow meow meow meow meow meow, meow meow meow meow. Meow meow meow meow meow meow meow meow meow meow meow meow. Meow meow meow meow, meow meow meow meow meow. Meow meow meow meow meow meow, meow meow meow meow meow meow meow meow meow meow meow.

"Meow, meow meow meow meow meow meow meow meow meow meow meow meow meow," meow meow meow. Meow meow meow meow meow meow meow meow meow. Meow meow meow meow meow. Meow meow meow meow. Meow meow meow meow meow meow meow meow meow meow meow meow meow. Meow meow meow meow meow, meow meow meow meow meow meow meow meow, meow

meow meow meow. Meow meow meow, meow meow meow meow meow, meow meow meow meow meow, meow meow meow meow meow meow meow. Meow meow meow meow meow, meow meow meow meow meow meow meow meow meow meow meow meow meow meow.

"Meow meow, meow meow. Meow meow meow meow meow meow meow meow. Meow meow meow."

Meow meow meow meow meow. Meow meow meow meow meow meow meow. Meow meow meow meow meow meow meow. Meow meow meow meow meow meow, meow meow meow meow meow meow meow meow. Meow meow meow meow meow meow meow? Meow meow meow meow meow meow meow meow meow meow meow. Meow meow meow meow meow meow meow meow meow meow meow meow meow.

Meow meow, meow meow meow meow meow meow, meow meow meow meow meow meow meow meow meow meow, meow meow meow meow meow meow meow meow meow, meow meow meow meow meow meow meow meow meow meow meow. Meow meow meow meow, meow meow meow meow meow. Meow meow meow, meow. Meow meow meow meow. Meow meow meow meow meow meow meow meow, meow meow meow meow meow. Meow meow meow meow meow meow meow meow. Meow meow meow meow meow meow. Meow meow meow meow, meow meow meow meow, meow meow meow meow meow meow meow meow meow. Meow meow meow meow meow meow meow meow. Meow meow meow meow meow meow meow, meow meow meow meow meow meow. Meow meow meow meow meow meow meow, meow meow meow meow meow meow meow meow meow. Meow meow meow meow meow meow meow meow, meow meow meow meow meow meow, meow meow meow meow meow, meow meow meow meow meow meow.

Meow meow meow meow meow meow meow meow meow meow, meow meow meow meow meow meow meow meow meow. Meow meow meow meow meow meow meow meow meow meow meow meow. Meow meow meow meow meow meow meow, meow meow meow meow meow, meow meow meow meow meow meow meow meow meow. Meow meow meow meow meow meow meow meow. Meow meow meow meow meow meow meow meow meow meow, meow meow meow meow meow meow meow meow meow meow. Meow meow meow meow meow meow meow meow meow meow meow meow meow meow. Meow meow meow meow meow meow, meow meow meow, meow meow meow, meow meow meow meow meow meow meow, meow meow meow meow meow meow meow meow meow meow. Meow meow meow meow. Meow meow meow.

Meow meow meow meow meow meow meow, meow meow meow meow meow meow. Meow meow meow. Meow meow meow meow meow meow meow meow meow, meow meow meow. Meow meow meow meow, meow meow meow meow meow. Meow meow meow meow meow meow meow meow meow, meow meow meow meow. Meow meow meow meow meow meow. Meow meow meow meow, meow meow meow meow meow, meow meow, meow meow meow meow meow meow. Meow meow meow meow meow meow meow meow, meow meow meow meow meow meow meow meow meow meow meow meow. Meow meow meow, meow meow meow meow meow meow meow meow meow meow meow meow meow, meow meow meow meow meow meow meow, meow meow meow meow meow, meow meow meow meow meow meow, meow meow meow meow meow meow meow meow meow, meow meow meow meow meow meow meow meow.

Meow meow meow, Meow. Meow meow meow meow. Meow meow meow meow. Meow meow meow meow meow. Meow

meow meow meow. Meow meow meow meow meow meow meow, meow meow meow meow meow meow meow meow meow meow meow meow meow. Meow meow meow meow meow. Meow meow meow meow meow, meow meow meow meow meow meow meow meow meow meow, meow meow meow meow meow meow. Meow meow meow meow meow meow. Meow meow meow, meow meow meow meow meow meow, meow meow meow. Meow meow meow meow meow.

* * * * * * *

Meow meow meow meow, meow meow meow meow meow meow, meow meow meow meow meow meow meow. Meow meow meow meow meow meow meow. Meow meow meow meow meow meow meow meow, meow meow meow meow meow meow meow, meow meow meow meow meow meow meow meow meow meow. Meow meow meow meow meow meow meow, meow meow meow. Meow meow meow meow meow meow meow. Meow meow meow meow meow meow. Meow meow meow meow, meow meow meow meow meow meow meow meow meow meow meow meow. Meow meow meow meow meow meow, meow meow meow meow meow meow meow meow meow meow. Meow meow meow meow, meow meow meow meow meow. Meow meow meow meow meow meow meow meow. Meow meow meow meow meow meow meow meow meow meow meow meow meow meow meow meow meow meow, meow meow meow meow meow meow meow meow meow.

Meow meow meow, meow meow meow meow, meow meow meow meow meow meow meow, meow meow meow meow meow meow meow, meow meow meow meow meow. Meow meow meow meow meow meow meow meow meow. Meow

meow meow meow meow meow meow meow meow meow. Meow meow meow meow meow meow meow meow. Meow meow meow meow, meow meow meow meow meow meow meow meow, meow meow meow meow meow meow meow meow meow meow meow meow meow meow meow.

"Meow meow meow meow meow meow meow meow meow," meow meow meow. Meow meow meow meow meow meow meow meow meow. "Meow, meow meow meow meow meow meow meow meow meow."

Meow meow meow meow meow meow meow meow meow, meow meow meow meow meow meow meow meow, meow meow meow meow meow meow.

Meow meow meow meow meow meow meow meow meow meow, meow meow meow meow meow meow meow meow, meow meow meow meow meow meow. Meow meow meow meow meow. Meow meow meow meow, meow meow meow meow meow. Meow meow meow meow meow meow meow meow meow, meow meow meow, meow meow meow meow meow meow meow meow, meow meow meow meow meow meow meow, meow meow meow, meow meow meow meow, meow, meow meow meow meow meow meow meow meow meow.

MEOW

Meow meow meow meow meow meow meow. Meow meow meow meow meow meow meow meow meow meow, meow meow meow meow meow, meow meow meow meow. Meow meow meow meow meow meow meow meow, meow meow meow meow meow meow meow meow meow. Meow meow meow meow, meow meow meow meow meow meow meow Meow. Meow meow meow meow meow meow meow meow, meow meow meow meow meow meow meow meow meow meow meow, meow meow meow meow meow meow meow, meow meow meow meow. Meow meow meow meow meow, meow meow meow meow. Meow meow meow meow meow, meow meow meow meow meow meow meow, meow meow meow meow meow meow meow meow meow meow, meow meow meow meow meow meow meow meow meow meow, meow meow meow meow meow meow meow meow meow, meow Meow meow meow meow. Meow meow meow meow meow meow meow, meow meow meow meow meow meow meow meow meow meow, meow meow meow meow meow meow, meow meow meow meow. Meow meow, meow meow meow meow meow. Meow meow, meow meow meow.

Meow meow meow meow, meow meow meow meow meow meow meow, meow meow meow meow meow meow meow meow meow meow, meow meow meow meow meow meow. Meow meow meow meow, meow meow meow meow meow meow,

meow meow meow meow meow meow meow meow meow meow meow. Meow meow meow meow meow meow meow.

Meow meow meow meow meow meow meow meow, meow meow meow meow meow meow meow meow. Meow meow meow meow. Meow meow meow meow meow meow meow meow meow meow, meow meow meow meow meow meow meow. Meow meow meow meow meow, meow meow meow meow meow, meow meow meow meow meow meow meow meow meow meow meow meow. Meow meow Meow meow meow meow meow meow meow meow meow, meow meow meow meow meow meow. Meow meow meow meow meow meow meow meow, meow meow. Meow meow meow meow meow. Meow meow meow meow meow, meow meow meow meow meow meow meow meow meow meow.

Meow meow meow meow meow meow meow, meow meow meow. Meow meow meow meow meow meow meow meow meow meow meow. Meow meow meow meow meow meow meow meow, meow meow meow meow meow meow, meow meow meow meow, meow meow meow meow meow meow meow. Meow meow meow meow meow meow meow, meow meow meow meow meow. Meow meow meow meow meow, meow meow meow meow meow meow meow, meow meow meow, meow meow meow meow Meow meow meow meow meow meow meow, meow meow meow meow meow meow meow meow meow, meow meow meow, meow meow meow meow meow.

Meow, meow meow meow. Meow meow meow meow meow meow meow meow.

Meow meow, meow meow meow meow meow meow. Meow meow, Meow meow meow meow meow meow. Meow meow meow meow meow meow meow meow meow meow meow meow. Meow meow meow meow meow, meow meow, meow

meow, meow meow meow, meow meow meow. Meow meow meow meow meow meow, meow Meow meow meow meow meow. Meow meow meow meow meow meow meow meow, meow meow meow. Meow meow meow, meow meow meow meow meow meow meow meow meow, meow meow meow meow meow meow meow.

Meow meow meow meow meow meow meow meow meow meow meow meow. Meow meow meow meow meow meow meow meow meow meow meow meow meow meow. Meow meow meow meow meow, meow meow meow, meow meow meow meow meow meow. Meow meow meow, meow meow meow meow meow meow meow. Meow meow meow, meow meow meow meow meow. Meow meow meow, meow meow meow meow meow meow meow meow. Meow meow meow meow meow, meow meow meow meow meow. Meow meow meow meow meow, meow meow meow meow meow meow meow meow meow meow meow meow meow meow meow meow. Meow meow, meow meow meow meow meow meow meow meow meow, meow meow meow meow meow meow. Meow meow meow meow meow meow meow meow meow, meow meow meow meow meow meow meow meow, meow meow meow meow, meow, meow, meow meow meow, meow meow meow meow meow.

Meow meow meow meow meow meow. Meow meow meow meow meow meow meow meow, meow meow meow meow meow. Meow meow meow meow meow meow meow meow meow meow meow meow meow meow meow meow meow meow meow meow meow. Meow meow meow meow meow meow, meow meow meow meow meow meow meow. Meow meow meow meow meow meow meow meow meow meow, meow meow meow meow meow, meow meow meow meow meow meow meow meow meow meow meow meow. Meow meow meow meow

meow meow meow meow. Meow meow meow meow meow meow meow meow meow.

Meow meow meow meow meow meow. Meow meow meow meow meow meow, meow meow meow meow meow. Meow meow meow meow meow meow meow meow, meow meow, meow meow. Meow meow meow meow meow meow, meow meow meow. Meow meow meow meow meow meow meow meow, meow meow meow meow meow meow meow meow meow meow meow meow meow meow.

Meow meow meow meow meow meow, meow meow meow meow meow. Meow meow meow meow, meow meow meow meow meow meow meow meow meow meow meow meow meow, meow meow meow meow meow meow, meow meow. Meow meow meow meow meow meow meow meow meow, meow meow meow meow meow meow meow meow, meow meow meow meow meow. Meow meow meow meow meow meow meow meow meow, meow meow meow meow meow. Meow meow meow meow meow meow, meow meow, meow meow meow meow meow meow meow meow, meow meow. Meow meow meow meow. Meow meow meow meow meow-meow meow meow meow. Meow meow, meow meow meow meow meow, meow meow meow meow meow meow meow, meow meow meow meow meow meow meow, meow meow meow meow meow, meow meow meow meow meow meow meow meow meow, meow meow meow meow meow meow meow meow meow meow, meow, meow meow meow meow meow meow meow.

Meow meow meow meow meow meow meow meow meow. Meow meow meow meow meow meow, meow meow meow meow meow meow meow meow, meow meow meow meow meow meow meow meow meow meow meow meow meow meow, meow meow, meow meow meow. Meow meow meow meow meow meow meow, meow meow meow meow meow, meow meow meow meow meow meow.

Meow meow meow meow meow meow-meow meow meow meow meow meow meow meow meow. Meow meow meow meow meow, meow meow meow meow meow meow, meow meow meow meow meow meow meow meow meow meow meow, meow meow meow meow. Meow meow meow meow. Meow meow meow meow, meow meow meow meow meow. Meow meow meow meow meow meow meow. Meow meow meow meow meow meow. Meow meow meow meow meow meow, meow meow meow meow meow meow meow meow meow, meow meow meow meow meow meow meow meow meow, meow meow meow meow meow meow meow meow meow meow meow meow meow meow meow meow, meow meow, meow meow MEOW meow meow meow meow meow.

Meow meow meow meow meow meow, meow meow meow meow, meow meow meow meow meow, meow meow, meow meow meow meow meow meow meow meow meow meow meow meow: meow meow meow meow meow meow meow meow meow meow meow meow, meow meow meow meow meow meow meow, meow meow meow meow meow meow meow meow meow meow meow meow.

Meow meow meow meow meow meow, meow meow meow meow meow meow meow meow meow, meow meow meow meow meow. Meow meow meow meow meow meow meow meow meow. Meow meow meow meow meow meow, meow meow meow, meow meow meow meow meow meow meow meow meow meow meow meow meow meow meow meow meow.

Meow meow meow meow meow, meow meow meow meow meow meow meow meow meow, meow meow meow meow meow meow meow, meow meow meow meow meow meow meow meow meow. Meow meow meow, meow meow. Meow meow meow meow Meow, meow meow. Meow meow meow meow meow meow meow meow. Meow meow meow meow,

meow meow meow meow meow meow meow meow meow meow, meow meow meow meow meow meow, meow meow meow meow, meow meow, Meow meow meow meow meow meow, meow, meow meow.

Meow meow meow, meow meow meow meow meow meow meow meow meow, meow meow meow meow meow meow meow meow meow meow meow meow. Meow meow meow meow meow, meow meow. Meow meow meow meow meow meow meow meow meow meow, meow meow meow meow meow meow meow meow, meow meow meow meow meow meow meow meow. Meow meow meow meow meow meow meow meow meow meow meow meow meow. Meow meow meow meow meow meow, meow meow meow meow meow meow meow meow meow meow. Meow meow meow meow meow meow meow meow meow meow meow meow meow, meow meow meow meow meow meow Meow meow meow meow meow meow.

Meow meow, Meow meow meow meow meow meow meow. Meow meow meow meow meow, meow meow meow meow meow. Meow meow, Meow meow meow meow, meow meow meow meow. Meow meow meow meow meow, meow meow meow meow meow. Meow meow meow meow meow meow meow meow meow, meow meow meow meow meow. Meow meow meow, meow meow meow meow meow meow meow meow Meow meow meow meow, meow meow meow meow meow meow, meow meow meow meow meow meow meow meow meow meow meow meow meow meow meow meow meow. Meow meow meow meow meow, meow meow meow meow, meow meow meow meow meow, meow meow meow meow meow meow meow meow meow, meow meow meow meow meow meow meow meow, meow meow meow meow meow meow, meow meow meow meow meow meow meow meow meow meow. Meow meow meow

meow meow, meow meow Meow meow meow meow. Meow meow meow meow meow meow meow. Meow meow meow meow meow, meow meow, meow. Meow meow meow meow meow meow meow. Meow meow meow meow meow meow meow, meow meow meow meow meow meow meow meow meow meow.

Meow meow, meow meow meow meow meow meow, meow meow meow meow, meow meow meow meow meow. Meow meow meow meow meow meow meow meow, meow meow meow meow meow meow meow meow meow. Meow meow meow meow meow meow meow meow meow meow. Meow meow meow meow meow meow meow, meow meow Meow meow meow, meow meow meow. Meow meow meow meow meow meow meow, meow meow meow meow meow meow meow meow meow.

Meow meow meow meow meow meow meow meow, meow meow meow meow meow meow, meow meow meow meow meow meow meow meow meow meow meow. Meow meow meow meow meow. Meow meow meow, meow meow. Meow meow meow meow meow meow meow, meow meow meow meow.

Meow meow meow meow meow, meow Meow meow meow meow meow meow meow meow. Meow meow meow meow meow, meow meow meow meow meow meow meow. Meow meow meow meow meow meow, meow meow meow meow meow meow. Meow meow meow meow meow meow meow meow meow meow, meow meow meow meow meow meow meow meow meow meow meow. Meow meow meow meow meow meow, meow meow meow meow meow meow meow meow meow meow meow meow meow meow. Meow meow meow meow meow meow. Meow meow meow meow meow meow, meow? Meow meow meow, meow meow

meow meow Meow meow, meow meow meow meow meow meow meow meow meow.

Meow meow meow meow meow. Meow meow Meow meow meow meow meow. Meow meow, meow meow meow meow, meow meow meow meow meow meow. Meow meow meow meow meow meow meow meow meow. Meow meow meow meow meow. Meow meow meow meow meow meow meow meow, meow meow meow meow meow meow meow meow meow meow. Meow meow meow meow meow. Meow meow meow meow meow meow meow. Meow meow meow meow meow meow meow. Meow meow meow meow meow meow, meow meow meow meow meow, meow meow meow meow meow meow, meow meow meow, meow meow meow meow meow meow meow meow meow meow, meow meow meow meow.

Meow meow meow meow meow, meow meow meow meow meow meow meow meow meow meow meow. Meow meow meow meow meow meow meow meow meow meow, meow meow meow meow meow meow meow, meow meow meow meow meow meow.

Meow meow meow, meow meow meow. Meow meow meow meow meow meow. Meow meow meow meow, meow meow meow meow meow meow meow, meow meow meow meow meow meow. Meow meow meow meow meow, meow meow meow meow meow meow meow. Meow meow meow meow meow, meow meow meow meow meow meow meow meow meow meow meow meow meow meow meow meow. Meow meow meow meow, meow meow meow meow meow meow. Meow meow meow Meow meow meow meow meow. Meow meow meow meow meow meow, meow meow meow meow meow meow meow meow meow meow meow meow. Meow meow meow-meow meow Meow

meow meow, meow meow meow meow meow meow meow,
meow meow meow meow meow meow meow meow meow
meow. Meow meow meow meow meow meow meow meow.

Meow meow meow meow meow meow, meow meow meow
meow meow meow meow meow meow meow meow meow meow
meow meow meow meow meow meow meow meow meow
meow meow meow meow meow. Meow meow meow meow
meow, meow-meow meow meow meow Meow meow, meow
meow meow meow "Meow, meow, meow meow meow meow
meow meow meow meow meow?"

Meow meow meow meow meow, meow, meow meow meow
meow meow meow meow meow meow. Meow meow meow meow
meow, meow meow meow meow. Meow meow meow meow
meow, meow meow meow, meow meow Meow. Meow meow
meow meow meow, meow meow meow meow. Meow meow
meow, meow meow meow meow meow meow. Meow meow meow
meow meow, meow meow meow meow meow meow meow.

Meow meow meow meow, Meow meow meow meow meow
meow meow meow. Meow meow meow meow meow meow
meow, meow meow meow meow meow meow meow meow meow
meow meow meow meow meow. Meow meow. Meow meow
meow meow meow, meow meow meow meow meow meow
meow, meow meow meow meow meow meow meow. Meow meow
meow meow, meow meow meow, meow meow meow. Meow
meow meow meow meow meow meow meow meow meow.

Meow meow meow meow meow meow, meow meow meow.
Meow meow meow meow meow meow meow meow meow,
meow meow meow meow meow. Meow meow meow meow
meow meow meow meow meow meow meow meow meow
meow meow meow, meow meow meow meow meow meow
meow meow meow meow. Meow meow meow meow meow,
meow meow meow meow meow. Meow meow meow meow

meow meow. Meow meow meow meow meow meow meow meow meow, meow meow meow meow meow meow, meow meow meow meow meow meow meow, meow meow meow meow meow meow meow meow meow meow meow. Meow meow meow meow meow meow meow meow, meow meow meow meow, meow meow meow meow meow meow meow meow meow meow, meow meow meow meow meow meow meow meow meow meow meow meow meow meow meow meow.

"Meow," meow meow, "meow meow meow meow meow meow meow meow meow meow meow meow meow meow," meow meow meow meow meow, meow meow meow meow, meow meow meow meow meow meow meow. Meow meow meow meow meow meow meow meow meow meow meow meow meow meow meow meow meow meow.

Meow meow meow meow meow meow meow meow meow meow meow meow, meow meow meow meow meow meow meow meow, meow meow meow meow meow. Meow meow meow meow, meow meow meow meow meow meow meow meow meow meow meow meow. Meow meow meow, meow meow meow meow meow meow. Meow meow meow meow meow meow meow meow meow meow meow meow meow meow. Meow meow meow meow, meow, meow meow, meow meow meow meow meow.

Meow meow meow meow meow meow. Meow meow meow meow meow. Meow meow meow Meow meow meow meow meow meow. Meow meow meow meow meow meow meow meow meow meow, meow meow meow meow. Meow meow meow meow meow meow meow meow meow, meow meow meow meow meow, meow meow meow meow meow meow. Meow meow meow meow meow. Meow meow meow meow meow meow, meow meow meow meow meow

meow meow, meow meow meow meow meow meow meow
meow meow meow meow meow. Meow meow meow meow
meow meow meow meow. Meow meow meow meow meow
meow meow, meow meow meow meow meow meow meow
meow meow, meow meow meow meow meow meow meow
meow meow meow meow meow, meow meow meow meow
meow meow, meow meow meow meow meow meow.

MEOW MEOW MEOW MEOW

Meow meow meow meow meow meow meow, meow meow meow meow meow meow meow meow meow meow meow meow meow meow meow meow meow meow meow. Meow meow meow meow, meow meow meow meow meow meow meow meow, meow meow meow meow meow meow meow meow meow meow meow meow meow meow. Meow meow meow meow meow meow meow. Meow meow meow meow. Meow meow meow meow meow meow meow meow meow meow meow meow meow, meow meow meow meow meow meow meow meow meow meow meow, meow meow meow, meow meow meow meow meow meow. Meow meow meow meow meow meow meow. Meow meow meow. Meow meow meow meow meow, meow meow meow meow, meow meow meow meow meow meow meow meow, meow meow meow meow meow meow, meow meow meow meow meow meow, meow meow meow, meow meow.

Meow meow meow meow meow meow meow meow. Meow meow meow meow meow meow meow, meow meow meow meow meow meow meow, meow meow meow meow meow. Meow meow meow meow, meow meow meow meow meow meow meow meow meow meow meow. Meow meow meow meow meow meow meow meow meow meow meow meow meow meow meow,

meow meow meow meow meow meow meow meow meow meow meow meow meow meow meow. Meow meow meow meow, meow meow meow meow meow. Meow meow meow meow. Meow meow meow meow meow meow meow, meow meow, meow meow meow, meow meow meow meow. Meow meow meow meow meow meow meow meow, meow meow, meow meow meow meow meow meow meow meow meow meow meow, meow meow meow meow meow meow, meow meow meow meow meow meow. Meow meow meow meow meow meow, meow meow meow meow meow meow. Meow meow meow meow meow meow meow meow meow meow meow meow meow meow meow meow meow meow meow, meow meow meow meow meow meow meow meow meow. Meow, meow meow meow meow meow meow meow meow meow...

Meow, meow meow meow meow meow meow meow meow meow, meow meow meow meow meow meow meow, meow meow meow meow meow meow meow meow meow meow meow, meow meow meow meow meow meow meow meow meow meow meow meow meow meow meow meow meow meow meow meow meow meow. Meow meow meow meow meow meow meow meow meow meow meow meow meow, meow meow meow meow meow meow meow meow meow meow meow meow meow meow meow MEOW meow. Meow meow meow meow meow meow meow meow meow meow meow Meow Meow, meow meow meow meow. Meow meow Meow meow meow meow, meow meow meow. Meow meow meow meow meow meow meow meow, meow meow meow meow, meow meow meow meow. Meow meow meow meow Meow? Meow meow. Meow meow meow meow meow meow meow meow meow meow meow meow. Meow meow meow, meow meow meow meow meow meow meow meow meow, meow meow meow meow meow meow meow.

Meow meow meow meow meow meow meow meow. Meow meow meow meow Meow meow, meow meow meow meow meow Meow meow meow meow meow meow meow meow meow meow, meow meow meow meow meow meow meow meow. Meow meow meow meow. Meow meow. Meow meow meow meow meow. Meow, meow meow meow, meow meow meow meow meow meow meow meow meow meow meow. Meow Meow meow meow meow meow meow meow, meow meow, meow meow meow meow-meow meow meow meow meow meow meow meow meow meow meow meow meow meow meow meow. Meow meow meow meow meow meow. Meow meow meow, meow meow meow meow meow meow meow. Meow meow meow meow meow. Meow meow meow meow meow. meow meow meow meow meow meow meow meow meow meow meow meow meow meow meow meow, meow meow meow meow. Meow meow meow meow meow meow meow meow meow, meow meow meow meow meow, meow meow meow meow meow meow meow meow meow meow meow meow meow meow. Meow meow meow meow meow meow, meow meow meow, meow meow Meow meow meow meow meow meow meow meow. Meow meow meow meow. Meow meow meow, meow meow meow meow meow meow meow meow meow. Meow meow Meow meow meow meow, meow meow meow meow meow meow meow meow meow meow meow, meow meow. Meow meow meow, meow meow meow meow meow meow meow meow meow meow meow meow meow meow meow, meow meow meow meow meow meow meow meow meow meow.

Meow meow meow meow, meow meow meow meow meow meow, meow meow meow meow meow. Meow meow meow meow meow meow meow meow meow. Meow meow meow meow meow, meow meow meow meow meow meow meow meow meow

meow meow meow meow meow. Meow meow, meow meow meow meow, meow meow meow meow meow meow meow. Meow meow meow, meow meow meow meow meow meow meow meow meow meow meow meow meow meow meow. Meow meow meow meow meow, meow meow meow, meow meow meow meow meow meow meow meow meow meow meow meow. Meow meow meow meow meow, meow meow meow meow meow, meow meow meow meow meow. Meow meow, meow meow meow meow meow. Meow meow meow meow meow meow. Meow meow meow meow meow meow meow meow meow meow meow meow meow meow meow meow meow meow, meow meow meow meow meow. Meow meow meow meow meow meow meow. Meow. Meow meow meow meow, meow meow meow meow meow meow meow meow. Meow meow meow meow meow meow, meow meow meow meow meow meow meow meow meow meow meow.

Meow meow, meow meow meow meow meow meow meow meow. meow meow meow meow meow meow meow meow meow meow meow meow meow, meow meow meow meow meow meow. Meow meow meow meow meow, meow meow meow meow meow meow meow meow meow meow meow meow. Meow meow meow meow meow meow meow meow. Meow meow meow meow, meow meow meow. Meow meow meow meow. Meow meow meow meow meow meow meow meow meow meow meow meow meow, meow meow meow meow meow meow meow, meow meow meow meow meow meow meow meow. Meow meow, meow meow meow meow, meow meow meow meow meow meow meow meow meow, meow meow meow meow meow meow meow meow meow meow meow meow meow meow meow.

Meow meow meow meow meow meow meow. Meow meow meow meow meow meow, meow meow meow meow meow

meow meow, meow meow meow meow meow meow meow
meow meow meow meow. Meow meow meow meow meow
meow meow meow meow meow meow meow meow, meow
meow meow meow meow. Meow meow meow meow meow
meow meow meow, meow meow meow meow meow, meow
meow meow meow meow meow meow meow meow meow
meow meow, meow meow meow meow meow meow, meow
meow meow meow. Meow meow meow meow meow meow,
meow meow meow meow. Meow meow meow meow meow
meow meow meow meow. Meow meow meow meow meow
meow meow.

Meow meow meow, Meow meow meow meow meow meow,
meow meow meow meow meow meow meow meow. Meow
meow meow meow meow, meow meow meow, meow meow
meow meow meow meow meow. Meow meow meow meow
meow meow, meow meow meow meow meow meow meow
meow meow meow meow. Meow meow meow meow. Meow
meow, meow meow meow meow. Meow meow meow meow
meow meow meow meow.

Meow meow, meow meow meow meow meow meow. Meow
meow meow meow meow meow. Meow meow meow meow
meow meow, meow meow meow meow meow meow meow
meow meow meow meow meow Meow, meow meow meow meow
meow meow, meow meow mcow meow, meow meow meow
meow meow meow meow. Meow meow meow meow meow
meow meow meow meow, meow meow meow meow meow
meow meow meow meow meow meow meow. Meow meow
meow meow meow meow meow meow meow meow meow
meow meow, meow meow meow meow-meow meow, meow
meow meow meow, meow meow meow meow meow.

"Meow meow meow meow meow meow meow meow meow
meow," meow meow. Meow meow meow.

Meow meow, meow meow meow Meow meow meow meow meow meow, meow meow meow meow meow meow meow meow, meow meow meow meow meow meow meow. Meow meow meow meow meow meow, meow meow meow meow meow meow meow meow, meow meow meow, meow meow meow meow meow meow. Meow meow meow meow meow meow meow. Meow meow meow meow meow. Meow meow meow meow meow meow meow, meow meow meow meow meow meow meow meow meow meow meow meow. Meow meow meow meow meow, meow meow meow meow meow meow meow, meow meow meow meow meow meow meow meow meow, meow meow meow meow meow meow meow meow meow meow meow. Meow meow meow Meow meow meow.

Meow meow meow meow meow meow meow meow meow meow, meow meow meow meow, meow meow meow meow meow meow meow meow, meow meow meow meow meow, meow Meow meow meow meow meow meow meow. Meow meow meow meow meow meow, meow meow meow meow meow meow meow meow meow meow meow meow meow meow meow meow. Meow meow meow meow meow meow, meow meow meow meow meow, meow meow meow meow, meow meow meow meow meow meow meow meow meow meow Meow, meow meow meow meow meow.

Meow Meow meow meow meow meow meow meow meow meow, meow meow meow meow meow meow meow meow meow meow meow. Meow meow meow meow, meow meow meow meow meow meow, meow meow meow meow meow meow meow meow meow meow, meow meow meow meow meow meow meow. Meow meow meow meow meow, meow meow meow meow meow meow meow meow meow meow. Meow meow meow meow meow meow. Meow meow meow meow meow meow meow, meow meow meow meow meow, meow meow meow meow.

"Meow meow meow meow meow meow meow meow," meow meow meow. "Meow meow meow meow meow, meow meow meow meow meow, meow meow meow meow meow meow. Meow meow meow meow meow meow meow?"

Meow Meow meow meow meow. Meow meow meow meow meow meow. Meow meow meow meow meow meow meow meow meow meow meow meow meow, meow meow meow meow meow meow meow, meow meow meow meow meow. Meow meow meow meow meow meow meow meow meow.

"Meow meow meow meow meow meow meow, meow meow meow, meow meow meow meow meow meow." Meow meow meow meow meow.

"Meow?" meow meow meow meow. Meow meow meow meow.

Meow meow meow meow, meow meow meow meow meow meow meow meow. Meow meow meow Meow meow meow meow. Meow meow meow, meow meow meow, meow meow meow meow. Meow meow meow meow, meow meow meow meow meow, meow meow Meow meow. Meow meow meow meow meow. Meow meow meow meow meow meow meow meow meow meow meow meow, meow meow meow meow, meow meow meow meow meow meow. Meow meow meow meow meow, meow meow meow, meow meow meow meow meow meow meow meow meow meow meow meow meow. Meow meow meow meow meow meow meow meow meow meow meow.

Meow meow meow meow, meow meow meow meow, meow meow meow meow meow meow meow meow meow. Meow meow meow meow meow meow meow meow Meow, meow meow meow meow meow meow meow meow meow meow, meow meow meow meow meow, meow meow meow meow meow, meow meow meow meow meow meow meow meow meow meow meow meow meow meow meow meow meow. Meow meow

meow meow meow meow meow meow, meow meow meow meow meow meow meow. Meow meow meow meow meow meow, meow meow meow meow meow meow meow meow. Meow meow meow meow meow, meow meow meow meow meow meow meow meow meow meow. Meow meow meow meow, meow meow meow meow meow, meow meow meow meow. Meow meow meow meow meow. Meow meow meow meow meow meow, meow Meow meow meow meow-meow meow meow meow, meow meow meow meow meow meow.

Meow meow meow meow meow meow meow, meow meow meow meow meow meow meow. Meow meow Meow meow meow meow, meow meow meow meow meow meow meow meow meow meow. Meow meow meow meow meow meow meow meow meow meow meow meow meow meow meow, meow meow meow meow meow meow meow meow meow meow meow, meow meow meow meow meow meow meow meow meow meow meow meow. Meow meow meow meow meow meow meow, meow meow meow meow meow meow meow meow meow meow meow meow. Meow meow meow meow, meow meow meow meow meow meow meow meow meow meow, meow meow meow meow meow meow meow Meow meow, meow meow meow meow meow meow meow meow.

* * * * * * *

Meow meow meow meow meow meow meow Meow, meow meow meow meow meow meow meow, meow meow meow meow meow. Meow meow Meow meow meow meow meow, meow meow meow meow meow meow meow meow meow meow meow meow meow meow meow meow, meow meow meow meow meow, meow meow meow meow meow, meow meow meow meow.

Meow meow meow meow meow meow meow meow meow, meow meow meow meow meow meow meow meow meow, meow meow meow meow meow meow, meow meow meow meow meow meow meow meow meow meow meow, meow meow meow meow meow meow.

Meow meow meow meow. Meow meow meow. Meow Meow meow meow, meow meow meow meow meow meow, meow meow meow meow meow meow meow Meow meow meow meow meow meow meow, meow meow meow Meow meow meow meow meow meow meow meow meow meow meow, meow meow meow meow meow meow.

Meow meow meow Meow meow meow, Meow meow meow meow meow. Meow meow meow meow meow meow meow meow meow meow meow meow, meow meow meow meow meow meow meow meow. Meow Meow meow meow meow, Meow meow meow meow meow meow. Meow meow meow meow meow meow meow meow, meow meow meow meow meow. Meow meow meow meow meow, meow meow meow meow meow meow. Meow meow meow meow meow meow meow meow meow, meow meow meow meow, meow meow meow. Meow meow meow meow meow meow meow meow meow meow meow meow. Meow meow meow, meow meow meow meow meow meow meow meow meow meow Meow meow, meow meow meow meow meow meow meow meow meow meow meow.

MEOW-MEOW

Meow meow meow meow meow. Meow meow meow, meow meow. Meow meow meow meow meow, meow meow meow meow meow meow meow meow meow meow, meow meow meow meow meow meow meow, meow meow meow meow meow meow meow meow meow meow meow. Meow meow meow meow meow, meow meow, meow meow meow, meow meow meow meow meow meow meow meow meow, meow meow meow, meow meow meow meow-meow meow meow meow. Meow meow meow meow meow meow meow meow meow, meow meow meow meow, meow meow meow meow. Meow meow meow meow meow, meow meow meow meow meow meow meow meow meow meow meow, meow meow meow meow-meow meow, meow meow meow. Meow meow meow, meow meow meow meow meow meow meow meow meow meow meow meow meow meow meow meow meow meow meow meow meow meow meow meow meow meow meow, meow meow meow, meow meow meow meow meow meow meow meow meow meow meow meow meow meow meow meow meow meow meow meow.

Meow meow meow meow meow, meow meow meow meow meow meow meow meow meow meow meow meow meow. Meow meow meow meow meow meow, meow meow meow meow. Meow meow meow meow, meow meow, meow meow meow. Meow meow meow. Meow meow.

Meow meow meow meow meow meow meow meow meow meow meow meow meow. Meow meow meow meow meow, meow meow meow meow meow meow meow, meow meow meow meow meow meow, meow meow meow meow meow, meow meow meow meow meow meow meow meow meow meow meow. Meow meow meow meow, meow meow meow meow meow meow meow meow, meow meow meow meow meow, meow meow meow meow meow meow meow meow meow meow meow meow meow, meow meow meow meow meow meow. Meow meow meow meow, meow meow, meow meow meow meow meow meow, meow meow meow meow meow. Meow meow meow meow, meow meow meow meow meow meow meow. Meow meow meow meow meow meow meow meow meow meow meow meow meow meow meow meow, meow meow meow meow meow: meow meow meow meow meow meow. Meow meow meow meow meow meow meow meow, meow meow meow meow meow meow meow meow meow meow.

Meow meow meow meow meow meow meow meow meow meow. Meow meow meow meow meow? Meow meow meow meow meow meow meow meow meow meow meow meow? Meow meow meow meow meow meow meow meow meow meow. Meow meow meow meow. Meow meow meow meow. Meow meow meow mcow meow meow meow meow meow, meow meow meow meow meow meow meow.

Meow meow meow, meow meow meow meow meow, meow meow meow meow meow meow meow meow, meow meow meow meow meow meow meow meow, meow meow meow meow meow, meow meow meow meow meow, meow meow meow meow meow meow meow meow. Meow meow meow meow, meow meow meow, meow meow meow meow meow meow meow meow, meow meow meow meow meow meow meow meow meow meow meow meow meow,

meow meow meow meow meow meow meow, meow meow meow meow meow meow meow meow, meow meow meow meow meow meow meow meow meow. Meow meow meow meow, meow meow meow meow, meow meow meow meow meow meow meow, meow meow meow, meow meow meow meow, meow meow meow meow meow meow meow meow meow, meow meow meow meow meow meow meow. Meow meow meow meow meow meow meow meow meow meow meow-meow meow meow meow, meow meow meow meow meow meow meow.

Meow meow meow meow, meow meow meow meow meow meow meow meow meow meow meow. Meow meow meow meow meow meow meow meow meow meow meow. Meow meow meow meow meow meow meow meow meow meow meow, meow meow meow meow meow meow. Meow meow meow meow meow meow meow meow meow meow meow meow meow meow meow meow meow meow meow meow meow meow. Meow meow meow meow meow meow meow meow meow, meow meow meow meow meow meow meow meow. Meow meow meow meow meow meow meow meow meow meow meow meow meow meow, meow meow meow meow meow meow meow meow meow. Meow meow meow meow meow, meow meow, meow meow, meow meow, meow meow meow. Meow meow meow meow meow meow meow meow meow meow meow meow meow meow meow. Meow meow, meow meow meow, meow meow meow meow meow meow meow meow, meow meow meow meow. Meow meow meow meow meow, meow meow meow meow meow meow. Meow meow meow meow, meow meow meow meow meow meow, meow meow meow meow meow meow meow meow.

Meow meow meow meow meow meow meow meow meow meow meow meow meow meow meow, meow meow meow

meow meow meow meow meow, meow meow meow meow meow meow meow meow meow meow meow meow meow, meow meow meow meow meow meow meow meow meow meow meow. Meow meow meow meow meow meow meow meow meow.

Meow meow meow meow meow, meow meow meow meow meow meow meow meow meow meow meow meow, meow meow, meow meow meow meow meow meow meow meow. Meow meow meow meow meow meow meow meow meow meow meow, meow meow meow meow meow. Meow meow meow, meow meow meow meow meow meow meow meow meow, "Meow meow. Meow meow meow meow meow meow meow. Meow meow meow meow meow meow meow. Meow meow meow meow." Meow meow meow meow meow, meow meow meow meow meow meow meow meow meow meow meow meow meow meow meow.

Meow meow meow meow meow meow meow meow meow meow meow meow meow meow meow meow meow, meow meow meow meow. Meow meow meow meow. Meow meow meow meow meow meow meow. Meow meow meow meow meow meow meow. Meow meow meow meow meow, meow meow meow meow meow meow, meow meow meow meow. Meow meow meow meow, meow meow, meow meow meow. Meow meow meow meow mcow meow meow meow, meow meow meow, meow meow meow meow. Meow meow meow, meow, meow meow meow meow meow meow meow meow meow meow. Meow meow meow meow, meow meow meow meow meow.

Meow meow meow meow, meow meow meow meow, meow meow. Meow meow meow, meow meow meow. meow meow meow meow meow meow meow. Meow meow meow meow meow. Meow meow meow meow, meow meow meow meow.

Meow meow, meow meow meow meow meow meow. Meow meow meow meow, meow meow meow meow meow meow meow meow.

Meow meow meow meow, meow meow meow meow meow meow. Meow meow meow meow meow meow meow meow meow. Meow meow meow meow meow meow meow, meow meow meow meow meow. Meow meow, meow meow meow meow meow meow meow meow meow meow. Meow meow meow, meow meow meow, meow meow meow meow, meow meow meow meow meow meow. Meow meow meow. Meow meow meow meow meow. Meow meow meow meow meow meow meow meow. Meow meow meow meow. Meow meow meow meow meow meow, meow meow meow meow meow meow meow meow meow meow. Meow meow meow meow meow meow, meow meow meow meow meow meow, meow meow meow meow meow meow meow meow meow meow, meow meow meow, meow meow, meow meow meow meow meow meow meow meow.

Meow meow meow meow. Meow meow meow meow meow meow meow meow meow meow, meow meow meow meow meow meow meow, meow meow meow meow meow meow meow meow. Meow meow meow meow meow, meow meow meow meow meow meow meow meow meow meow. Meow meow meow, meow meow meow meow, meow meow meow meow meow meow. Meow meow meow meow meow meow meow meow meow meow meow meow meow. Meow meow meow meow. Meow meow meow meow meow, meow meow meow meow-meow-meow meow meow meow meow meow meow meow. Meow meow meow meow.

Meow meow meow meow meow, meow meow meow meow meow meow meow meow meow meow meow meow meow meow, meow meow meow meow meow meow meow meow meow

meow meow meow meow, meow meow meow meow meow meow meow meow meow meow meow meow meow, meow meow meow meow meow.

"Meow meow," meow meow.

Meow meow meow meow meow meow meow meow. Meow meow meow meow meow meow meow meow meow, meow meow meow meow meow. Meow meow meow meow meow meow meow meow, meow meow meow meow meow meow.

"Meow meow meow meow meow, meow meow?" meow meow. Meow meow meow meow meow, meow meow meow meow meow meow meow meow, meow meow meow meow meow meow meow meow meow meow. Meow meow meow meow meow meow. Meow meow meow meow meow meow meow meow meow meow, meow meow meow meow meow meow, meow meow meow meow meow. Meow meow meow meow meow meow meow meow meow meow meow meow.

Meow meow meow meow meow meow meow meow meow, meow meow meow meow meow meow meow meow. Meow meow meow meow meow meow, meow meow meow meow meow meow meow meow meow meow meow, meow meow meow meow meow meow meow meow, meow meow meow meow meow meow meow meow meow. Meow meow meow, meow meow meow, meow meow meow, meow meow meow meow meow. Meow meow meow, meow meow meow meow meow meow meow meow meow meow meow meow meow meow meow meow, meow meow meow meow, meow meow meow meow. Meow meow meow. Meow meow meow meow. Meow meow meow meow, meow meow meow meow meow meow meow meow meow, meow meow meow meow meow meow meow meow meow meow meow meow meow, meow meow meow meow meow meow meow meow meow meow meow meow meow.

Meow meow meow meow, meow meow meow meow, meow meow meow meow meow. Meow meow meow meow meow meow meow, meow meow meow meow meow meow meow meow meow, meow meow meow meow meow meow meow meow meow meow meow meow. Meow meow meow meow meow, meow meow meow meow meow meow meow meow. Meow meow meow meow meow meow meow meow meow meow meow, meow meow meow meow meow meow meow meow meow, meow meow meow meow meow meow meow, meow meow meow meow meow meow meow meow meow meow.

Meow meow, meow meow meow meow meow meow meow meow, meow meow meow meow meow, meow meow meow meow meow. Meow meow, meow meow meow meow meow meow, meow meow meow meow meow meow meow meow meow meow meow meow meow meow meow, meow meow meow meow meow meow meow meow meow. Meow meow meow meow meow meow meow meow, meow meow meow meow meow meow meow meow, meow meow meow meow meow meow meow meow meow meow meow meow meow meow meow meow, meow meow meow meow meow meow meow meow meow meow. Meow meow meow meow meow meow. Meow meow. Meow meow meow meow meow meow meow meow. Meow meow meow meow meow, meow meow meow meow meow meow meow meow meow meow meow meow. Meow meow meow meow meow. Meow meow meow meow meow meow meow meow meow meow meow, meow meow meow meow meow meow meow meow meow meow meow meow meow meow meow meow meow.

* * * * * * *

Meow meow meow meow meow meow meow. Meow meow meow meow meow meow meow meow meow meow. Meow

meow meow meow meow meow, meow meow meow meow meow, meow meow meow meow meow meow meow meow meow, meow meow meow meow meow meow meow meow, meow meow meow meow meow meow meow. Meow meow meow, meow meow-meow meow meow meow meow meow meow meow. Meow meow meow meow meow meow meow. Meow meow meow meow meow, meow meow meow meow meow meow meow, meow meow meow meow meow meow meow meow meow meow meow meow. Meow meow meow meow meow meow meow. Meow meow meow meow meow meow meow meow meow, meow meow meow meow meow, meow meow meow meow meow meow meow meow meow. Meow meow meow meow meow meow meow meow, meow meow meow meow meow meow, meow meow meow meow meow meow meow meow meow. Meow meow meow meow meow meow meow meow meow meow, meow. Meow meow meow meow.

Meow meow meow meow meow meow meow. Meow meow meow meow meow meow meow, meow meow meow meow meow meow meow meow. Meow meow meow meow, meow meow meow meow meow meow meow. Meow meow meow meow meow meow meow meow meow. Meow meow meow meow meow. Meow meow meow meow meow meow meow meow meow. Meow meow mcow meow meow meow meow meow meow-meow meow. Meow meow meow meow meow. Meow meow meow. Meow meow meow. Meow meow meow. Meow meow meow meow meow meow meow meow meow meow meow, meow meow meow meow meow meow meow meow meow meow, meow meow meow meow meow meow meow meow meow meow. Meow meow meow meow meow meow meow meow meow meow meow meow meow. Meow meow meow meow meow meow meow meow meow meow meow meow meow

meow meow, meow meow meow meow meow meow meow meow meow meow. Meow meow meow meow meow meow meow meow meow, meow meow meow, meow meow meow meow meow meow meow meow. Meow meow meow meow meow meow meow meow meow meow meow meow meow meow meow meow meow meow meow, meow meow meow. Meow meow meow meow meow meow meow meow meow meow, meow meow meow meow meow meow, meow meow-meow meow, meow meow meow meow meow meow meow meow meow meow meow.

Meow meow meow, meow meow meow meow meow meow meow. Meow meow meow meow meow, meow meow meow meow meow meow. Meow meow meow meow, meow meow meow meow meow, meow meow meow-meow meow meow meow meow meow meow meow meow meow.

Meow meow meow meow meow meow meow meow. Meow meow meow meow meow meow meow meow meow meow. Meow meow meow meow meow meow, meow meow meow meow meow meow meow meow meow, meow meow meow, meow meow meow meow meow meow, meow meow meow meow meow meow meow. Meow meow meow meow meow meow meow meow. Meow meow meow, meow meow meow meow meow meow meow meow meow meow, meow meow meow, meow meow meow meow meow meow. Meow meow meow meow meow meow. Meow meow meow meow, meow meow meow meow meow meow meow meow meow meow.

"Meow, meow" meow meow, meow meow meow meow meow meow meow, meow meow meow meow meow, meow meow meow meow meow meow meow meow meow meow meow meow, meow meow meow. Meow meow meow meow meow meow, meow meow meow meow meow meow. Meow

meow meow meow meow meow meow meow meow meow meow meow, meow meow meow, meow meow meow meow meow meow meow meow meow meow. Meow meow meow meow meow meow? Meow meow meow meow meow meow meow meow meow meow meow meow meow meow meow.

Meow meow meow meow meow meow, meow meow meow meow meow meow meow. Meow meow meow meow meow meow, meow meow meow meow. Meow meow, meow meow meow meow meow meow meow meow meow meow meow, meow meow meow meow meow. Meow meow meow meow, meow meow meow meow meow meow meow meow meow, meow meow meow meow meow meow meow meow meow, meow meow, meow meow meow, meow meow meow meow meow. Meow meow meow.

Meow meow meow meow meow meow meow meow meow. Meow meow meow meow meow meow meow meow, meow meow meow meow meow meow-meow meow, meow meow meow meow meow meow. Meow meow meow meow meow meow meow meow. Meow meow, meow meow meow meow, meow meow meow meow meow meow meow. Meow meow meow meow, meow meow meow. Meow meow meow meow meow meow meow meow meow meow meow meow, meow meow, meow meow meow meow meow meow meow meow: meow meow meow meow meow meow meow meow. Meow meow meow meow meow meow. Meow meow meow meow meow meow meow meow meow.

Meow meow meow meow, meow meow meow meow meow meow meow meow. Meow meow meow meow meow meow meow meow meow meow meow meow meow meow. Meow meow meow, meow meow meow meow meow meow meow meow meow meow meow meow meow meow. Meow meow meow meow meow meow, meow meow meow meow meow meow meow meow,

meow meow meow meow meow meow meow meow meow
meow, meow meow meow meow meow meow meow. Meow
meow meow meow meow meow meow meow meow meow
meow meow meow. Meow meow meow meow meow meow
meow meow, meow meow meow meow meow meow meow
meow meow meow.

"Meow meow meow meow meow meow meow, meow
meow. Meow meow meow meow meow meow," meow meow
meow. Meow meow meow meow meow meow meow meow.
Meow meow meow meow meow meow, meow meow meow
meow meow meow, meow meow meow meow meow meow
meow meow meow. Meow meow meow meow meow meow
meow meow. Meow meow meow meow, meow meow meow.
Meow meow, meow meow meow meow meow meow meow
meow meow meow meow meow meow meow meow meow
meow meow. Meow meow meow meow meow meow meow
meow meow meow meow meow meow. Meow meow meow,
meow meow meow meow meow. Meow meow meow meow
meow meow meow, meow meow meow meow meow meow
meow. Meow meow meow meow meow meow. Meow meow
meow, meow meow meow meow meow, meow meow meow
meow meow meow meow.

Meow meow meow meow meow meow meow meow meow,
meow meow meow meow meow meow meow, meow meow
meow. Meow meow meow meow meow meow meow meow
meow, meow meow meow meow meow meow meow meow
meow meow meow, meow meow meow meow meow meow
meow meow meow meow meow. Meow meow meow meow
meow meow. Meow meow meow meow meow meow, meow
meow meow meow meow. Meow meow meow meow meow
meow meow meow. Meow meow meow meow meow meow,
meow meow meow meow meow meow meow meow meow

meow meow meow meow meow meow meow meow meow meow meow meow meow. Meow meow meow meow meow meow meow.

"Meow m'eow meow meow?" meow meow, meow meow meow meow meow meow meow meow. Meow meow meow meow, meow meow meow meow meow meow meow meow, meow meow meow meow meow meow meow meow meow meow meow meow meow. Meow meow meow meow meow meow meow meow meow meow meow meow. Meow meow meow meow, meow meow meow meow meow meow meow meow. Meow meow meow meow meow meow meow, meow meow meow meow meow. Meow meow meow meow meow meow meow, meow meow meow meow meow meow meow meow meow, meow meow meow meow meow meow meow meow meow, meow meow meow meow meow meow meow meow meow meow meow meow meow. Meow meow meow meow meow meow meow meow, meow meow meow meow, meow meow meow meow meow meow meow meow. Meow meow meow meow meow meow meow meow meow meow meow meow meow.

Meow meow meow meow meow meow, meow meow meow meow meow meow meow meow, meow meow meow meow meow meow meow meow meow meow meow meow meow, meow meow meow meow meow meow meow meow meow meow meow meow, meow meow meow, meow meow meow meow meow meow meow meow. Meow meow meow meow meow meow meow meow meow meow meow, meow meow meow meow meow meow meow meow meow meow meow. Meow meow meow meow meow. Meow meow meow meow, meow meow meow meow meow meow. Meow meow meow.

Meow meow meow meow. Meow meow meow meow meow meow meow meow meow meow meow meow meow, meow meow

meow meow. Meow meow meow meow meow meow meow meow meow, meow meow meow meow meow meow meow meow meow meow. Meow meow meow meow meow meow meow, meow meow meow meow meow meow meow. Meow meow meow meow meow meow meow meow meow meow meow meow meow meow. Meow meow meow meow meow meow meow meow meow.

Meow meow meow meow meow meow meow meow meow. Meow meow meow meow meow meow, meow meow meow meow meow meow meow, meow meow meow meow meow meow, meow meow meow meow meow, meow meow meow meow meow meow meow meow meow meow, meow meow meow meow meow meow meow meow. Meow meow meow meow meow.

Meow meow meow meow meow meow meow meow meow meow meow meow, meow meow meow meow meow meow meow meow, meow meow meow meow meow meow meow meow meow meow meow meow. Meow meow meow meow meow meow meow. Meow meow meow meow meow meow. Meow meow meow meow meow, meow meow meow meow meow-meow meow meow meow meow meow meow meow meow meow meow. Meow meow meow meow, meow meow meow meow meow. Meow meow meow meow meow meow meow meow meow meow meow meow, meow meow meow meow. Meow meow meow meow meow, meow meow meow meow meow meow meow meow meow meow meow meow, meow meow meow meow meow meow meow meow. Meow meow, meow meow meow meow meow meow meow meow meow. Meow meow meow meow, meow meow meow meow meow meow meow.

Meow meow meow meow meow, meow meow meow meow meow. Meow meow meow. meow meow meow meow meow meow.

Meow meow meow meow meow meow meow meow meow meow. Meow meow meow meow meow meow meow, meow meow meow meow Meow. Meow meow meow meow meow meow meow, meow meow meow. Meow, meow meow meow meow, meow meow meow meow meow meow meow meow. meow meow meow meow meow, meow meow meow meow, meow meow meow. Meow meow meow meow meow meow. Meow meow meow. Meow meow meow meow meow. Meow meow. Meow meow meow meow. Meow meow meow.

MEOW?

Meow meow meow meow meow meow, meow meow meow meow meow meow meow. Meow meow meow meow meow meow meow meow meow, meow meow meow meow meow meow. Meow meow meow meow meow. Meow meow meow meow meow meow meow meow meow, meow meow meow meow meow meow meow. Meow meow meow meow meow meow meow meow meow meow, meow meow meow meow meow, meow meow meow, meow meow meow, meow meow meow meow meow meow meow meow meow meow meow, meow meow meow meow meow meow meow meow meow meow. Meow meow meow meow meow meow meow. Meow meow meow meow meow meow meow meow meow meow meow. Meow meow meow meow meow meow meow, meow meow meow meow meow meow meow, meow meow meow meow meow meow meow. Meow meow meow meow meow meow, meow meow meow meow meow meow meow meow meow meow, meow meow meow meow meow meow meow meow. Meow meow meow meow, meow meow meow, meow meow meow meow meow-meow meow, meow meow meow meow meow.

Meow meow meow meow meow meow meow meow meow meow, meow meow meow meow meow meow meow, meow meow meow meow meow, meow meow meow meow. Meow meow meow meow. Meow meow meow meow meow, meow meow

meow meow meow meow. Meow meow meow meow meow meow meow meow meow meow meow. Meow meow meow meow meow meow meow. Meow meow meow meow meow meow meow meow meow, meow meow meow meow meow meow meow meow, meow meow meow meow meow meow meow meow meow.

"Meow meow meow meow meow meow meow meow," meow meow meow, meow meow meow meow meow meow meow meow meow meow meow meow.

Meow meow meow meow meow meow, meow meow meow meow meow, meow meow meow meow meow meow meow meow meow-meow meow, meow-meow meow meow meow, meow meow meow meow, meow meow meow meow meow meow meow meow meow, meow meow. Meow meow, meow meow meow meow meow, meow meow meow meow meow meow meow meow, meow meow, meow meow meow meow meow meow meow meow, meow meow meow meow. Meow meow meow meow meow, meow meow meow meow meow meow meow meow. Meow meow meow meow meow meow meow meow, meow meow meow meow. Meow meow meow meow meow meow meow, meow meow meow meow meow meow. Meow meow meow. Meow meow meow meow meow meow, meow meow meow meow meow meow meow meow, meow meow, meow meow meow meow meow meow meow meow meow meow meow meow meow.

Meow meow meow meow meow meow meow meow meow, meow meow meow meow meow meow meow, meow meow meow meow meow meow meow meow meow, meow meow meow meow meow meow meow, meow meow meow meow meow meow, meow meow meow meow, meow meow, meow meow meow meow meow meow meow meow meow. Meow meow meow meow meow meow meow meow meow meow, meow meow meow meow meow. Meow meow meow meow. Meow meow meow meow meow meow, meow meow meow

meow meow meow meow meow meow meow meow meow meow meow meow. Meow meow meow meow. Meow meow meow meow meow meow, meow meow meow meow meow meow. Meow, meow meow.

Meow meow meow meow meow meow, meow meow meow meow meow meow meow. Meow meow meow meow meow meow meow meow meow meow meow, meow meow meow meow meow meow meow meow. Meow meow meow meow meow meow meow meow meow, meow meow. Meow meow meow meow meow, meow meow meow meow meow meow meow meow meow, meow meow meow meow meow meow meow, meow meow meow meow meow meow meow meow meow. Meow meow meow meow meow meow meow meow meow meow, meow meow meow meow meow. Meow meow meow meow meow.

"Meow meow meow meow meow. Meow meow meow meow meow meow," meow meow meow meow meow meow meow meow meow.

Meow meow meow meow meow, meow meow meow meow meow meow meow meow, meow meow meow meow meow. Meow meow meow meow meow meow meow meow meow meow meow meow meow meow meow, meow meow meow meow meow meow meow. Meow meow meow meow meow meow meow meow. Meow meow meow meow meow, meow meow meow meow meow meow meow meow meow meow meow meow meow meow meow. Meow meow meow meow meow meow meow meow meow meow meow meow meow.

Meow meow meow meow meow meow meow meow meow, meow meow meow meow meow meow meow meow meow meow meow meow meow meow. Meow, meow meow meow meow meow meow meow, meow meow meow meow meow,

meow meow meow meow meow meow meow. Meow meow meow meow meow, meow meow meow meow meow, meow meow meow meow meow meow meow. Meow meow meow meow meow. Meow meow, meow meow meow meow meow, meow meow meow meow meow meow meow meow. Meow meow meow meow meow, meow meow meow meow. Meow meow meow meow meow, meow meow meow meow meow meow meow, meow meow, meow meow, meow meow, meow meow meow meow meow meow meow meow meow meow meow meow meow, meow meow meow meow meow meow, meow meow meow meow meow meow.

* * * * * * *

Meow meow meow meow. Meow meow meow meow meow meow meow meow meow meow meow. Meow meow meow meow meow meow meow meow. Meow meow. Meow meow meow meow, meow meow meow meow meow meow meow meow meow meow meow meow meow meow. Meow meow meow meow meow, meow meow meow meow meow meow meow-meow meow. Meow meow meow meow, meow meow meow meow meow, meow meow meow meow. Meow meow meow meow meow. Meow meow meow meow meow meow meow, meow meow meow meow meow, meow meow meow, meow meow meow meow meow meow meow. Meow meow meow meow meow meow meow meow. Meow meow meow meow meow meow, meow meow meow meow meow meow meow, meow meow meow meow meow meow, meow meow meow meow meow meow meow.

Meow meow meow meow meow meow, meow meow meow, meow meow meow meow meow meow meow meow meow meow meow meow meow meow meow meow meow. Meow meow meow

meow meow meow, meow meow meow meow. Meow meow meow meow meow meow meow, meow meow meow meow meow, meow meow meow meow meow meow meow, meow meow, meow meow meow meow meow meow meow, meow meow meow meow. Meow meow meow meow meow meow meow, meow meow, meow meow meow meow meow meow meow meow meow meow. Meow meow meow meow meow meow meow meow meow meow meow, meow meow meow meow meow meow meow meow, meow meow meow meow meow meow meow. Meow meow meow meow meow meow meow meow meow meow meow, meow meow meow meow. Meow meow meow meow meow meow meow meow meow meow. Meow meow meow meow meow meow meow meow meow meow meow meow, meow meow meow meow meow meow meow meow meow meow meow meow meow meow meow meow.

Meow meow meow meow meow meow, meow meow meow meow meow meow meow meow, meow meow meow. Meow meow meow meow. Meow meow meow meow meow meow meow, meow meow meow meow meow meow meow meow, meow meow meow, meow meow meow meow, meow meow Meow Meow meow meow meow. Meow meow meow meow meow meow, meow meow meow meow meow meow meow, meow meow meow meow meow meow meow meow meow meow meow meow meow, meow meow meow meow meow, meow meow meow meow meow, meow, meow meow meow meow meow meow meow meow. Meow meow meow meow, meow meow meow meow meow meow, meow meow meow meow meow meow meow meow meow, meow meow meow meow meow meow meow meow. Meow meow meow meow meow meow meow meow meow meow meow, meow meow meow meow, meow meow meow meow meow meow meow meow meow meow meow,

meow meow meow meow meow. Meow meow meow meow meow meow meow meow meow meow, meow meow meow meow, meow meow meow meow meow meow meow. Meow meow meow meow meow meow meow meow, meow meow. Meow meow, meow meow meow meow? Meow meow meow meow meow, meow meow meow Meow Meow meow meow meow. Meow meow meow meow, meow meow meow meow meow meow meow meow, meow meow meow meow meow meow meow meow meow. Meow meow meow.

Meow meow meow, meow meow meow meow, meow meow meow meow meow. Meow meow meow meow meow, meow meow meow meow, meow meow meow meow meow meow meow meow meow, meow meow meow meow meow meow meow. Meow meow meow meow, meow meow. Meow meow meow meow meow meow meow meow-meow, meow meow meow meow meow meow, meow meow meow. Meow meow meow meow meow meow meow meow meow, meow meow meow meow meow meow. Meow meow meow meow meow meow meow. Meow meow meow meow meow meow, meow meow meow meow meow meow meow, meow meow meow meow meow meow, meow meow meow meow meow meow meow. Meow meow meow meow meow meow meow meow meow meow meow Meow.

"Meow meow meow meow meow meow meow meow meow, meow meow mcow meow meow meow," meow meow, meow meow meow meow meow meow meow meow. Meow meow meow meow meow meow meow meow meow, meow mcow meow, meow meow meow meow meow meow meow meow meow meow meow meow meow meow meow meow.

Meow meow meow meow meow meow meow meow.

Meow meow meow meow meow, meow meow meow meow, meow meow meow meow meow, meow meow meow-meow meow, meow meow meow meow meow meow, meow meow meow

meow meow meow. Meow meow meow, meow meow meow meow meow meow, meow meow meow meow meow-meow meow meow meow meow meow meow meow meow meow meow meow meow meow meow meow meow. Meow meow meow meow meow meow meow meow meow meow meow meow meow meow meow, meow meow meow meow meow meow meow meow meow meow meow meow, meow meow meow meow meow meow meow meow meow, meow meow meow meow meow meow meow meow meow meow meow meow, meow meow meow meow meow meow, meow meow meow meow meow meow meow meow meow meow meow meow.

Meow meow meow meow meow meow meow meow. Meow meow meow meow meow, meow meow meow meow meow. Meow meow meow meow meow meow meow meow meow, "Meow meow meow meow Meow!"

Meow meow meow, meow meow meow meow meow meow meow-meow meow, meow meow meow meow meow, meow meow meow meow meow meow meow. Meow meow meow meow meow meow meow meow meow meow meow, meow meow meow meow meow meow meow meow meow meow. Meow meow meow meow meow meow meow meow meow, meow meow meow meow meow meow, meow meow meow meow meow meow meow meow. Meow meow meow meow meow meow meow meow meow meow meow meow meow meow meow, meow meow meow meow meow. Meow meow meow meow meow, meow meow meow meow meow meow meow meow meow. Meow meow meow meow meow meow meow meow meow meow, meow, meow meow meow meow meow meow meow. Meow meow meow meow meow meow meow meow meow.

Meow meow meow meow meow meow meow meow meow meow. Meow meow meow meow meow meow meow MEOW, meow meow meow, meow meow meow meow meow meow.

Meow meow meow meow meow meow, meow meow meow meow meow meow meow meow, meow meow meow meow meow meow meow meow.

Meow meow meow meow meow meow, meow meow meow meow meow meow. Meow meow meow meow, meow meow meow meow meow meow meow meow meow. Meow meow meow meow, meow meow meow meow, meow meow meow meow meow meow. Meow meow meow, meow meow meow meow. Meow meow meow meow. Meow meow meow meow meow meow meow meow meow Meow meow meow. Meow meow meow meow meow meow meow meow meow, meow meow meow.

Meow meow meow meow meow meow. Meow meow meow meow meow meow meow meow meow meow, meow meow meow meow meow meow meow meow, meow meow meow meow meow. Meow meow meow meow meow meow, meow meow meow meow meow meow meow meow meow meow meow. Meow meow meow meow meow meow meow meow meow.

Meow meow meow meow meow meow, meow meow meow meow meow meow meow meow meow, meow meow meow meow meow meow meow meow meow, meow meow meow meow meow meow meow meow meow meow meow. Meow meow meow meow, meow meow meow meow. Meow meow meow meow meow. Meow meow meow meow meow. Meow meow meow meow meow meow meow Meow. Meow meow meow meow meow meow meow meow meow meow meow. Meow meow meow meow meow meow, meow meow meow meow meow meow meow, meow meow meow meow meow meow meow. Meow meow meow meow meow meow.

MEOW

Meow meow meow meow meow meow, meow meow meow meow meow Meow meow meow meow meow. Meow meow meow meow meow, meow meow meow meow meow meow meow meow, meow meow meow meow, meow meow meow meow, meow meow. Meow meow meow meow meow meow meow meow meow. Meow meow meow meow meow meow meow meow meow meow meow meow meow meow, meow, meow meow meow meow meow meow meow, meow meow meow meow meow meow meow meow. Meow meow meow meow meow meow meow meow meow meow meow meow, meow meow meow meow meow meow, meow meow, meow, meow meow meow. Meow meow meow-meow. Meow meow meow meow meow meow meow meow. Meow meow meow meow meow meow meow meow. Meow meow meow meow meow meow meow, meow meow meow meow meow, meow meow meow, meow meow meow.

Meow meow meow meow meow meow, meow meow meow meow meow meow, meow meow. Meow meow meow meow meow meow meow meow meow meow meow meow meow meow meow meow meow meow meow, meow meow meow meow meow meow meow meow meow meow. Meow meow meow meow meow meow meow meow meow meow. Meow meow meow meow. meow meow meow meow meow meow. Meow meow meow meow meow meow meow meow, meow meow meow

meow meow meow meow meow. Meow meow meow meow meow, meow meow meow meow meow meow meow, meow meow meow meow meow, meow meow meow meow meow meow meow, meow meow meow meow meow meow meow meow, meow meow meow meow meow, meow meow meow meow meow meow meow meow meow meow meow. Meow meow meow meow meow meow meow meow, meow meow meow meow meow meow meow meow meow meow. Meow meow meow meow meow meow meow. Meow meow meow meow meow meow meow, meow meow meow meow meow meow, meow meow meow meow.

Meow meow meow meow meow meow, meow meow meow meow meow meow meow meow. Meow meow meow meow meow meow, meow meow meow, meow meow meow meow meow meow, meow meow meow meow meow meow meow meow meow meow, meow meow meow meow meow meow. Meow meow meow meow meow meow meow meow meow meow meow. Meow meow meow meow meow meow. Meow meow meow meow meow meow meow meow meow, meow meow meow meow meow meow meow meow.

Meow meow meow. meow meow meow meow meow meow meow meow meow, meow meow meow meow meow meow, meow meow meow. Meow meow meow. Meow meow meow meow meow. Meow meow meow meow meow meow meow, meow meow meow meow. Meow meow meow. Meow meow meow meow meow meow, meow. Meow meow meow meow meow meow. Meow meow meow meow meow meow meow meow, meow meow meow meow meow meow, meow Meow meow meow. Meow meow meow meow meow, meow meow meow meow meow meow meow meow meow

meow meow meow meow meow meow meow meow, meow
meow meow meow meow. Meow meow meow meow meow
meow meow meow meow, meow meow meow meow meow
meow meow meow, meow meow meow meow meow meow
meow meow. Meow meow meow meow meow meow, meow
meow meow meow meow meow, meow meow meow meow
meow meow meow meow meow. Meow meow meow, meow
meow meow meow meow meow meow meow meow meow
meow meow. Meow meow meow meow, meow meow meow
meow meow meow meow meow meow meow meow, meow
meow meow meow, meow meow meow meow, meow meow
meow meow meow meow meow, meow. Meow meow meow
meow meow meow meow meow.

Meow meow meow meow meow meow meow meow meow.
Meow meow meow meow meow. Meow meow meow meow
meow. Meow meow meow meow. Meow meow meow, meow
meow meow meow, meow meow meow meow. Meow meow
meow meow meow. Meow meow meow meow meow meow,
meow meow meow, meow meow meow meow. Meow meow
meow meow meow meow meow meow meow meow. Meow
meow meow meow. Meow meow meow meow, meow meow
meow meow meow meow, meow meow meow meow meow meow
meow meow. Meow meow meow meow meow meow meow.

＊＊＊＊＊＊＊

Meow meow meow meow meow meow meow meow meow
meow meow meow meow meow meow meow meow meow,
meow meow meow. Meow meow meow meow meow meow
meow meow, meow meow meow meow meow meow meow
meow meow meow meow meow. Meow meow meow, meow,
meow meow meow meow meow meow meow, meow meow

meow meow meow meow. Meow meow meow meow meow
meow meow meow, meow meow, meow meow meow meow
meow, meow meow, meow meow meow meow, meow meow
meow meow. Meow meow meow meow meow meow meow
meow meow meow meow, meow meow meow meow meow
meow, meow meow meow meow meow meow meow meow
meow. Meow meow meow. Meow meow meow.

Meow meow meow. Meow meow meow meow meow meow
meow. Meow meow meow meow meow meow. Meow meow
meow meow meow meow meow meow meow, meow meow
meow meow meow, meow meow meow meow meow. Meow
meow meow meow meow meow meow meow, meow
meow meow meow. Meow meow meow meow meow meow
meow meow meow, meow meow meow meow meow meow
meow. Meow meow meow meow.

Meow meow meow meow meow, meow meow meow meow
meow meow. Meow meow meow meow meow meow meow
meow. Meow meow meow meow meow meow meow, meow
meow meow meow, meow meow meow meow meow meow
meow meow. Meow meow meow, meow, meow meow meow
meow meow meow, meow meow meow meow meow meow.
Meow meow. Meow meow meow meow meow, meow meow,
meow meow meow meow, meow meow meow meow. Meow
meow meow meow meow meow meow meow meow meow
meow, meow meow meow meow meow meow, meow meow
meow meow meow meow meow meow meow meow. Meow
meow meow. Meow meow meow.

Meow meow meow. Meow meow meow meow meow meow
meow meow. Meow meow meow meow meow meow meow.
Meow meow meow meow meow, meow meow meow, meow
meow meow meow meow, Meow Meow Meow. Meow meow
meow meow meow. meow, meow, meow meow. Meow meow

meow meow meow meow meow meow meow meow meow meow meow, meow meow meow meow meow, meow meow meow meow, meow meow meow meow meow meow meow meow, meow meow meow meow meow meow meow. Meow meow meow meow meow meow meow. Meow meow meow meow meow meow meow meow, meow Meow meow meow meow meow, meow meow meow meow meow meow meow meow meow meow meow. Meow meow meow meow meow meow meow, meow meow meow meow meow, meow meow meow meow meow meow meow meow meow. Meow meow meow meow meow meow meow, meow meow meow meow meow, meow meow meow meow meow meow meow meow.

Meow meow meow meow meow. Meow meow Meow. Meow meow meow meow meow meow meow meow meow meow meow meow meow meow meow meow meow meow. Meow meow meow meow meow meow meow meow meow meow meow, meow meow meow meow, meow meow meow meow meow meow meow meow meow meow.

Meow meow meow meow meow meow meow. Meow meow meow meow meow.

Meow meow meow meow. Meow meow meow meow meow, meow meow meow meow meow meow meow meow meow meow. Meow meow meow meow meow meow meow meow meow meow meow, meow meow meow meow meow meow meow meow, meow meow meow meow meow meow meow meow meow meow meow meow meow meow meow. Meow meow meow meow meow meow meow meow. Meow meow meow meow meow meow. Meow meow meow meow, meow meow meow meow meow.

Meow meow meow, meow meow meow meow. Meow meow meow. Meow meow meow meow meow meow meow meow meow, meow. Meow meow meow meow meow meow meow

meow meow meow meow meow meow meow meow, meow
meow meow meow meow meow meow meow meow meow,
meow meow meow meow meow meow meow. Meow meow
meow meow meow meow meow meow. Meow meow meow,
meow meow meow meow meow meow. Meow meow meow
meow meow meow meow meow meow, meow meow meow
meow meow meow meow, meow meow meow meow meow
meow meow. Meow meow meow meow meow meow meow
meow meow, meow meow meow meow meow meow, meow
meow meow meow. Meow meow meow meow meow, meow
meow meow meow meow meow meow meow meow meow meow
meow meow meow meow. Meow meow meow meow, meow
meow meow meow meow meow meow meow meow meow.

Meow Meow meow meow, meow meow meow meow meow
meow. Meow meow meow, meow meow meow meow meow
meow meow meow meow meow meow meow meow, meow meow
meow meow meow, meow meow, meow meow meow meow
meow meow meow meow meow meow.

* * * * * * *

Meow meow meow meow meow, meow meow meow meow
meow. Meow meow meow meow meow meow meow meow,
meow meow meow meow meow meow meow meow meow, meow
meow meow meow meow meow meow-meow meow,
meow meow meow meow meow meow meow meow. Meow
meow meow meow meow meow meow, meow meow
meow meow. Meow meow meow meow meow meow meow
meow meow meow meow meow, meow meow meow meow meow
meow, meow meow meow meow meow. Meow meow meow
meow meow meow meow meow, meow meow meow, meow
meow, meow meow meow meow meow meow. Meow meow meow

meow meow meow meow meow meow meow meow Meow meow meow meow meow meow. Meow meow meow meow, meow, meow meow meow meow meow meow meow meow meow, meow meow meow meow meow meow meow meow meow meow meow meow. Meow meow meow meow meow meow meow meow meow meow meow meow meow. Meow meow meow meow meow meow meow meow meow meow. Meow meow meow meow meow meow, meow meow meow meow Meow meow meow meow meow. Meow meow, meow meow meow meow meow meow meow. Meow meow meow meow meow meow meow meow meow meow meow.

Meow meow meow meow, meow meow meow meow. Meow meow meow meow meow meow meow meow meow meow, meow meow meow meow meow, meow meow meow, meow meow meow meow, meow meow meow meow meow meow. Meow meow meow meow, meow meow meow meow meow, meow meow meow meow. Meow meow meow meow meow MEOW meow meow. Meow meow meow meow, meow meow meow meow meow meow meow, meow meow meow meow. Meow meow meow meow meow, meow meow meow meow meow meow, meow meow meow meow meow meow. Meow meow meow meow meow. Meow meow meow meow meow meow. Meow meow meow meow meow meow meow meow. Meow meow meow meow meow meow.

Meow meow meow meow meow meow meow meow meow meow meow meow meow, meow meow, meow meow meow meow meow. Meow meow, meow meow meow meow meow meow meow, meow meow meow meow meow meow meow meow meow meow meow meow meow. Meow meow meow meow meow meow meow. Meow meow meow meow meow meow meow meow. Meow meow meow meow meow meow meow meow, meow meow meow meow meow

meow meow meow meow. Meow meow meow meow meow meow meow meow meow meow meow. meow meow meow meow meow meow meow meow meow meow. Meow meow meow meow meow, meow meow, meow meow meow meow meow meow meow meow meow meow meow, meow meow meow meow meow, meow meow meow meow meow. Meow meow meow. Meow meow meow meow meow meow meow meow meow meow? Meow meow meow meow meow meow, meow meow meow, meow meow. Meow meow meow. Meow meow meow meow meow meow, meow meow meow meow meow meow, meow meow meow meow meow meow, meow meow meow meow meow. Meow meow meow meow meow meow meow, meow meow meow meow meow meow. Meow meow meow meow meow meow meow, meow meow meow meow meow meow meow meow meow meow. Meow meow meow meow meow meow meow meow meow.

Meow meow meow meow meow meow meow, meow meow meow meow meow. Meow meow meow meow meow meow meow, meow meow meow meow meow meow meow meow meow meow meow, meow meow meow meow meow meow. Meow meow meow meow meow meow, meow meow meow meow meow meow meow meow, meow meow meow meow meow meow meow meow, meow meow meow meow, meow meow meow meow meow meow meow meow. Meow meow meow meow meow meow. Meow meow meow meow meow, meow meow meow, meow meow meow meow meow meow, meow, meow meow meow meow. Meow, meow meow meow meow meow meow meow. Meow meow meow meow meow meow, meow meow meow.

Meow meow meow meow, meow meow. Meow meow meow meow meow meow meow meow meow, meow meow meow, meow meow. Meow meow meow meow meow meow meow

meow, meow meow meow meow meow meow meow, meow, meow meow meow meow.

"Meow meow meow meow meow meow, meow?" meow meow meow meow meow meow meow meow meow meow meow.

"Meow, meow meow meow, meow meow meow meow meow meow. Meow meow meow meow meow meow meow meow meow meow."

Meow meow meow meow, meow meow meow meow meow meow meow meow meow meow. Meow meow meow meow meow, meow meow meow meow meow. Meow meow meow meow meow meow meow meow meow, meow meow meow meow meow meow meow meow. Meow meow meow meow meow meow meow? Meow, meow meow, meow meow meow meow.

Meow meow meow meow meow meow meow meow meow meow meow meow, meow meow meow meow, meow meow meow, meow meow meow meow meow meow meow meow. Meow meow meow meow, meow meow meow. Meow meow meow meow meow, meow meow meow meow meow meow meow, meow meow meow meow meow, meow meow meow. meow meow meow. Meow meow meow meow meow meow, meow meow meow meow meow meow meow, meow meow meow meow meow meow meow meow meow meow.

Meow meow meow meow meow. Meow meow, meow meow meow meow meow, meow. Meow meow meow meow meow meow meow meow meow meow meow meow, meow meow meow meow meow, meow meow meow meow meow meow meow meow meow meow meow meow, meow meow meow meow meow meow meow meow meow meow meow meow meow meow meow. Meow meow meow meow meow meow, meow meow meow meow meow meow meow meow meow meow, meow meow meow meow meow meow meow meow

meow meow meow meow meow meow meow, meow meow meow meow: meow meow meow meow meow meow meow.

Meow meow meow meow meow meow meow meow meow meow meow meow.

Meow meow meow meow meow meow meow meow, meow meow meow meow meow meow meow meow meow. Meow meow meow meow meow meow meow. Meow meow meow meow, meow meow meow meow meow meow meow. Meow meow meow, meow meow meow meow meow, meow meow meow meow meow meow meow meow meow meow meow meow, meow meow meow meow.

Meow meow meow, meow meow meow meow, meow meow meow, meow meow meow meow meow meow meow meow meow. Meow meow meow meow meow meow, meow meow meow meow. Meow meow meow meow meow meow meow. Meow meow meow meow meow meow meow meow, meow meow meow meow meow meow meow meow meow meow meow. Meow meow meow meow meow meow meow meow? Meow meow meow meow meow meow meow meow meow?

Meow meow meow meow meow meow meow meow meow. Meow meow meow meow meow meow, meow meow meow meow meow meow meow meow meow, meow meow meow meow meow meow meow meow, meow meow meow meow meow. Meow meow meow meow meow meow meow meow meow meow meow meow, meow meow meow, meow meow meow meow meow, meow meow meow meow meow meow meow meow meow meow. Meow meow meow meow meow meow meow, meow meow, meow meow meow meow meow meow meow meow. Meow meow meow meow meow, meow meow meow meow meow meow meow meow meow meow.

MEOW

Meow meow meow meow meow meow. Meow meow meow meow, meow meow meow meow meow. Meow meow meow meow meow meow, meow meow, meow meow meow meow meow meow meow meow meow, meow meow meow meow. Meow meow meow meow meow meow meow meow.

Meow meow meow meow meow meow. Meow meow meow meow meow meow meow meow, meow meow meow meow meow meow, meow meow meow meow meow meow meow meow meow, meow meow meow meow meow meow meow meow meow meow meow, meow meow meow meow, meow meow meow meow meow. Meow meow meow meow. Meow meow meow. Meow meow-meow meow meow meow meow meow meow meow meow meow meow meow meow, meow meow meow meow meow meow meow meow meow meow-meow-meow. Meow meow meow, meow meow meow meow. Meow meow meow meow meow meow.

Meow meow meow meow meow meow meow meow meow meow meow meow. Meow meow meow meow meow meow meow meow meow meow. Meow meow meow meow, meow meow, meow meow meow. Meow meow meow meow, meow meow meow meow meow meow meow. Meow meow meow meow meow meow meow, meow meow meow meow meow meow. Meow meow meow meow meow meow meow. Meow

meow meow meow meow. Meow meow meow meow meow meow meow meow. Meow.

Meow meow meow meow meow meow meow meow meow meow meow meow meow meow, meow meow meow meow meow meow meow, meow meow meow meow meow meow meow meow, meow meow meow meow meow meow meow meow meow meow, meow meow meow meow meow meow. Meow meow meow meow meow meow meow.

Meow meow meow meow meow, meow meow meow, meow meow meow meow, meow meow meow meow meow meow meow meow. Meow meow meow meow meow meow meow meow meow meow. Meow meow meow meow meow, meow meow meow meow meow meow meow, meow meow meow meow, meow meow meow meow. Meow meow, meow meow meow meow meow meow, meow meow meow meow meow, meow meow meow meow meow. Meow meow meow meow meow meow meow meow. Meow meow meow. Meow meow meow meow meow meow meow, meow meow meow meow. Meow meow meow meow meow meow meow meow meow meow meow meow meow meow. Meow meow meow meow meow meow meow meow, meow meow meow. Meow meow meow meow meow meow meow meow meow meow, meow meow-meow meow, meow meow meow, meow meow meow meow meow meow meow meow, meow meow meow meow meow meow meow meow meow meow.

Meow meow meow meow meow meow, meow mcow meow meow, meow meow meow meow meow meow meow meow meow, meow meow meow, meow meow meow meow meow meow meow meow meow meow meow meow meow meow, meow meow meow meow. Meow meow meow meow meow meow, meow meow meow meow meow meow meow meow. Meow meow meow meow meow. Meow meow meow, meow

meow. Meow meow meow meow meow meow meow meow meow meow meow meow meow meow, meow meow meow meow meow. Meow meow, meow meow meow meow meow meow meow. Meow meow meow meow, meow meow meow meow, meow meow meow meow meow meow.

Meow meow meow. Meow meow meow meow meow meow meow. Meow meow meow meow meow meow meow, meow meow meow meow meow. Meow meow meow meow meow meow meow meow meow meow meow meow. Meow meow meow meow meow meow, meow meow meow meow meow meow meow meow meow meow, meow meow meow meow meow meow. Meow meow meow meow, meow meow meow meow meow. Meow meow meow meow meow meow meow meow meow meow, meow meow meow meow meow meow meow meow meow, meow meow meow meow meow meow meow meow meow meow meow meow meow meow meow.

"Meow meow meow meow meow meow meow meow meow meow meow meow meow, meow meow meow meow meow meow," meow meow meow. Meow meow meow meow meow meow meow, meow meow, meow meow meow meow meow meow meow meow meow meow meow.

Meow meow meow meow meow. Meow meow meow meow meow meow meow, meow meow meow meow meow. Meow meow meow, meow meow meow meow meow meow meow meow meow meow. Meow meow meow meow meow meow meow, meow meow meow meow meow.

Meow meow meow meow meow meow. Meow meow meow meow meow. Meow meow, meow meow meow meow meow meow meow meow meow meow meow-meow meow meow meow meow. Meow meow meow meow meow meow meow. Meow meow meow meow meow meow, meow meow meow meow meow meow meow meow meow. Meow meow meow meow.

Meow meow meow, meow meow meow meow. Meow meow meow meow meow meow meow meow, meow meow meow meow meow meow meow meow meow meow meow. Meow meow meow meow meow meow meow, meow meow meow meow meow meow. Meow meow meow meow-meow meow meow. Meow meow meow meow meow meow meow, meow meow, meow. Meow meow meow meow meow meow meow meow meow meow meow meow, meow meow meow meow, meow meow meow meow meow meow. Meow meow meow. Meow meow meow meow meow. Meow meow meow meow meow meow, meow meow meow meow, meow meow meow meow meow meow meow. Meow meow meow meow meow. Meow meow meow meow meow meow meow. Meow meow meow meow meow, meow meow meow meow meow meow meow meow.

Meow meow meow meow meow meow meow meow meow meow, meow meow meow meow meow meow meow, meow meow meow meow meow meow. Meow meow meow meow meow meow meow, meow meow meow meow meow meow meow. Meow meow, meow. Meow meow meow meow meow meow meow, meow meow meow meow meow meow meow meow, meow meow meow meow. Meow meow meow meow meow, meow meow meow meow meow meow meow. Meow meow meow meow meow meow.

Meow meow meow meow meow meow meow, meow meow meow meow meow meow meow meow meow meow. Meow meow meow meow meow meow. Meow meow meow meow meow meow. Meow meow, meow meow meow meow. Meow meow meow meow meow meow meow meow, meow meow meow meow. Meow meow meow meow meow meow meow meow, meow meow meow meow meow. Meow meow meow meow meow meow meow. Meow meow meow meow meow

meow meow meow. Meow meow meow meow meow meow, meow meow meow meow meow meow meow meow meow meow. Meow meow meow meow meow meow.

Meow meow meow meow meow meow meow meow, meow meow meow meow meow. Meow meow meow meow meow meow meow meow, meow meow meow meow meow meow meow meow, meow meow meow meow meow meow meow meow-meow meow meow meow, meow meow meow meow meow meow meow meow meow meow meow meow. Meow meow meow meow meow meow meow meow meow, meow meow meow meow, meow meow meow meow meow meow, meow meow meow meow. Meow meow meow meow meow meow meow, meow meow meow meow meow meow meow meow meow meow meow meow meow meow. Meow meow meow meow meow, meow meow meow, meow meow meow meow, meow meow meow meow meow meow meow. Meow meow meow meow meow meow, meow meow meow meow, meow meow meow meow meow meow meow, meow meow meow meow meow meow. Meow meow meow meow. Meow meow meow meow meow meow meow meow meow meow meow meow meow meow. Meow meow meow meow meow meow meow, meow meow meow meow. Meow meow meow, meow meow meow meow meow, meow meow meow, meow meow meow meow meow meow meow. Meow meow meow meow.

Meow meow meow meow meow meow meow meow meow, meow. Meow meow meow meow meow meow. Meow meow meow meow meow meow meow meow meow meow meow, meow meow meow, meow meow meow meow meow meow meow meow. Meow meow meow meow meow, meow meow meow meow meow meow meow, meow meow meow meow meow meow. Meow meow meow meow meow meow meow,

meow meow meow meow meow meow meow meow. Meow meow meow. Meow meow meow meow meow meow meow. Meow meow meow meow meow meow, meow meow meow meow meow meow, meow meow meow meow meow meow. Meow meow meow meow meow meow meow meow meow, meow meow meow meow meow, meow meow meow meow meow meow meow meow meow. Meow meow meow meow meow, meow meow meow. Meow meow meow meow meow meow meow meow meow meow meow meow meow, meow meow meow meow meow meow. Meow meow meow meow meow, meow meow meow meow meow meow meow meow meow meow meow. Meow meow meow meow meow meow meow, meow meow meow meow meow. Meow meow meow. Meow meow meow meow meow meow meow meow meow meow meow meow.

Meow meow meow meow, meow meow meow meow. Meow meow meow meow meow, meow meow meow meow meow meow meow meow meow, meow meow meow meow meow. Meow meow meow meow meow meow. Meow meow meow meow meow meow meow. Meow meow meow meow meow, meow meow meow. Meow meow meow meow. Meow meow meow meow, meow meow meow meow meow. Meow meow meow meow, meow meow meow meow meow meow meow meow meow meow meow meow meow, meow meow meow meow meow meow. Meow meow meow meow meow, meow-meow. Meow meow meow meow meow meow, meow meow meow meow meow meow, meow meow.

Meow meow meow, meow meow meow meow meow meow meow meow meow meow meow meow meow. Meow meow meow meow meow meow meow. Meow meow meow meow meow meow meow meow meow meow meow, meow meow meow, meow meow meow meow. Meow meow meow meow meow meow

meow meow, meow meow meow meow meow meow meow
meow. Meow meow meow meow meow meow meow meow.
Meow meow meow meow meow meow. Meow meow meow
meow meow meow meow meow meow, meow meow meow
meow. Meow meow meow meow meow meow meow.

Meow meow meow meow meow meow meow meow meow
meow meow meow. Meow meow meow. Meow meow meow
meow meow meow meow. Meow meow-meow. Meow meow
meow meow meow meow meow meow meow, meow meow
meow meow meow meow meow meow meow meow meow.

Meow meow meow meow meow, meow meow meow meow
meow meow meow meow, meow meow meow meow meow
meow meow. Meow meow Meow meow meow meow meow
meow. Meow meow meow meow, meow meow meow, meow
meow meow. Meow meow meow meow meow meow. Meow
meow meow meow meow meow meow meow. Meow meow
meow meow meow meow meow, meow meow meow meow
meow meow. Meow meow meow meow meow meow meow
meow meow meow meow. Meow meow meow meow meow
meow meow meow, meow meow meow meow meow. Meow
meow meow meow meow meow, meow meow meow
meow meow meow. Meow meow meow meow meow meow
meow. Meow meow meow, meow meow meow meow.

Meow meow meow meow meow meow meow. Meow meow
meow meow meow meow meow. Meow meow meow meow
meow meow meow meow meow, meow meow meow meow
meow meow meow meow meow meow meow. Meow meow
meow meow, meow meow meow meow meow, meow meow
meow. Meow meow meow meow. Meow meow meow meow
meow, meow meow meow meow meow meow. Meow meow
meow, meow meow meow meow meow meow meow meow.
Meow meow meow, meow meow meow. Meow meow meow

meow. Meow meow meow meow, meow meow meow, meow meow meow meow meow meow meow meow. Meow meow meow meow meow meow. Meow meow meow meow meow, meow meow meow meow meow meow meow, meow meow meow meow meow, meow meow meow meow meow meow meow. Meow meow meow meow meow. Meow meow meow.

Meow meow meow meow meow meow meow, meow meow meow meow, meow meow meow meow meow meow meow. Meow meow meow meow meow meow meow meow, meow meow meow meow. Meow meow meow meow meow meow meow, meow meow meow meow meow. Meow meow meow meow meow meow meow meow meow meow meow meow, meow meow meow meow, meow meow meow meow meow meow. Meow meow, meow meow meow meow, meow meow meow meow meow, meow meow meow meow meow meow meow, meow meow meow meow meow meow meow meow meow, meow meow meow meow meow meow meow. Meow meow meow meow meow meow meow meow. Meow meow meow meow meow meow meow, meow meow meow meow meow meow meow meow meow, meow meow meow meow, meow meow meow meow meow meow. Meow meow meow meow meow meow, meow meow, meow meow meow meow meow meow meow meow meow meow meow meow meow, meow, meow-meow. Meow. Meow meow mcow meow meow meow.

Meow meow meow meow meow meow meow? Meow meow meow meow meow. Meow meow meow meow meow meow meow meow meow meow meow meow meow meow meow, meow meow meow meow meow? Meow meow meow meow meow meow meow meow meow meow meow? Meow meow meow meow meow.

Meow meow meow meow meow meow meow meow meow meow. Meow meow meow? Meow meow meow meow meow,

meow meow meow meow meow. Meow meow meow meow meow meow meow. Meow meow meow meow meow meow, meow meow meow. Meow meow meow meow meow meow meow meow. Meow meow meow meow meow meow. Meow meow meow meow meow meow meow, meow meow. Meow meow meow meow meow meow, meow meow meow meow. Meow meow meow meow meow meow meow meow, meow meow meow meow meow meow meow meow meow meow meow meow meow meow meow, meow meow meow, meow meow. Meow meow meow meow meow meow meow meow. Meow meow meow meow meow meow, meow meow meow, meow meow meow meow meow meow meow meow meow meow, meow meow meow meow meow meow meow meow meow, meow meow meow meow meow meow meow meow meow.

Meow meow meow, meow meow meow. Meow meow meow meow meow meow meow meow. Meow meow meow, meow meow meow meow meow, meow meow meow meow meow meow meow meow. Meow meow meow meow meow. Meow meow meow meow meow meow meow. Meow meow meow, meow. Meow meow meow meow meow meow meow meow meow meow, meow meow meow meow meow meow, meow meow meow meow meow meow, meow meow meow meow meow meow meow meow meow meow meow.

Meow meow meow meow meow meow meow meow meow. Meow meow meow meow meow meow meow meow. Meow meow, meow meow meow meow meow meow meow meow, meow meow meow meow meow meow meow. Meow meow meow meow meow meow meow meow meow meow meow. Meow meow meow meow, meow meow meow meow meow meow meow meow. Meow meow meow meow meow meow, meow meow meow meow meow meow meow meow meow. Meow meow meow meow meow meow, meow meow meow meow

meow meow, meow meow meow meow meow meow meow meow meow meow meow meow meow meow meow. Meow meow meow meow meow meow meow meow.

Meow meow, meow meow meow meow meow meow, meow meow meow meow meow meow meow meow. Meow meow meow, meow meow meow meow, meow meow meow meow, meow meow meow meow meow meow meow meow meow meow meow meow meow. Meow meow meow meow, meow meow meow meow meow, meow meow meow meow meow meow meow. Meow meow meow meow meow meow meow, meow meow meow meow meow meow meow meow meow meow, meow meow meow meow meow meow. Meow meow meow meow meow meow. Meow meow meow meow meow meow meow meow. Meow meow meow meow meow, meow meow meow meow. Meow meow meow meow meow meow meow meow, meow meow meow meow meow meow meow meow. Meow meow meow meow meow meow, Meow, meow meow meow, meow meow meow meow meow meow meow, meow meow meow meow meow meow meow meow, meow meow meow meow meow meow meow meow meow, meow meow, meow, meow, meow, meow meow. Meow meow meow meow meow meow meow meow meow meow meow meow meow, meow meow meow meow meow meow meow, meow meow meow meow meow. Meow mcow meow meow meow meow meow meow, meow meow meow meow meow meow. Meow meow meow meow meow. Meow meow meow meow.

Meow meow meow meow meow meow meow meow meow meow, meow meow meow meow meow meow. Meow meow meow meow, meow meow meow meow meow meow meow, meow meow meow meow meow meow meow meow meow meow meow. Meow meow meow meow meow meow meow, meow meow meow meow meow, meow meow meow meow meow

meow meow. Meow meow meow meow meow. Meow meow meow meow meow meow meow meow meow meow meow meow, meow meow meow meow meow meow meow meow meow Meow Meow. Meow meow meow meow, meow. Meow meow meow meow. Meow meow meow meow meow meow meow meow meow, meow meow meow meow meow meow meow. Meow meow meow. Meow meow meow meow meow. Meow meow meow. Meow meow meow meow meow meow meow meow, meow meow meow meow meow. Meow meow meow meow meow meow meow meow meow, meow meow meow meow meow meow, meow meow. Meow meow meow meow, meow meow meow meow meow meow. Meow meow meow meow meow meow.

Meow meow meow meow meow meow meow, meow meow meow meow meow meow meow meow meow, meow meow meow meow meow meow meow meow meow, meow meow meow meow, meow meow, meow meow meow meow meow meow. Meow meow meow meow. Meow meow meow meow meow. Meow meow meow meow meow meow meow meow meow meow, meow meow meow meow meow meow, meow meow, meow meow meow. Meow meow meow. Meow meow meow meow meow, meow meow meow meow meow meow meow meow. Meow meow meow meow meow meow, meow meow meow meow meow meow meow. Meow meow meow meow meow meow meow meow meow meow, meow meow meow meow. Meow meow meow Meow, meow Meow Meow. Meow meow meow meow meow Meow. Meow meow meow meow meow meow meow meow meow meow meow meow meow meow, meow meow meow meow meow meow, meow meow meow meow meow meow, meow meow meow meow meow. Meow meow meow meow meow meow. Meow meow meow meow meow meow, meow meow

meow meow meow meow. Meow meow meow meow meow meow meow meow meow meow.

Meow meow meow meow meow, meow meow meow meow meow meow meow, meow meow, meow. Meow meow meow meow meow. Meow meow meow meow meow meow meow meow meow.

Meow meow meow meow meow meow meow, meow meow meow meow meow meow. Meow meow meow meow meow meow meow. Meow meow meow meow meow, meow meow meow meow meow meow. Meow meow meow meow meow meow meow meow meow meow meow meow, meow meow meow, meow meow meow meow, meow meow meow. Meow meow meow, meow meow meow meow meow meow meow meow meow. Meow meow meow meow meow.

Meow meow meow meow meow meow meow. Meow meow meow meow meow meow meow, meow meow meow meow meow meow meow meow. Meow meow meow meow meow meow, meow meow meow meow meow meow meow meow. Meow meow meow meow meow, meow meow meow meow meow meow meow meow meow meow, meow meow meow meow meow meow meow meow meow meow meow meow meow meow. Meow meow meow meow meow, meow meow meow meow meow meow meow.

Meow mcow meow meow meow, meow meow meow meow meow, meow meow meow meow meow meow meow meow. Meow meow meow meow, meow meow meow meow meow mcow meow meow meow, meow meow meow meow meow meow meow meow meow meow meow meow.

Meow meow meow meow meow meow meow meow, meow meow meow meow meow meow meow meow meow, meow meow Meow. Meow meow meow meow. Meow meow meow meow meow meow meow. Meow meow meow meow meow

meow meow. Meow meow, meow meow meow meow, meow meow meow meow, meow meow, meow meow meow. Meow meow meow meow meow meow. Meow meow meow meow meow meow meow meow meow meow meow.

Meow meow meow meow meow meow meow meow meow meow meow, meow meow meow meow meow meow. Meow meow meow meow meow meow meow meow meow. Meow meow meow meow meow, meow meow meow meow meow meow meow meow meow meow meow meow meow meow. Meow meow meow meow meow meow. Meow meow meow meow, meow meow meow meow meow meow meow meow meow meow. Meow meow meow. Meow meow meow meow. Meow meow meow meow meow meow. Meow meow meow meow meow meow meow meow meow meow meow.

Meow meow meow meow meow, meow meow meow meow meow meow. Meow meow meow meow meow meow meow meow meow meow meow. Meow meow meow meow meow meow meow meow meow meow meow meow meow. Meow meow meow, meow meow meow meow meow meow. Meow meow meow meow meow meow meow. Meow meow, meow meow meow meow meow meow meow, meow meow meow meow meow meow meow meow meow meow meow meow. Meow meow meow meow meow meow. Meow meow meow, meow meow meow meow meow meow. Meow meow meow meow meow.

Meow meow meow. Meow meow meow meow meow meow meow meow meow meow. Meow meow meow meow meow meow meow meow, meow meow meow, meow meow meow meow meow meow. Meow meow meow meow meow meow meow meow meow, meow meow meow.

Meow meow meow meow meow, meow meow meow meow meow meow, meow meow meow meow meow meow meow. Meow

meow meow. Meow meow meow meow meow meow meow
meow meow meow. Meow meow, meow meow meow meow
meow meow meow.

Meow meow meow meow meow meow, meow meow, meow
meow, meow meow meow meow meow. Meow meow meow
meow meow meow meow.

Meow meow, meow meow meow meow, meow meow, meow
meow meow, meow, meow meow meow. Meow meow meow
meow meow meow meow meow meow meow, meow meow
meow meow meow meow, meow. Meow meow meow meow
meow meow meow meow, meow meow. Meow meow meow
meow meow. Meow meow meow meow meow meow meow
meow, meow meow meow meow meow meow meow meow. Meow
meow meow meow meow meow meow meow. Meow meow
meow meow. Meow meow meow meow meow meow meow
meow meow meow meow.

Meow meow meow meow meow meow, meow meow meow
meow meow meow, meow meow meow meow meow meow,
meow meow meow meow meow meow. Meow meow meow
meow meow meow meow meow meow meow meow meow
meow.

"Meow meow meow meow meow meow?"

"Meow meow," meow meow meow meow meow meow
meow meow, meow meow meow meow meow.

Meow meow meow, meow meow meow meow, meow meow.
meow meow meow, meow meow meow meow, meow meow
meow meow meow meow, meow meow. Meow meow meow,
meow meow meow meow meow, meow meow meow meow
meow meow meow meow meow. Meow meow meow meow.
Meow meow meow meow meow. Meow meow meow meow
meow meow, meow meow meow meow meow meow meow,
meow meow meow meow meow. Meow meow meow meow,

meow meow meow, meow meow meow meow. Meow meow meow, meow meow meow meow meow meow meow.

Meow meow meow meow, meow meow meow. Meow meow meow meow meow, meow meow meow, meow meow meow meow meow meow meow meow. Meow meow meow meow meow meow. Meow meow meow, meow meow meow meow meow, meow meow meow meow. Meow MEOW meow meow meow.

Meow meow meow meow-meow meow meow meow meow meow meow. Meow meow meow meow meow meow meow meow. Meow meow, meow. Meow meow meow meow meow meow meow meow. Meow meow meow meow meow meow meow meow meow, meow meow meow. Meow meow meow meow meow meow meow meow, meow meow meow meow meow meow meow meow meow meow. Meow meow meow meow meow meow meow meow meow meow, meow meow meow. Meow meow meow meow meow meow meow meow meow. Meow meow meow meow meow meow. Meow meow meow, meow meow meow meow meow.

Milton Keynes UK
Ingram Content Group UK Ltd.
UKHW031104280724
446129UK00001B/44